THE LAST
GENRO

Date Loaned

Oc1 38M	Mr8'43N		
	Ja7'45		
Fe21 39M			
Oc29'40M	OCT 1 3 1982		
No5'40P	NOV 0 7 1984		
No26'40P			
De2 40K			
Dec20'40N			
Jan6'41N			
My8'41P			
Fe9'42N			
Fe26'42L			
Oc23'42V			
Oc30 42B			
Nov6'42B			
No13'42H			
No25'42I			
Ja27'43V			
Ja30'43V			
Feb6'43V			
Fe13'43M			
Fe20 43M			
Mr1'43N			

Pictures, Inc., Photo.

PRINCE KIMMOCHI SAIONJI

THE LAST GENRO

PRINCE SAIONJI
The Man Who Westernized Japan

By

BUNJI OMURA

PHILADELPHIA & NEW YORK

J. B. LIPPINCOTT COMPANY

LONDON

TO
PRINCE KIMMOCHI SAIONJI

FOREWORD

When a Nipponese speaks of the 'fathers' of his country, he refers to them as Genros, elder statesmen. They participated in the wars of the Meiji Restoration, and in 1889 under Emperor Meiji they drew up the Imperial Constitution upon which the present political system is based. The Genros continued to serve as guardians of that document and as advisers to the Emperor. Their most important duty was to recommend a choice of Premiers to His Majesty.

In 1916 death had so thinned their ranks that the survivors recommended for their body a man who had fought with them in 1868 when he was a young courtier. They had sought his counsel before. This man, the President of the Privy Council, the second President of the Seiyukai Party, twice a Premier, and Nippon's Chief Delegate to the Paris Peace Conference, was Kimmochi Saionji, or as the Nipponese say, Saionji Kimmochi.

All the other elder statesmen have died. Since the Constitution makes no mention of this office, Prince Saionji, now eighty-eight years old, will be the last Genro.

The story of Saionji's long years embraces the history of New Nippon, which the West has chosen to call Japan. In 1849, when he was born, the government had been in the hands of the Tokugawa Shoguns for over two and a half centuries. Saionji was eighteen when Emperor Meiji ascended the throne. Under him a united nation began her progress.

That progress had been given an impetus by the arrival of Commodore Perry in 1854. Western commerce and civilization roused the Island Empire. Liberal ideas of the nineteenth century crossed the seas.

Following the Franco-Prussian War, Saionji spent some time in France where among other leaders he met Clemenceau.

He returned home ready to put his new ideas into practice in his brief editorship of a radical newspaper. His convictions became less arbitrary when he entered political life, but throughout his public career he was known as a liberal.

In his childhood he had been a favorite of Emperor Komei and was appointed the Emperor's Child-Chamberlain and Middle General; under Emperor Meiji, whose close personal friend he was, he served twice as Premier. It was under Emperor Taisho that he was sent to the Paris

Peace Conference, and at present he acts as the sole Councillor to His Majesty. In these various capacities his influence resulted in the appointment of thirteen Premiers, among them the latest, Prince Konoe Fumimaro.

During Saionji's lifetime, up to this writing in June 1937, Nippon engaged in four major conflicts: the Sino-Nipponese War in 1894-1895, the Russo-Nipponese War in 1904-1905, the World War in 1914-1918 and the 1931-1932 Manchurian Expedition.

Industrially, some small undertakings have grown into vast monopolies, notably, the Mitsui, Mitsubishi and Sumitomo Houses, the last headed by Saionji's younger brother Kichizayemon who was adopted into the Sumitomo family. Socially, the Nipponese have turned from their centuries-old customs to a widespread adaptation of Western ways.

Through the maze of readjustment, Nippon looks to Saionji as her guide. When too much modernization threatens her national integrity, she values his leadership, for he has seen the old order and the new, and whatever the 'Grand Old Man of the Empire' thinks suitable for the nation is acceptable to the man in the street. Reactionary political factions have not always agreed: there have been threats against his life when the extreme nationalists resented his opposition to their demands. Moralists at home and abroad did not approve when the seventy-year-old statesman brought his third young common-law wife with him to the Paris Peace Conference. Nor has the legend about his theoretical bachelorhood condoned in their eyes the fact that he has not troubled to marry any of his successive mistresses, although he had children by them. But these are the trivia of small souls. Throughout Nippon there is a vast awe for the man who lives alone in his Okitsu home, one hundred miles south of Tokyo.

Basing this romance on authentic historical facts, I have with all sincerity attempted to reproduce the life of Prince Saionji Kimmochi, the *Last Genro* of Nippon.

BUNJI OMURA

NEW YORK CITY
June 1937

CONTENTS

I

❧

COURTIER

CHAPTER I

COURTIER

I<small>T WAS IN KYOTO IN</small> 1862.

In his home within the enclosure of the Imperial Palace, a twelve-year-old boy sat on the matted floor, reading. Beside him lay a *biwa*.

He heard the whinny of a horse. The book slid to the mat, and his hands reached hastily for the musical instrument.

"Kimmochi, we are going to ride."

Tokudaiji Kinzumi stood looking at his son who had been adopted ten years ago by the house of Saionji. Tokudaiji was wearing a simple courtier garb, a riding *hakama* and a short sword. The small upright headgear was tied under his chin. A black mustache with twisted ends heightened his dignity. Both father and son had round brown eyes, an aristocratic nose and an oval face. Severity marked the man's features.

"The steward has brought out your horse. Come, come!" Tokudaiji's eyes went from the book to the silent *biwa*. Kimmochi nodded, fastened a few stray hairs into his black topknot and placed the short sword at his hip. He followed his father.

Wordless, the two riders dodged the pine branches and blossoming cherry trees of the palace grounds and came into the street. Buddhist temple bells rang out in the spring dawn and the sun's rays spread above the tip of the Higashiyama.

Tokudaiji gave a signal; both tightened the reins, and set spur to their horses.

After a while they were sitting on the bank of the Kamo River. The cloud of dust had settled behind them and the horses nibbled at the grass. Some distance away, scores of women, their kimono skirts tucked up, were singing as they bleached their homespun clothes in the fast-running, crystal water.

"We rode early this morning, Father," the boy said as he wiped his high forehead.

Tokudaiji spoke in formal courtier fashion: "I have received discouraging reports about you from every source. Since the death of your foster father you are the head of the Saionji house, so that I, even though you are by birth my son, have no jurisdiction over you. But when the very members of the Saionji family complain to me

15

about your conduct, I feel obliged to speak." He touched his eye-brows and mustache with a small, printed towel.

"Did Sagami complain about me?"

Tokudaiji smiled in spite of himself. "Sagami, who taught you to drink and smoke, and all the other so-called social graces when you were only ten years old, who adores the ground you walk on—did Sagami bring any tales? You know better. No, she did not. But your new uncles—do you know what they say about you?"

A mischievous light played in the boy's dark eyes. He mimicked the precise accents of the uncles: "They say to their small sons: 'Don't imitate Kimmochi's ways. He is a disgrace to the family and will come to no good end. Be like his elder brother, Sanenori, who will succeed his father as the head of the Tokudaiji house. But stay away from Kimmochi.' They are afraid of me," Kimmochi concluded with boyish pride.

Tokudaiji's lips twitched. His favorite son had already aroused jealousy because of his fast promotions at court. At the age of two, he had been adopted by the important but childless Saionji family. When he was past three years old, he had acted as child-chamberlain to the Emperor. Now at twelve he had been relieved of the menial services and appointed Middle-General of the Right Imperial Guard. Gossips said that Emperor Komei regarded him as dearly as his own son, who was later to be called Emperor Meiji. It made Tokudaiji's heart swell with gratitude and pride. But there were also grave charges against Kimmochi.

"I previously thought that your major vice was this idle reading of books, but I have discovered that you also act in open defiance of the rules which the Tokugawas at Edo have laid down for us who live in the court circles. Our duties here are to serve His Majesty and nothing more. We must leave the management of the country's af-fairs to the Tokugawa Shogun. You know, furthermore, that we courtiers are not permitted to consort with people from out of the district. Yet you have received on these palace grounds visitors from outside. I hear that men from Satsuma and Choshu, the 'Sat-cho,' have frequently been invited to your house. You know how severely the Shogun punishes such transgressions. You think it is yourself whom these Sat-cho seek out, but did it ever occur to you that they want your popularity with the Mikado for their own advancement? How do you know that they are not mere sycophants?"

Kimmochi was throwing pebbles into the water. He said nothing.

"Thirdly, you practice the forbidden art of fencing. If you persist, I fear that you will be drastically punished. It is not only that you yourself are involved, but your adopted family, the long illustrious Saionji and their immediate relatives, may also be disgraced.

"These counts would be severe against a grown man. But neither your youth nor your privileged relationship with the Emperor, which does not add to the Shogun's liking for you, will long protect you if the Tokugawa men find out about your behavior. As I suspected, your constant book-reading is making a rebel of you. The rebel's way leads to destruction. Follow the example of the patriot and reap prosperity as a reward. And appreciate a little more your family heritage of *biwa* music. I fear you neglect it altogether."

Tokudaiji sighed after this long speech. Kimmochi looked up, a pebble in his hand.

"But, Father, why can't I read the nation's history books, especially those which tell of our Fujiwara ancestors, the Tokudaiji and the Saionji, many centuries ago when they in the name of the Imperial House actually governed the people? And as for the Sat-cho men, what if they are really honest? If the Sat-cho do conquer the Tokugawas for the Emperor, will they still be rebels? It will be they who are the patriots and the saviors of the country." His long smooth face was radiant against the sun. After a moment he began again. "Father, is it not the duty of every noble to defend the Mikado and himself against the enemy?"

"Yes."

"Then why does the Shogun forbid fencing?"

"Because he will have it so."

"Is it not the duty of every loyal Nipponese to unite his strength with that of every other countryman for the Emperor's greater glory?"

"Nominally, yes, but our Government does not wish us court nobles to mingle freely with outsiders, particularly with the Satsuma and Choshu *samurai* who are plotting its overthrow."

"They are the true patriots and the friends of the Divine Ruler of our country," the boy declared stubbornly. "The Tokugawas are impostors. Great Nippon does not need a Shogun. We owe allegiance only to the Emperor. His Majesty must make the decisions, not the Shogun—for instance, on whether the 'Red-hairs' may trade with us—"

"You are merely repeating what the Sat-cho men advocate—"

"But by what right can the Tokugawa Shogun, who does not even live in Kyoto, dictate to us? How does he dare to keep the Emperor's friends from him? Isn't it as I said—the Sat-cho are the real patriots? I believe you think so, too."

His round eyes flamed.

Tokudaiji looked sharply at his son.

"I will be frank with you, although I think you have divined my thoughts. For two hundred and sixty years, off in Yedo, the Tokugawa house has, as you say, held the reins of Government. They have run things to suit themselves. They have kept the Emperor in poverty and seclusion here in Kyoto, so that he has become almost legendary in the minds of the Nipponese. Your friends the Choshu and Satsuma men especially are dissatisfied with this state of affairs. They say it is a disgrace that the Tokugawas receive eight million koku a year from the nation's income, while the Imperial House has only an annual allowance of a hundred thousand koku, from which we all draw our meagre share. They say it is shameful that all His Majesty's powers have gone into the hands of the Shogun." Tokudaiji spoke with concern, but doubt crept into his vioce. "I do not know how sincere these two clans are. They have strength and courage and ingenuity on their side. They say that we can oppose the inroads of the Dutch, English, French and American traders by union under His Majesty. But perhaps the Sat-cho wish to usurp permanently these powers for themselves when they are temporarily entrusted with them. I may be unjust to them, but it is human to take advantage of such a situation. However, while the Shogun still rules, it is the better policy to conform to his laws. You are too young to accomplish good by disobedience. I would have you remain a child a little while longer. You will have a long life in which to prove your devotion to the Imperial House, as did many of the Tokudaiji and the Saionji forefathers about whom you have been reading."

"Some were generals and many were premiers, according to the book," the boy interrupted.

"I am particularly obliged to your adopted parents. When they were alive, they were very proud of you and entertained great hopes for your future."

"My foster father was very handsome I was told."

"When he adopted you he said that the Saionji family would once more be able to offer His Majesty a premier. Don't fail him."

They rode home side by side, each with his own thoughts. From temple bells in every section of the ancient city, the morning hour of eight rang out.

At parting, the boy's father gave one more piece of advice.

"I hear that you admire antiques. I hear that you spent several hundred yen on a teapot. That is extravagance."

Saionji nodded.

At the time of Saionji's birth, which occurred on October 23, 1849, Kyoto had been a quiet city for a long time. This town, the seat of the Imperial Court, was the nominal capital of Nippon, and the Mecca of art, literature and learning, but for two and a half centuries, government and commerce had flourished in Edo, now Tokyo. A contemporary journalist described Kyoto as a center of pretty women, nobles and priests. 'Things abundant are: temples, women and makers of clogs. Things scarce are: *samurai*, half-drunkards, bars and crows. People walking in the streets do not pick quarrels. In their homes they do not swear at each other. The atmosphere is peaceful and elegant.' It was said that *samurai* were so rarely seen that when one did visit Kyoto, the common people made sport of him, because the two swords at his side had a ridiculous resemblance to fried bean curd on its bamboo sticks.

During Saionji's childhood this haven of peace was overrun by strangers, and savagery was rife. The long plotting of the Satsuma and Choshu insurgents was having its effect. The tide of political change came in. When the Emperor, who had kept within the royal gates for many generations, appeared in the streets with his guards to pay tribute at the various national shrines, people rubbed their eyes in amazement. His Majesty was actually a human being.

Discontented *samurai* and masterless warriors called *ronin* secretly trooped to Kyoto. Every year brought in more, from sections so remote that even their names were unknown. Some were in sympathy with the rebellious clans and others with the Shogun at Edo, but all looked for satisfactory employment. They came on foot, on horseback, hungry and in rags, sometimes in disguise.

Various dialects from the north and the south grated suddenly on the air; peddlers hawked their wares, and peculiar costumes mingled in the streets. Hold-ups, robberies, shootings and slayings occurred every hour. Skirmishes and fighting between the two contending groups of the *samurai* occurred, first under cover and later in the open, scores on each side, high and low, old and young, losing their lives. Lawlessness took the place of order in the once peaceful city. People were irritable and fearful by day, and cried out in their sleep at night. Even the ordinary explosion of bamboo burned as firewood sounded like a deadly shot.

Meanwhile the nation had its troubles with the 'foreign invasion,' particularly in Satsuma and Choshu where, independently, the foreigners were challenged. Until several years before only the Dutch had been tolerated and that only in their special quarter at Nagasaki, the sole port through which they had been allowed to conduct their traffic with the natives. Then the Nipponese were forced to open trading posts, one by one, to others, beginning with the Americans. Now the British, French and Russians were anchored in their harbors, sailing off with Nipponese silk and gold and leaving behind a great wanderlust.

The Shogun increased his arms to ward off the threat to his power. Every measure which could possibly save him was tried.

Those were exciting days in Kyoto, when Saionji was a boy. He lived in sunlight and shadow. There were hours spent on penmanship, writing poetry, reading, the tedious pursuit of *biwa* music, and attendance on His Majesty. Then Choshu and Satsuma visitors would burst in upon him with another 'restoration plan,' and it would seem that the quiet of the palace was to yield to the clamor of battle.

Once when the Choshu *samurai*, several hundred strong, were attacking the Tokugawa men at Hamaguri Gate of the Imperial Palace, Saionji almost forsook his court duties to join his friends. But Governess Sagami was stern.

"It is not your affair. Your duty is to protect His Majesty. Later, if the Emperor acknowledges this cause as his own, you may go to war, my master. Keep your head cool."

So he went by a rear path to the Palace, and guarded the Mikado there until the Choshu, defeated, had to give up the fight. Saionji chafed at his bonds. But the time was approaching when he would distinguish himself in a real battle, the only bloody encounter in his career.

The quarrels between the two forces reached a crisis. Emperor Komei died and was succeeded by his son, fourteen-year-old Mutsuhito, later Emperor Meiji. His advisers decided to give the Sat-cho cause the Imperial blessing.

The Shogun was forced to surrender his title, and tried to save the remnants of his power. Fifteen thousand men were sent to Kyoto, on the pretext of carrying a petition to His Majesty. Opposed at every step of the way, they finally reached Toba and Fushimi, the southern gateway to the capital.

On January 4, 1868, from the palace one could see the sky red with the burning of the Toba-Fushimi towns. And yet the Imperial forces had not begun their concerted action. For in the government office there were still those who advised waiting or flight, since the Mikado's soldiers, mostly from the Satsuma and Choshu clans, numbered only sixty-five hundred men. And against the advice of the older courtiers, these rough men would consent to march under only two leaders. One was Prince Komatsu and the other was Saionji Kimmochi, now eighteen years old.

At home, Sagami, Saionji's governess, laid down her sewing. The wind rattled the paper screens. Outside was the roar of cannon.

She listened intently. Then she took up her sewing again, her face feverish with haste.

A roundish woman burst in, fear distorting her eyes.

"Oh! That booming sound frightens me to death, Sagami-sama. It shakes the house, doors and trees, and it scares all my thoughts away. I came to tell you something, but I can't remember what. Oh, that noise stops my heart-beats and makes my knees shake. You know, the picture of hell at the Buddhist temple came to my mind when my man and I were on the hill watching the skies over the towns where the fight is.

"My man said if the loyalists—I don't know who they are, and I don't care to know who they are—lose their battle, the Toku'wa *samurai*—I don't know them either—would storm the city in no time. And he says that invaders kill men and women and aged and young; they snatch things away from anybody and anywhere, homes or temples or shrines; they carry away pretty women for their own pleasure. You see, I don't think I am good-looking, but my man says they will take even me; I'd rather stay with him than to go with someone I don't know. Oh, dear, oh, dear! He thinks they will even burn this beautiful ancient city to the ground. I wouldn't believe it if I hadn't seen the burning towns last night." The gatekeeper's wife wagged her head. "Do you think they will come? You think so? Or don't you? Why don't you do something? It's no time to be sitting in the house and mending things; everybody is running around.—D-d-d-d-d-o-n! Oh, dear, dear, there it goes again!"

"Where is your husband, Miyo?" Sagami did not look up as she spoke. "He has not reported for gate duty this morning. What is he doing? It is unusual for him to be late."

"Oh, him. That's what I was going to tell you. I forgot it entirely. The noise put it out of my mind with thinking how the *samurai* might run off with me. Oh, he? My man?"

"Miyo, answer me. Where is your husband?"

"He is hiding our belongings underground for fear if the Toku'wa people come they'll take them. The neighbors are doing it, too. Oh, do you think the Toku'was would want our poor little cracked dishes and things? He said he's coming soon, my man is. That's what I meant to tell you."

Sagami tried to stop the flow of words, but Miyo went on:

"Sagami-sama! What is all this terrible killing and burning about? Who makes the trouble?"

"The trouble is between the Satsuma and Choshu men on one side and the Tokugawa *samurai* on the other—"

"Why don't somebody put the trouble-makers out? Where do they come from?"

"The Tokugawa, mostly from the northwest, are fighting against the Imperial House. We call them rebels; the Satsuma and Choshu men, from the southwestern section of the country, are the loyalists who are defending His Majesty. Years ago we called the Satsuma and Choshu men rebels and the Tokugawa loyalists. Can you understand that?"

"But who makes the trouble?"

"The Tokugawa, by insisting that they want to come to the capital to present a petition to the Emperor, so the loyalists are trying to stop them at those towns before they enter this city."

"Do you think they can?"

"We don't know yet. There are over fifteen thousand rebels and only about sixty-five hundred of the Emperor's men. But the loyalists have the Emperor's blessing."

"If there aren't enough men there, why don't they send more? Not a single *samurai* did I see marching, nothing but *ashigaru* in rags."

"I'm busy, Miyo. I have no time to lose. Will you do this?" She showed her the princely martial robe of woven hemp which had been patterned after the one worn by a great ancestor, General Saionji, six hundred years before. Sagami had cut and sewn the new robe herself; she hoped to finish embroidering the coat-of-arms, but the time was growing short. Soon both women were busy with their needles, and Miyo's tongue rattled on.

"All the ladies in the court ask me about our lord every time I meet them, you know," she went on, unabashed. "What is 'Commander-

General' and 'Councillor'? Such long words. The ladies say they never heard of 'Councillor' before, even in books. What do those words mean?"

Sagami sighed. "Well, our lord was taken into a group of wise men, that's where he has been these days. And he may be ordered to lead the big army for the Mikado. Then he would be the Commander-General. Now do you understand?"

"Will he really lead the army?"

"I hope so, Miyo. I very much hope so." For a moment Sagami rested her hands and stared into space.

Someone came up the road. Sagami dropped her needle, and the scissors clattered to the floor.

One of the two high stewards of the Saionji house ran into the room. "Sagami!"

"Well, Sir Steward?"

"There isn't a horse on the market. Not even the ghost of an animal is there! What is our lord going to do? He can't ride our old nag."

"I suppose they are all bought up for the war. And Saionji, of all people, to be without one! Let me think awhile. You'd better get your things ready for tomorrow."

"Are the Prince's robe and other belongings ready?"

"Yes, we can finish them before evening. I am expecting his sword and armor from the repair shops at any minute."

"Sagami"—he turned at the door—"do you think I have to accompany our lord to the palace tomorrow when he receives the sword and the Imperial Banner of Golden Brocade from the hands of His Majesty?"

"In the first place, we don't know that he will be Commander-General. There are many who think he is too young."

The head steward persisted. "But if he does, do I have to go with him? Those formalities—"

"If you don't, who would? It's your job. Anyway, I thought you were an authority on that subject."

"Yes, yes, but for centuries the ceremony never actually took place. And now I, the chief steward of the new Commander-General, am to accompany him into the Audience Hall of the Palace. *Bow before stepping over the sill, head parallel with the knees*—" He enumerated the old ceremonial forms on his knobby fingers.

"How often you've bored us with your recitation of the court etiquette! Now let's see you put it into practice."

"But that's different! All I know is what I read in books. I never saw it done or did it myself before. What if I forget something or my knees shake as they're doing right now at the very thought of it? Couldn't someone else go?"

Sagami was not listening. There was the sound of hurrying footsteps on the road.

"Steward, I beg your pardon, but I think this is the messenger from the Shrine with the talisman."

The governess laid a packet in the alcove.

"Miyo," she said, "make a little bag. See, this is from the National Shrine at Ise; this one is from the Hachiman Shrine of the god of war; that is from Narita Temple at Sakura to keep him healthy and invulnerable to bullets and sword-blades; the last one is from the Shirakumo Shrine, the Saionji family altar. This bit of goods left from the robe is just big enough to hold all the amulets."

"Is the lord going to wear this?"

"Yes, very close to his heart."

The cold, gloomy day came to an end. The Buddhist and Shinto buildings on the hills surrounding the city were lighted with large paper lanterns. Guns from the Toba-Fushimi front were still audible and occasionally a loud explosion shook the air.

The household awaited Saionji's return from the government office. Three days he had been away. Surely he would come home tonight with good news. Good news, if Saionji were made Commander-General! Such an honor would distinguish the family from all others.

But the night came on, and still there was no sign of him. The stewards took turns at walking down the road. Fingering their sword-hilts, they looked anxiously towards Toba-Fushimi.

Sagami, alone in the garden, thinking of the rider for whom no horse was provided, prayed to *Kwannon*, Goddess of Mercy.

There was no sound but her breathing.

She called one of the stewards to her. A few words and he was running down the road, Sagami watching him. Much later she entered the house and went to the family altar where stood a replica of the Shirakumo Shrine. She pulled up the wick in the dish filled with vegetable oil and lighted it. Then she knelt.

All night the distant cannon roared. All night the vain waiting for Saionji. As the first cock crowed the stewards put on their field attire.

Then in the uneasy dawn there came a war-cry that rang through the neighborhood. The head steward standing on the veranda saw a paper lantern in the distance. Gradually he made out the approaching attendant, the emblems on the lantern, Saionji on foot, and a steward behind him.

The crowd in the yard was motionless.

Saionji came closer. He glanced at the household and they followed him inside. He smiled at the sight of the robe with the coat of arms, the talisman bag, the green armor, the headgear, and the long sword lying in the recess.

After he had changed to formal dress, he called the household to form a semi-circle around him in the guest hall.

The steward asked: "What is the final decision on the government's plan, my lord?"

Saionji's voice was clear. "To fight to the end! Many conservative people advise a truce, but we must strike down the enemies!"

"Your part, sir?"

"As we hoped! Yes, I shall lead the army into Tamba Province to pave the way to the southwest. Should our side lose at Toba-Fushimi and the enemies march into the city, we must remove the Imperial Train to safety. In past centuries when the Imperial Throne was threatened, it took refuge in the Hiyei Mountains and other places near the capital, but this time we may accompany His Majesty to Choshu and even as far as Kyushu."

"Sagami!" His eyes rested on the governess.

"Yes, my master?"

"I must take all the stewards and vassals with me; so I leave everything to you. You have been my dearest mother and teacher all these years. I thank you for that! And for your faithful services, too, my stewards and vassals, I thank you," he said, turning to the others.

All bowed low.

"And now let us depart. It is the fate of *samurai* to die in combat. Let none of us show the coward's heel. Remember, we must give the others a good example of knighthood. Let us not disgrace the glorious names of our ancestors!"

Cold sake was poured into shallow earthen saucers. Saionji was served first and then each in turn, according to the order of his rank in service, drank the rice wine.

At that moment there was shouting at the gate. "A horse! A horse!" A strong steed, in full trappings, led by a Satsuma man, cantered to the gate. Sagami breathed a prayer of relief. The Satsuma camp had granted her request.

Saionji mounted his horse while the beating of drums came nearer on the chill morning wind.

"Follow me." He tightened the reins in his hands, and gave a backwards glance at the members of the household standing along the fence.

The gatekeeper dug his knuckles into his eyes. His father, and his father's father, had served the family, but never had they beheld such horsemanship.

"Farewell," Saionji's voice cried from a distance. "And now to headquarters and to the Imperial Palace!"

The next hour passed like a dream. Whether he and the chief steward stumbled into His Majesty's presence, or whether they observed every measure of the ceremony, Saionji did not remember. He only knew that after a while the steel was in his trembling hands, and the beloved Emperor was murmuring:

"With this sword we empower thee to conquer our enemies and this Imperial Banner shall lead our forces." The voice broke: "Return to us in safety, Kimmochi, and help us with the more arduous tasks of state."

Then they were marching behind the Golden Brocade. Crowds cheered the flying Banner. War drums and gongs, echoing against the mountains, led the formation. The Commander-General saw his father, Tokudaiji. Like the others, he was squatting on the ground. He took off the headgear, and touched the earth with his brow as the Banner passed before him. When he raised his face, Saionji saw in it pride and approval.

The victorious tide of the Imperial expeditionary forces was still sweeping northeastward through Honshu, the largest island of Nippon. The fifteenth Tokugawa Shogun had long since yielded his Edo castle, the feudal headquarters, to the Emperor's men, and retired into seclusion. Most of his relatives and their supporters had surrendered, forgetting their oath to stand together in loyalty to the hereditary overlord until the last 'bow and arrow' was broken. Only a few small contingents in the north were still battling for the lost cause in the early spring of 1869.

Edo, now renamed Tokyo by an Imperial decree, was plunged into confusion. The streets were deserted, the people who had not joined the daily exodus from the city grew apprehensive. All business and social activities were paralyzed, except for the bustle of the Sat-cho and their commandants who had marched in as conquerors.

One of them, his ebony-black hair drawn into a courtier's topknot above his aristocratic face, his arms folded in the sleeves of his silk kimono, a pair of swords on his hip, had passed Ryogoku bridge and was coming towards the Koto, the lower east bank of the Sumida River. Above him hung heavy clouds that oppressed even the gay temper of the natives of Tokyo. His clogged footsteps sounded dull.

A flock of black crows flew over his head.

His eyes and footsteps followed their flight and soon the teahouses of the once prosperous gay quarters loomed before him. These long two-storied buildings with their balconies and verandas under black-tiled roofs were already, after a few days' stay, familiar to him. His choice had been the Nakamura-ro, which, like some of the others, had a building in the rear, parallel to it. The two houses were joined by passages at both ends, forming an inner garden, where twin ponds reflected the cold, gray sky.

Saionji proceeded to the shallower of the ponds which held fantailed goldfish in the summer. The water was still. Rocks and miniature promontories lined the shore of the deeper pond. The black and red carp were in hiding and he saw only weathered stalks of Nipponese iris and lotus. A series of single boards reached from the shore to the largest of several islands. Saionji walked gingerly along the dilapidated bridge to the shrine with its red *tori-i* dedicated to the 'Fox' deity.

He retraced his steps and curiously studied the arbor fashioned like the Golden Pavilion, with its background of artificial hills, weeping willows, shrubs, dwarfed pines, cherry and plum trees. A few white plum blossoms that had clung through the winter added to the bleakness of the scene. The balconies, which opened out onto this garden so that all the rooms except those facing the front had access to it, were empty now, and the colored paper lanterns hung limp and tattered. Saionji leaned against a pillar. With his eyes closed he could imagine how festive it would all be later, with the lighted lamps and lanterns reflected in the water, the tinkling of wind-bells, and the gaily-dressed geisha flitting in and out.

He started at the sound of a voice.

"Oh, *Okuge-sama*, I'm sorry to disturb your peace." A woman in her forties was carrying a basket of fish-food.

"Huh, *Josho*, don't treat me so courteously. Please don't say, '*Okuge-sama*.'"

"How modest you are, Prince Saionji! Until a few years ago, the name of your family sounded to us people of Edo like the name of an angel. I never even dreamed of having such a high personage in my humble quarters." The operator of the Nakamura-ro came a few steps towards him and continued: "When we think of the Sat-cho—even the lowest footmen—how boastful and rude they are—we appreciate your friendliness and unassuming attitude. My household, employees, and acquaintances are deeply impressed by the contrast." She went to the ponds and emptied the basket. "You have many callers these days, Prince Saionji—"

"Huh, how did you find out my real name? I registered here as 'Boto Ichiro' when you consented to lodge me. I didn't want you to address me formally."

Dimples showed in her face. She said: "When I saw you for the first time with your merrymaking friends, I guessed your origin—I was not mistaken. Your callers nowadays ask for Prince or Saionji *Okuge-sama* or the Commander-General or the Governor of Echigo. Do they come to—"

"To get me back into the government office I held last—and my military mentor, General Omura Masujiro, is coming after me this evening, too."

"Then the rumor is correct that you and General Omura are very close friends?"

"Huh, he taught me his military tricks." Pointing to the garden, Saionji inquired: "Why have you neglected its care?"

"Because I can't make any money these days."

"But don't you have many men and young girls in good kimonos here?"

"I have all classes, *Okuge-sama*, although they may look alike to you. There are geisha of different ranks, and the men are *hokan*, male entertainers. Besides them there are servants—"

"My governess used to tell me about the *hokan* and the geisha—"

Saionji strolled over to her side. "I thought all the girls were geisha. The *hokan* and geisha are supposed to live somewhere else, are they not?" He looked at her inquisitively.

"Yes."

"You have young girls, too?"

"The small ones are the *maiko* who dance to the accompaniment of the geisha's music. They become *oshaku* when they have learned the art of entertaining. They must spend a little while as *oshaku* and wait on the guests and learn everything connected with this profession. They frequently dance and play instruments too. The geisha are the highest class and when they get too old for that they teach the *maiko*, if they are good at instruments or singing."

"How do you get the little girls—"

"Poor parents bring their little one to be trained in this calling. But often the charge turns out to be hopeless, and then we put her into the kitchen or at other menial tasks. I have one girl now. She is very tender-hearted and obedient, but she has neither musical talent nor a pleasing appearance—"

"Huh, the girl running around with the broom, the button-nose one?"

"Ho, ho, yes, Prince."

"So geisha must be pretty?"

"Well, yes, now; but in the past when they were introduced as a branch of the Yoshiwara prostitutes, the brothel operators barred pretty girls from entering the geisha profession, because they were afraid they might outshine and perhaps snatch away the courtesans' guests. Since the brothels and the teahouses became independent of each other, the competition is very keen, and if a geisha has natural beauty and talents, she will become a star. There is a girl in my—"

"That takes a long time, I suppose?"

"It differs according to the individual. We keep her as a *maiko* until she is ten or twelve. Then she is an *oshaku* for two or three years. Then with great ceremony we introduce her as a full-fledged geisha. But you see, *Okuge-sama*, these days we get girls from another class. The young daughters of the poor and defeated *samurai* come to us. They are usually well-mannered, besides knowing the principles of music, singing, dancing and the like, so that it takes only a short time for them to learn our ways.—As I was going to say, in my house there is a young girl named Okiku, who is of *samurai* origin. Everybody expects her to be the most popular geisha in Tokyo. She is pretty, too."

"Do they make money any other way?" He grinned self-consciously.

"They are not supposed to, but most of them do, selling their charms." She smiled too, and added: "See, Prince, in former days, when times were good in the geisha occupation, everything was controlled under the co-operative system through registry houses called the *kemban*, where the *maiko* used to be trained, too. They regulated the geisha wearing apparel, individual conduct in the presence of guests and in off-duty hours, and the handling of her earnings. For instance, she could not wear *tabi* on her feet, no matter how cold it was, and she was not allowed to wear any but a cheap, plain kimono. She could not sit close to the guest, and she was not permitted to receive her pay from him directly—that went to her *kemban*, from which she got a monthly return, minus her dues to the organization."

"Huh."

"If the *kemban* discovered that a girl had misbehaved, she would, after an investigation, be thrown out at once. Her kimono and other belongings would be exhibited in front of that house to warn would-be violators to obey the rules. The ousted girl could not get any connection with other *kemban*."

"And now?"

"Now, with the prosperity of the brothels and teahouses, geisha discipline has gone to the winds. As a matter of fact, our business is at the verge of ruin. Countless *kemban* and teahouses have already been dissolved."

"So the geisha have degenerated?"

"Well, *Okuge-sama*, they must live somehow. They don't know any other trade and there aren't any jobs. They try anything—rather than die of starvation like grasshoppers in a barren field."

"And so they all come to you?"

"My business is not a *kemban*, but a teahouse. In the past I rented rooms for parties and furnished feasts. However, as I explained, many *kemban* went out of business and promising entertainers were stranded. I couldn't stand to watch them go shelterless and hungry, so I decided to keep them as long as I could, provided they retained their professional standard and morals. I've built up my business this far; I'm willing to die fighting for its recovery, Prince Saionji."

"Huh."

There was a stir in the pond.

"I think it will snow this evening, *Okuge-sama*, the fish are restless."

"So this is where the young hero hides himself." General Omura Masujiro looked up and down the walls, scrutinized the elaborate folding screen, and glanced briefly at the scroll. He thrust out his lower lip. The puffy cheeks which had won him the title *Dharma*, the name of the 'god who blows on the fire,' swelled out. "A fine place, an excellent place for our prodigy."

Saionji kept silent. His hands rested in the folds of his simple kimono.

Omura's vast kettle-body creaked as he squatted beside a charcoal brazier on the straw mat. He had laid his big sword in the holder in the alcove.

Saionji was lighting a candle on the stand.

"It's really true, then. The hero of Tamba and Echigo has nothing better to do than to settle himself in Edo.

"Wait a minute. Edo—we call it Tokyo the Eastern Capital, now.

"And he can't find a better occupation than to spend his days and nights here at the Nakamura-ro in this Koto gay quarter? The usual decline and fall of the hero."

A faint smile drifted across Saionji's face.

"General Omura, if I did not know you so well, I would think you were jealous!"

"Jealous! Jealous? You little 'priestling'! Jealous? What would I be jealous of?" His thick black brows came close together.

"Do you think because your name is on every lip, that I don't know where the credit is due? Listen! I was the brains of all the military campaigns. I, *Dharma* Omura. For years I studied European fighting methods. Do the Europeans put their best generals out to be massacred the first thing? They do not! They keep them behind the front lines. What good are a thousand soldiers if they've lost their leader? We with our notions of bravery—bah! For years our stupid gray-heads wouldn't listen to me. They exiled me for my foreign heresy. Only Kido Koin had sense enough to bring me back where I belonged. Kido gave me my chance and I took it.

"*I* planned the whole scheme against the Tokugawas. *I* applied the military tactics of the Westerners, and kept myself, the brains, and those handsome, brave generals and that darling Saionji where it was safe for us to be. And that's why the Shogun is gone and the Imperial cause is victorious. That's why Nippon is united now, and that's why the innocent *Okuge-sama* was made governor of Echigo province.

"And now, after all my work, that same darling *Okuge-sama* of the people has nothing better to do than to rest his elbow on a geisha-house brazier. For nothing at all I'd apply the *moxa* on that slender backside. At least he couldn't be sitting then."

Saionji bowed, nettled by the *Dharma's* vehemence.

"And what does General Omura wish me to do?"

"What does General wish? Doesn't your own common sense tell you that? I want you to go back to Echigo Province, where you were appointed governor, and pick up more knowledge of my profession in your spare time."

"But why must I, if I don't want to?—if I have something better in mind?"

"Better in mind! A geisha, I suppose. Listen—there was a time when I had nothing to do. I admit that I spent months with the females of such quarters as this and in the Yoshiwara. I had to wait until the tide turned. And I certainly understand how a young man wants to have his day. But right now you have to learn. You are needed. You did a good job on the battle front. I won't underestimate it. Not many could have kept those Sat-cho hot-heads united. That's why I looked you up. You think I run after just anybody? You've had a lifetime of experience in a year. You're headed for real statesmanship. It's your heritage, but that alone is not enough from now on. I want someone to take my place when I go. Is Nippon to writhe under the heel of the foreigner, or of another Tokugawa, just because one fat, ugly Omura gets a shot in the back one of these days? You are my successor, and I want you to stick to business."

"Perhaps General Omura is ignorant of my own humble plans. I want to ask Councillor Kido when he comes—"

"May we interrupt, masters?" A gentle voice came from behind the paper screens separating the room from the veranda. "Tea time, sir."

"Yes." Saionji looked relieved.

Near the screens knelt two girls, one with a tea set on her tray, and the other with a bowl of pickled plums. They placed the trays on the mat and touched the floor with their foreheads. Then they served the green tea.

Saionji whispered to one of the servants.

"Well, you certainly are at home, Saionji-san. Those girls have you under their thumbs all right. It is one of those two? Well, it wouldn't be so bad to have a little feminine touch for a change. Brings back the past, as it were."

When the general beamed, his eyes almost disappeared in the folds of flesh.

Between the room in which they were sitting and the house entrance were many matted guest-chambers. All were separated from each other by paper screens which could be slid together and taken out of their sills to make one large room where several smaller ones had been.

Outside it was already dark. The paper lanterns were lit. The February snow fell on the branches of the trees and withered grasses in the garden. Beyond the wooden fence, everything was quiet, for after sundown no one dared venture out. The discharged *samurai* still made the streets unsafe.

The *josho*, following her usual custom of greeting her guests, was asking permission to be allowed in for a few moments.

"It is our great pleasure to have you with us." She bowed low a few times. "Please be at ease and enjoy the evening. Though humble and incapable, we shall be at your service," she said, addressing General Omura.

"I am of—"

"From Choshu. You know—" Saionji began.

"You are General Omura! We heard much about you from the Prince, and your name is on every lip, sir, since you commanded the Imperial troops against the Shogi-tai on our Uyeno Hills—"

"Ha, so he did mention me!"

She bowed low again: "It is our unusual honor, sir, to have you, the person whom the Prince respects most!"

With many bows she left the room.

"I was saying that I want to ask Councillor Kido a favor. What is he doing now?"

"Many things, Saionji-san. He has most ambitious plans." The General lowered his voice and continued: "You see, the Tokugawa Shogun and his supporters are gone, but the country is actually still divided into hundreds of provinces under the local *daimyos* who, as you know, rule their domains like independent countries. Kido wants to wipe out that system to make Nippon a united nation, a nation solid like a ball. He will try to persuade them to return their fiefs to the Mikado. But if they don't"—the General swung his right arm—"there again my service will come in handy."

"Huh."

"That's the beginning. The Government will be brought here to rehabilitate this city. A system of national currency is being considered. There will be many reforms in the political system and industry on European models. For instance, Kido favors the creation of a parliament on a small scale to give the people some idea of governing themselves as the Westerners do, and he advocates the building of a steam railroad." Omura shook his black mane. "And soon we'll have a national army. All the armed forces in the country will belong to His Majesty. That was *my* suggestion. But Kido has a greater plan. He confided to me his idea of the colonization of Korea—at first on a small scale. We agree that we must protect our people with troops. He thinks that mobilization will help unify the nation and open the way for the country's expansion. That's what Kido and I are going to discuss tonight. I shall map out the actual campaign."

His eyes shone.

"See, to carry out all these ideas—it may take many years—everybody must get busy: sacrifice, hard work, European training for our future leaders. Kido wants to send our most promising youths abroad to study modern methods—"

"General Omura!"

"What?"

"Do you think I might be able to join them?" Saionji's face flushed.

"Is *that* what you are thinking about?"

"Par—don!" The troop of maids on the veranda came into the room, each holding, almost level with her eyes, a square lacquer tray with neatly arranged plates. Crane-necked porcelain sake bottles and 'thimble' cups, some of which were in a bowl filled with water, and many lighted candles were brought.

"What's this formality? And on such a big scale! However, not bad, not bad, eh, Prince? Frankly, I love things on a big scale. Do you really live here?"

"Yes, you see, the operator is willing to let me have this room cheap as her business is dull—my relatives and friends of course urged me not to stay here—"

"I sympathize with them. But the new Government is penniless. Did you get your salaries?"

The young man smiled.

"Ah, you are a noble soul. If your relatives object to these accommodations, why don't you buy a mansion? I know some property for sale at 500 yen; it was formerly owned by one of the daimyos. It will be worth a fortune when times get better."

The General's eyes were travelling over the trays. As the *oshaku* sat down—the signal that the party was ready to begin—he said: "For many moons I haven't been near a magnificent feast like this or did I smell such fragrant sake, not to speak of having the intimate company of the fair sex. Saionji-san, why this big celebration?"

"General, this is a humble token of my appreciation of you. With your permission, I'll start."

As the host, Saionji spoke formally, and bowed. He picked up a small *sakazuki* from the water bowl.

An *oshaku* with a warm sake jar slid over to him and poured liquor.

The host bowed again before he drank. He rinsed his cup in the bowl and offered it to the General whose bony fingers seized the tiny cup like an octopus attacking its food: "Well, this was certainly unexpected!" He beamed, and gulping the liquor, licked the fragrant sake from his lips. His eyes twinkled. "Well, Saionji-san, I guess you have learned to drink by this time. 'Sake is the king of all medicines,' we say. Say, if you don't mind my frankness, this formality is rather irksome. How about our using the larger cups on our trays?" The General held up his own and glanced at the extra tray. "I wish Kido were here too."

Saionji merely smiled.

"Well, here's a toast to my protégé!" Omura shouted.

One after another, plates kept coming in for them. There was clear shrimp soup in lacquer-ware; then deftly their chopsticks flew from servings of sliced raw fish or nicely grated radishes and horse-radish, to a bowl of chopped chicken, cooked with vegetables. General Omura continued to drain his larger sake cup, and still the meal went on. The pink roasted *tai*, lying on its decorations of bamboo, pine, and plum twigs, its mouth and eyes bulging, its fins spread, was brought in. Innumerable times, the *sakazukis* exchanged hands, until the porcelain jars were empty of the warm wine. Then they heard a noise on the veranda.

The folding screen was taken away and the paper screens separating the next room were removed. The geisha, *hokan*, *maiko*, and the carriers of drums, tabors, and samisen boxes entered with mincing steps. The girls holding up their sweeping kimono skirts, and the *hokan* with fans in their hands, bowed and greeted their patrons with artificial smiles. Then they tuned the three-stringed samisens.

The geisha took the instruments on their laps and cleared their throats. The dainty *maiko* were ready for the first formal dance. Rather slowly, almost in a monotone, the geisha began to sing, touching the taut silken strings. The dancers rose from their knees, holding their right kimono sleeves with their left hands and their heavy dance fans with their right hands.

Everyone clapped at the end of the first performance, and the ice was broken; the newcomers were given sake, and the jars were refilled; the exchange of the cups began again. Another samisen solo and the little girls as well as the *oshaku* and geisha danced; the tabors and drums came into play. The *hokan* recited their jests and presented nude dances, the masculine bodies reflecting the candle-light.

It had been a long time since the Nakamura-ro had seen such merriment.

"Guest in!" came a call from the counter.

A tall *samurai*, led by the maid, appeared on the veranda. He was
about thirty-five years old, with broad shoulders and a high forehead,
a dignified, yet gentle expression on his face.

His black *haori* with the white crests cloaked a kimono of the same
material and the striped hakama. His swords on the hip were heavier
and longer than usual. The top-knot was carefully combed. One hand
rested on the side and in the other he held his *ogi*, the folding fan.

The entertainers placed their sake cups and instruments on the tray
and mats as Saionji, somewhat befuddled, attempted to sit back properly. General Omura became sober enough to recognize the newcomer.
He waved his right hand and struggled to his feet.

"Glad, glad to see you. Very glad. Very, very glad."

The guest smiled: "Oh, Saionji-san, it has been many seasons since I
met you last in Kyoto. That was before you left for the scene of your
famous victories."

"Cut that short, my friend! Don't make it too formal. You—you—"

"I see the party has progressed. It is rare to see General Omura so
relaxed."

All present laughed at the remark, including the General, who was
still pursuing some elusive fancy.

Although she was drunk, one of the geisha managed to kneel formally and receive the new guest's sword. She laid it in the alcove.

Omura had a moment of clarity.

"You'd all better get acquainted with this man, this great man in the
new Imperial Government! Satsuma people are proud of Saigo and
Okubo, but we Choshu clansmen are still prouder of him my good
friend. Courtier Iwakura, the two Satsuma men and this one, these
four men, are the b-b-BUILders of the new Nippon. And he is the most
liberal, best-informed though he is younger than I'm—"

"Well, now, Omura, isn't that enough?"

"Say, *Dharma-san*, you didn't tell us his name," the youngest and
prettiest of the geisha said. The whole company laughed.

"Didn't you hear me? I, I said he is Councillor Kido Koin, yes, yes,
Kido, get it?" His eyes shut tightly and he rubbed his round, reddish
chin. "Bring a big red lacquer sake cup for him. He is a whale. You
can't make him drunk with a *sakazuki* like this, smaller than the tip of a
thumb."

"*Okuge-sama*, on which side did you fight?" The young geisha handed her cup to Saionji. "My, m-my— I mean my geisha name is Tama, if you want to know." She went on: "My real name is Okiku—"

Her eyes were bloodshot, her hair and dress disarranged. While the clamor was going on, Saionji studied this Tama.

She seemed to be fourteen or fifteen, though her manner was mature. She was tall for a Nipponese woman. The inverted-fan or Fuji-san-shaped hairline on her forehead drew one's eyes to the straight black hair dressed in *shimada*. The new-moon-shaped eyebrows over the brown eyes, the well-balanced nose, full mouth and somewhat pointed chin marked the typical beauty of feudal days.

She used thick make-up. Her voice was clear and her pleasing manner had little trace of artificiality. She matched her older companions in every branch of the entertaining art this evening, yet, like the others, her head and chest were bent forward in traditional Nipponese feminine submissiveness and grace.

Tama wore a silk crepe kimono of light purple. The back and each sleeve had a white crest in 'hawk-feathers' pattern. A small pink maple-leaf design on the collar of her dress blended with her complexion and the kimono color. Her sash was tied in a drum shape, *taiko musubi*. Under the crested dress she wore a crepe *nagajiban* of lighter color with a delicate design of wild chrysanthemum. Its dainty collar peeped out from beneath that of the kimono, and the skirt showed when she walked or danced.

But Saionji was not impressed. He preferred the court ladies and Kyoto beauties he had known. The Kyoto women were more elegant and passive than these Tokyo girls.

Suddenly Tama asked again: "Did you fight for the Tokugawas or for the Sat-cho, you young *Okuge-sama?*"

"I fought for the Imperial House."

"What is that? Is that what threw my father and brother out? Disgraceful! Driving people from their places which were inherited through generations!" She brought a cup to her lips.

"We, all the Tokyo people, still think you are rebels. Look here, you destroyed this business, too. Even in our Nakamura-ro, every room is now covered with spider-webs. Thousands are moving out of the city. You newcomers are nothing but poor, unkempt rascals!"

"Hey, keep your mouth shut or I'll tear it to pieces!" the half-dreaming Omura suddenly exploded. "Such abuse of the Imperial Government!"

"Hush, Omura!" Kido whispered. "Let her alone, I want to sound out the sentiment around here. She's drunk, and I'll learn how we stand with the people in Tokyo. They won't talk when I'm around."

She railed against the invaders. "Maybe the Tokugawas were inhumane and fools, but one thing you must admit. They were confronted with a rising tide of changes over which they had no control. You couldn't have done any better if you had been in their place. Even so, if they had stuck together, we would have died for them. You would not have had a chance to capture this city intact. But there wasn't even a major battle. The city was just handed over to you fellows. Because you brought over a few shabby troops and a couple of cannon, the Tokugawa leaders, who knew nothing but luxurious living, lost even their code of honor. And who suffers? Not the Tokugawa. Not you. The common people who have lived here peacefully for centuries. Look, the people are starving. Their daughters are in brothels and in the geisha profession!" Her voice rose to a scream.

"Listen! My father was of the honorable *hatamoto* class, the Shogun's immediate vassal, and far above you Sat-cho *ashigaru* who call yourselves our masters. To save my family from starvation I became a geisha girl. Once I sang for my parents' pleasure. Now I entertain strangers—the Sat-cho themselves."

She was dazed, her face lifeless, her eyes closed. Her pretty *nagajiban* skirt parted at her knees. At every sentence she threw back the dishevelled strands of long black hair falling on her face.

There was no sound of music or song or whispering in the room, except Omura's snoring. Kido's arms were folded; the others had lowered their eyes.

Tama breathed a long sigh and picked up another cup filled with stale liquor.

"Oh—well—well—maybe you people have a cure for Tokyo's troubles. If you have, I'm—I'm—" Suddenly she slumped down and was fast asleep on the matting, like a rain-soaked cherry blossom in the moonlight.

The spell was broken by the entry of the *josho* and her chief clerk, the *banto*. They bowed low, their eyes towards Kido, and thanked him for his payment for the party and the ample tips to the entertainers and the Nakamura-ro household.

Then the geisha, *oshaku*, *maiko*, and *hokan* also bowed.

Saionji, the host, was bewildered, and pale with sake.

"Councillor Kido, I gave this party. I didn't want anybody to pay—"

The councillor, with a smile on his reddened face, raised his hand: "Let's not talk about money matters. Let me share your burden—it's my expression of thanks for your association with us—"

The voice and manner were gentle but decisive.

Kido offered Saionji the red lacquer cup: "We'll cement our friendship. Pass it to General Omura after you drink—"

More sake and plates arrived. The *josho* announced that these were the Nakamura-ro's tribute to the distinguished guests.

The merriment began again.

Towards dawn the entertainers slipped out, one by one.

Saionji looked at Tama who was still sleeping. "One wouldn't have thought—" he murmured.

A hand rested on his shoulder: "Kido and I are leaving now. We'll see you tomorrow. And—take care of that girl."

II

STUDENT

CHAPTER II

STUDENT

"Prince, are you up?" came the cheerful voice of Okiku, the young geisha who some months before had made the bold speech at the Nakamura-ro party.

"Almost ready, Okiku."

"Here is your basin of water and a towel, sir. I brought them myself."

"I guess you snatched them from the maid, huh?"

The warm sunshine was already radiant on the paper screens.

While waiting for Saionji to come out, she bent over the water to study her reflection. She took a comb from the folds of her sash.

"I see you, Okiku. Your pretty shadow is on the screen."

"Don't tease me, Prince."

"Were you up late last night?"

"No, sir. No merrymaking these days. Times are getting from bad to worse."

"Why is it so dull?"

"Why? Oh, you *Okuge-sama!* Don't you know anything? You are just as bad as those *daimyo*." She dipped the comb into the water and drew it through her hair.

"Started again!"

"The Shogun and *daimyo* used to get their money from all over the country and spend it in allowances to the *hatamoto* and other retainers. That finally came down to us geisha." She powdered her nose and reddened her lips with *beni*.

"Huh."

"But the Shogun is gone. The people have no jobs."

"I see!"

Okiku's delicate fingers and comb were still busy.

"If all that's true, why are you so concerned about your make-up?"

"You are really mean! Don't you think I want you to—I mean I want to look decent at any time. What keeps you in bed so long, anyway?"

"Huh, now you're teasing me, huh?"

"Tired from too much drinking?"

43

"No. I am used to that now, but I am thinking—thinking, not drinking. I am much puzzled these days. Many things have come to my attention—"

"Things whose existence you never guessed. So you're growing serious. Well, I was that way too, when I came away from my people. You had never been out of the Kyoto palace grounds?"

"Only the last fourteen months of my life."

"You are just an infant in the hard and cold reality of the world. I am now at home in it."

"To hear you talk one would think you knew something."

"Maybe I do."

"If I were to be honest, I would have to admit that you have taught me some things. Say, Okiku, about the *Go-Isshin*, the New Start, you know—"

"I hear *Go-Isshin* everywhere, too. It's a slogan, but I don't know what it means."

"Huh, some think we are going to start back in the period of the multiple gods."

"That sounds like nonsense to me. How can we go back to cave life after we have lived many centuries of refinement? I don't want to change my silk kimono, though it's old, to a piece of bark or a leaf of hemp-palm, for instance. But talking about changes, how would you like the way of the Westerners, the civilized people?"

She was still bent over the mirroring water, and turned her head from side to side. Saionji, in a *tanzen*, stood behind her unnoticed.

"Prince, aren't you going to get up? Don't you want my company?— Oh, you frightened me!" Okiku gasped as she saw his handsome face reflected beside hers.

Laughing, she left the basin.

When he had finished washing, Saionji stepped into his clogs, that stood on the clay pavement outside the veranda. He walked about in the inner garden. Okiku followed him.

"I hadn't noticed this *yamazakura* here. Oh, it has several flowers open! Aren't they graceful?" He pointed to a branch with young buds.

"This cherry is a very early variety, Prince."

"And look at that plum tree—no more flowers, all green leaves. It still had blossoms left when you made your famous speech in our company when General Omura and Councillor Kido were here. You don't make speeches any more."

She was embarrassed. "I remember I met those distinguished people, but I don't remember what I said. The others often refer to it."

"Councillor Kido was much moved by your eloquence. He repeatedly said, 'The drunkard tells the truth!' "

"Let's not talk about it.—What are you going to do today, Prince?"

"Well, I'll take a walk after breakfast. I don't know anything about Tokyo—which is the business section, or which is the residential part, even. So I'd better look around a little. Won't you come with me?"

"I?"

"Are you busy?" They circled the ponds.

"No. You see, you are an *Okuge-sama* of the Imperial Court, and a Commander-General, and so on. I am a geisha girl. Of course I might like to. But what would your relatives and friends think of you if you appeared in the streets with me?"

"What of it? This is the time of the New Start. I am for the abolition of all the social castes which make us class-conscious and cause prejudices and hatreds among us. Personally, I hope that they will take away the discriminating term *eta* from the outcasts and make everybody equal in Nippon. To prove my point, I'd even marry an *eta*."

"Are you serious?" Okiku laughed convulsively and asked again: "Are you serious?"

"Certainly. This is the new era. Our leaders say that all Nipponese are now the Emperor's *Sekishi*, the true children. If that is so, there mustn't be any differences in the family."

"My! So you'll show them the way. The young handsome *Okuge-sama* takes a bride from the *eta* group. Well, I will tell you your fortune free of charge. The courtier and distinguished Commander-General Saionji Kimmochi, the thirty-third successor to the noted Fujiwara family, will soon be engaged to a princess of the Imperial scion."

Okiku was half-laughing. They returned to Saionji's room.

Otake, whom he had named 'Button-nose,' had cleaned his room and packed the bedding in a closet behind the slides. She was bringing in his breakfast.

Okiku sat on the edge of the veranda.

"I'd like to wait on you some day."

"Huh."

"Really, Prince. You alone, no one else."

"From now on, don't call me Prince; call me by my name."

After eating, he changed his *tanzen* to a street kimono. Okiku was still lingering in the garden.

"This is really a fine spring day. I feel as if this carefree life were soon coming to a stop. But it's pleasant while it lasts.—Say really, will you take a walk with me?" Saionji insisted.

"Maybe."

"Where shall we go? To Uyeno Hills? Are there early cherry trees?"

"Some. But it's not a good section to go to. That's where General Omura's men killed those three thousand *Shogitai* volunteers."

"He told me something about that battle."

"Yes, the Uyeno is no place for sight-seeing now. All the fine Tokugawa temples and other buildings were burned down to the ground, and nothing has been done except to remove the bodies."

"Then let's walk along the bank of Sumida River, up to Ryogoku and to Nihombashi."

"Don't think you're going to see clear and fast-moving water like that of the Kamo River in your old home town, Prince. Our Sumida is dirty and almost still."

"I've read about your river in poetry. But our Kamo makes silk textiles very lustrous, and it's good for the complexion, too. That's why Kyoto girls are pretty."

"I suppose you mean that other women are ugly." Okiku adjusted her kimono collar.

"No, that's just an expression of love for my native town."

"Provincial pride—or are you homesick for some Kyoto beauty?"

"Don't be jealous. Let's go."

They strolled out into the street and to the river bank, she at some distance behind. It took repeated urging to make her walk beside him, in the 'new way.'

"Prince, do you see that boat below us? That's a *yakatabune*. It belongs to the Nakamura-ro."

"It's very shabby."

"It's been idle for years. In good times people used to pay a lot of money to take geisha and have feasts on that boat at night. They lighted the paper lanterns and plied up and down the stream."

"That, too, has been told in literature. Okiku, I'll have a surprise for you pretty soon. You'll be amazed. I have a big parcel coming from Kobe. My first European suit of clothes, with shirts, shoes, hat, cane, gloves, and everything."

"How funny you'll look. So you begin your *Go-Isshin* by changing your clothes."

"In a way, yes. I'll go to Yokohama in the next few days to have my hair cut by a European barber who's attached to the foreign marines there."

"So far away?"

"Yes, one or two barbers opened in Tokyo, but they're crude."

"It's expensive, too, going twenty miles for that, and anyway, do you have to cut off your beautiful long hair, topknot and all? It almost makes me weep to think of it." She studied his noble profile.

"It is *Go-Isshin*. We must get rid of the obstacles in the way of the new life. A man's topknot is one of them and the *samurai* sword is another. Anyway, I'll go to Yokohama. If I have it done at all, it must be a thorough job, by an expert."

"As usual."

They were conscious of the many eyes their novel appearance attracted, as they walked through the winding streets lined with low-framed storehouses, and came to the Ryogoku bridge, over the romantic Sumida River.

They were leaning over the railing in the middle of the bridge. Saionji asked: "Those boats with rush-mat awnings like thatched roofs are the famous *tomabune*, aren't they? The water along both banks is literally covered with them. I've read many stanzas about their sake and rice cargoes and the lovely songs of their boatmen, but I never thought I'd see them.—Do you have training in *waka*, thirty-one syllable-poetry, Okiku?" he asked suddenly.

"Just a little, Prince. My mother was fond of it, and taught me when I was a girl. I studied it until I became a geisha."

"Why are all the boats idle? Where are the crews?"

"There's nothing for them to do."

"Why?"

"No cargoes, no jobs."

"I suppose this, according to you, is also due to the fall of the Tokugawa. I am beginning to believe some of the things you and the *josho* told me. First I thought it was just hearsay."

There was a group of young, flat-nosed girls with babies on their backs, singing in low nasal tones:

> If you want to see pretty Tokyo, see it now.
> This great flowery city will soon be a barren field.

"Did you hear what they sang, Prince? It's true."

They walked down the bridge road.

"About marrying an *eta*," she stammered. "Would you marry her because you loved her, or just to be *Go-Isshin?*"

"What a question. Love is just for poetry and songs. In marriage there is a principle at stake."

"What principle?"

Her mouth trembled, and for a long time there was silence.

"Your stores seem to be shutting up, too," he finally said, indicating the carts laden with shop and household goods.

"They're going to the country. When seven hundred thousand of the two million people move out of Tokyo, the stores go with them. Only those who are too poor to go, stay here."

"What will they do?"

"Oh, plant the vacant lots with tea and mulberry as the new Government ordered.—Shall we walk as far as the signboard at Nihombashi and then come back along the canal, Prince? We'll be heading for the fish markets that way, though."

"Huh."

"An *Okuge-sama* wouldn't like smells and mud. That would be too much for your delicate upbringing."

"Why, Okiku—you never talked that way before. You seem angry. I didn't mean to hurt you." Saionji paused. "Well, here's the signboard. Three hundred and twenty-six miles to Kyoto. It's like the other end of the world, such a great distance. Oh, and here's an announcement. Okiku, your Tokyo will be prosperous again. The Emperor is coming here. To live—next month! Isn't that fine?" Saionji was sincerely glad.

They turned to the left.

"Since we started this way, we'll continue even if the mud is knee deep." The two picked their way carefully over the drying pools in the road.

"But is this the fish market? Where are the people?"

"Poor people get up early, Prince. They don't lie abed all morning. They get up at midnight and work until noon."

"Okiku, you are sharp-tongued today. I don't like you that way."

"Or any other way," she said before she thought.

"Okiku, why do you walk behind me again? Here, I'm so grateful to you. You have opened my eyes. My days of indolence are over. From now on, I'm going to devote my time to the real *Go-Isshin*. Outward reforms are not enough. I will study the translations of political economy that Kido has. I shall learn the foreign languages. Who knows, perhaps I shall even go to Europe. I shall really serve the new

Nippon. And it's all due to you. Don't shake your head. Come, to celebrate my new intentions, I'll treat you. We'll go to Asakusa Temple
Square and eat *sukiyaki* there. It's a mixture of sliced beef and vegetables cooked in front of one. How would you like that? Would you
be my sweet little Okiku again?"

"*Sukiyaki?* I've heard about it, but I wouldn't like to eat the flesh
of a cow. The cow is Buddha's messenger."

"Those are old ideas; when food is tasty and good you should eat it."

Saionji was walking from his Nakamura-ro home to the headquarters
of the new Government in Edo Castle, whence the former Tokugawa
Shogun had been banished for all time.

It was a late spring morning.

The odorous warmth brought beads of perspiration to Saionji's
brow. "Such weather the first time I wear them," he murmured to
himself. He was uncomfortable. There were painful blisters on his
heels and toes, his arms felt stiff, as if they were in a brace. A choking
sensation closed his throat, and the bobbing on his head kept time to
his cautious gait.

He was a new man. The topknot and two swords had disappeared.
His black hair was carefully barbered in the latest European fashion.
A high silk hat, a black frock-coat with flapping tails, black and
gray striped trousers, patent leather shoes, an uncertain bow-tie and
white gloves completed his costume. In his hand he twirled a Malacca
cane.

Many curious eyes were peering from behind creaking paper screens.
Saionji did not dare stop or turn back. His head up, he stubbornly
continued on his way, consoling himself with the memory of his image
in the looking-glass.

Gradually the haze drifted away, taking the fish smell with it. In
the distance, the snow-cap of Fujisan loomed.

Saionji entered the zone of the *daimyo* mansions where the large
houses stood like the cast-off shells of cicadas—empty. Small companies
of *samurai*, assigned to patrol duty, paced the deserted streets.

Unmindful of their stares, steeling himself against the scratching and
creaking and chafing of his new garments, Saionji managed to keep
up an even pace until he had reached the main entrance of Edo Castle.
Between him and the stone gate was a deep moat. A wooden bridge
arched over the reflections of the white clouds and the blue sky on
the water. On the massive gray stone walls surrounding the grounds,

grew aged green pines. Farther on stood the three-storied castle tower with a sloping black tiled roof.

Everyone stopped dead to stare at the strange apparition. To Saionji his own footsteps sounded like thunder on the planks of the bridge.

"Halt! Who are you? Where are you going?" demanded one of the *samurai* in front of the gate. A score of Choshu men glared at the newcomer.

"I am Saionji Kimmochi. I am going to headquarters to see Councillor Kido." The sworded men fell back and saluted him.

"Attention! Attention! Attention! Guards!"

Saionji and the sentries turned their eyes to look beyond the bridge. They saw a company of *samurai*, their leader like a huge tea-kettle on horseback, his short fat legs extending stiffly on either side of the steed. He was bareheaded, and his thick hair waved down to his shoulders.

In front of the guards he dismounted. He gave the reins to his follower, and proceeded with the rest.

"Who's that?" He walked towards Saionji.

"Ah, Saionji-san! Well, well, well—it's our Commander-General, Courtier Saionji Kimmochi himself. Ha! Ha!" He came close to Saionji and looked him up and down: "Say, they do it this way, don't they?" To the young man's amazement he took the slender hand into his massive grasp and shook it up and down. "That's the way my Dutch acquaintances do it." He took a few steps backward and slowly walked around Saionji.

"This is certainly ultra-modern. Splendid stuff and tailoring. Convenient. Neat. How would I look in an outfit like that?" He took the silk hat and put it on his immense head. His gaze travelled from Saionji to his own bulk and back again.

Shaking his mane, he set the hat back on its owner's head. With habitual cynicism he curled his thick lips.

"And a little over a year ago you were happy to wear your ancestral armor, and martial robe. You carried the Emperor-bestowed sword, and gallantly rode your brown steed under the Mikado's Banner of Golden Brocade."

Tapping the narrow shoulder with his stubby hand, he added: "How would you have looked on the Tamba front in that? A scarecrow for the vultures." His glances, nevertheless, were filled with secret admiration.

At every tap, Saionji was afraid his hat would fall off. His blisters burned painfully.

Turning to the guards, Omura said: "You men! This is Prince Saionji, once my disciple. Then he was a Commander-General, a Chief of Staff, and Governor of Echigo, even if he does look like a Dutch fashion-plate for statesmen and diplomats now." Then he turned back to Saionji. "And whom did you want to see here?"

"I have a petition to present at headquarters."

"That's not my field. Okubo or Kido's inside. Ask him. I have to go on an inspection tour. I'm supervising the military guards for the entry of the Imperial Train when it comes next week."

With a grudging "Good luck, young diplomat!" the general rode away. Under the escort of two guards, Saionji reached the temporary administration office in Edo Castle.

When he entered the vast hall, which was formerly the waiting-chamber for the *daimyo* and their followers, the doorkeeper ordered him to remove 'those things.' Gratefully, his swollen feet met the straw mat. As he passed between the rows of low desks, the entire office force, from one end of the hall to the other, got up on their feet to see their countryman in European clothes. By this time, stares and comments were an old story to Saionji. He was beginning to enjoy the excitement that rolled up behind him.

Kido was busy at his desk in the furthest corner, but the commotion penetrated his thoughts.

Kido rose.

"What's this, friends?" His low, weighty voice rang through the hall. Those who caught the piercing, imperturbable eyes began a quick retreat to their places.

Out of the receding mass, Saionji emerged, holding his hat in one hand and his cane and gloves in the other—Western fashion.

"Saionji-san! So that's what the noise was about." Kido's face broke into a smile.

Saionji wiped his forehead busily with a handkerchief.

"I had this ordered through Governor Ito Hirobumi of Hyogo."

"Ah, ah, Ito handled it for you." With folded arms Kido studied his visitor. He squatted on the mat and watched the young man do likewise.

The sharpness of the crease in his trousers showed that they were about to be sat in for the first time. After much ado, Saionji finally managed to sit cross-legged.

Kido said: "Hah! That's the only way to do until our houses are furnished to suit the European ways of living. I always thought that sitting on our matted floor would be very difficult in such clothes. Where did you leave your shoes?"

Saionji told him.

"So you've got to take them off too before you step on the mat. What do you call this style?"

"I don't know."

"It must be like our *montsuki haori.* I saw the European ministers wearing something like that on formal occasions. Well, what brings you here?"

"Councillor Kido, I want you to do three things for me."

Encouraged by Kido's smile, he went on.

"Huh, I want to resign at once from the governorship of Echigo, as I requested some months past; secondly, I would like to have some Nipponese translations of European works on political economy; and the third—well, it's in this," he said, laying a folded paper on Kido's desk.

"I'll try, Saionji-san. Are the books for you?"

"Yes, Councillor Kido. I'm going to study!"

"That's fine, that's encouraging. Do you want to join the government's 'resident students abroad'?"

"Yes! That is the third request in my petition."

"Good!" Kido tapped his desk and continued: "So you are ready to throw all your privileges, inherited and earned, into the air like last year's blackened calligraphy notes, and practically start your life anew in keeping with the fundamental spirit of the *Go-Isshin!* To what country do you want to go, Saionji-san?"

"France."

"Good! Some go to America, others to England, and still others to Prussia and Russia. I am going to send my son. Councillor Okubo's two sons, who are very young, will join you. You people will make the nation one of the first-class world powers some day after we are gone. It is still confidential, but some of us councillors, say Okubo and me, for instance, are anxious to see Western countries, too, to learn their ways of handling public affairs. When we complete some major projects on the agenda, we'll come to see you there. What are you going to study in Europe?"

"Law. Although General Omura originally wanted me to take up military science, I told him I didn't like that—"

"He won't care. He is an expert on military strategy and tactics, but he is also broad-minded and a scholar himself.—Now, if you want to study in France, you must take up their language. Recently we appointed a Frenchman named Pouchet as an instructor of the language at the *Kaisei-sho* school, now our highest institution of learning. You study under him for a while, then you'll be sent to Nagasaki for some months for advanced training before you take your long trip. You can start your French tomorrow, if you wish. Is that too soon?"

"No, sir!"

"Good! How is the geisha who made the speech that night when I visited you at the Nakamura-ro? Have you called her again to any of your parties?"

The young man blushed the color of a roasted lobster.

"Saionji-san, don't be bashful! I am a veteran in that field of scarlet skirts, too! I sympathize with you. Give my regards to her when you see her next. I got several hints from her drunken eloquence! And, a geisha often becomes a model wife, virtuous, devoted, nice appearance—"

Saionji laughed.

"Huh, I forgot to thank you for your kindness in calming my relatives about my present living arrangement. Thanks to you, I can live where I want to."

"Don't mention it!"

Saionji found his shoes where he had left them, but he had no shoehorn. While he labored, a crowd assembled to watch the difficult performance.

On the way home he debated with himself about the advisability of continuing to wear this novel but inconvenient new outfit.

"Good morning, Prince! May I come in?"

"Otake, yes!" Button-nose was already folding up Saionji's bedding. Her cheeks resembled red turnips, and her legs were like half-gallon sake jugs. A towel was wound around her head.

"These days you are up so early," she said without stopping her work. "I used to clean your room last, in my forenoon duties. Now yours comes first, yes, sir!"

Saionji was at the desk.

"What's that, Prince? You are always mumbling something, like frogs in the rainy season. When they get angry they make that sound, 're, ra, res.' I've heard you the last three or four months. Are you trying to say them ten thousand times or more? Doesn't make sense to me!"

She went on and on while Saionji concentrated on his French pronunciation. Like all his countrymen, the *l* sound was one of the most difficult for him to master. For example, he could not distinguish *roi* from *loi*. To get it correctly, every morning before he began his day's work, he sat down at the desk and tried *le, la, les* and similar words.

The Nakamura-ro household knew when he was up by the noise of his practicing.

"I still can't do it," he murmured to himself in disgust, and went on, "I think it's all right, but Professor Pouchet laughs at me."

The maid was sweeping with a broom of hemp-palm. "Oh, something like my work, Prince. I think I do a good job, but the Big Sister tells me, 'Otake, would you go over there and see what you left undone!' Ha, ha, ha!"

"Button-nose, it is no joke!" He turned toward her. "And don't stir up so much dust."

"That's right, it aren't, Prince! If I don't keep Big Sister satisfied, I lose my job. No joke, no, sir!"

"Would you tell the *josho* to have a *jinrikisha* ready for me, Otake?"

"What, sir?"

"*Jin-ri-ki-sha!* Do you understand? Just tell her the new carriage!"

"Oh, that man-pulled thing. I saw one yesterday on the Ryogoku Bridge. The crowd watched the pretty geisha in it. They said she would fall out."

He was amused. "Did she?"

"No, but while I watched she was going up and down on it like a wave," Otake said, swinging both her arms. "Prince, you'd better walk or take a palanquin instead. Only one wheel on each side and a man in front pulling. He can't see his customer, he won't know when he loses him on the street. The palanquin is far better 'cause two men carry you, one in front and one in back.—Well, I hope to see you here tomorrow morning doing 'ra' stuff, instead of lying somewhere with your pretty face all scratched up."

The jinrikisha was at the gate.

"*Danna*, where do you want to go?" asked the half-naked jinrikisha-man.

"To Shinagawa, and to Kyoto, and on to Nagasaki—"

"*Danna*, I can't haul you to Shinagawa. That's too far, over six miles. Some day I hope to pull you fifteen miles in one stretch. At present two miles is all I can run. The wheel is new—"

"Go as far as you can."

Saionji climbed in. They started slowly towards the Shinagawa road.

At the Nakamura-ro, Button-nose was shouting: "*Jin-riki-ya-san*, rikishaman, bring him back alive! Don't upset him into the water."

Saionji's long-cherished hope to go abroad to study was at last to be fulfilled in January 1871, the fourth year of Meiji. It was one of the most momentous years in the reconstruction period under the new Imperial Government. That very summer, the last vestige of the old order, the holding of territorial possessions by the local *daimyo*, came to an end, thereby clearing the ground for genuine political and social reforms.

The former Commander-General and Governor of Echigo had been officially relieved of his public duties in July 1869, and his French courses at Nagasaki were finished. An American ship, the S.S. *Costa Rica*, was to carry more than thirty government students, young and old, across the Pacific from Yokohama to San Francisco. While many were to remain in America, others, like Saionji, were destined for Europe.

The steamer was an odd-looking craft with paddle wheels. The appearance of the Nipponese passengers differed greatly; some were in native attire with topknot, kimono, two swords, and clogs; some had hair closely cropped; still others, though uncomfortable, were proud of their complete European outfits. Their pursuits, with military science predominating, were as varied as their clothing.

In due time, Saionji reached the Atlantic Coast. While most of his companions proceeded directly to their destinations, he with a few others came to Washington, D. C., and was received in audience by President Grant. He was impressed by woman's place in American society. Wherever he went, women appeared in public with their husbands. Though he was an ardent advocate of the abolition of social castes among the people in his native land where women were usually neither seen nor heard, he was startled to see social equality between the sexes accepted as a matter of course.

Via London, he came to Paris in the spring of the same year.

At first Paris reminded him of the sad and defeated Nipponese cities he had conquered during the civil wars.

The pessimistic atmosphere in the French capital, which had surrendered to the Prussian army less than two months before his arrival, depressed him. His exhausting trip and his difficulty with the language, particularly in speaking, added to his disillusionment.

His vague intention to study French law became more vague. He was too old to enjoy the mechanical work of memorizing, yet he could not go back home without obtaining the laurels for which he had set out. Furthermore, scores of fellow students, mostly younger than he, were now in Europe and America. He could not admit defeat.

He knew only that Sagami and Okiku and the mistress of the Nakamura-ro were several worlds away; that he would have exchanged all of France with its thick stone walls, its modish clothes and chattering crowds, for a hempen kimono, a matted floor and a dish of pickled plums.

Saionji and a Parisian girl were entering the Café Américain on the Boulevard des Capucines.

There in the restaurant was another young Nipponese. His smart clothes and his conversation with a *demi-mondaine* made him conspicuous. As he entered, Saionji noticed that the man was flushed from drinking.

Shortly, he approached Saionji's table.

"What is *furyu?*" asked the immaculately dressed intruder.

"To flirt just as tenaciously with a woman as you do!" Saionji replied quickly.

"Ha, ha, ha, you are sarcastic. But your ready wit is simply startling—"

"Ha!"

"You are all right, friend! I am Komyoji Saburo." He pulled out his handkerchief, drenched with perfume, and wiped his face.

"I am Saionji Kimmochi."

"Glad to see you!"

They bowed to each other.

Saionji's companion looked on.

"Let's join and make merry. I have already had plenty of good wine, though!" Komyoji sat down at the table.

"It's wonderful to find a countryman and be able to talk whole sentences without thinking of words, words, isn't it, Saionji-san?"

"I agree with you one hundred per cent." They talked in Nipponese, sang native songs, and forgot the girl.

She had a hard time keeping her eyes open when she heard the tunes that sounded like religious chants to her.

"Have you been in Paris long?" asked Komyoji.

"No. But it seems years to me, on account of the inconveniences, and my unsuccessful attempts to pursue my major studies—"

"Yes." Komyoji nodded.

Both were temporarily dejected.

"Saionji-san, this is the only way to forget our troubles and amuse ourselves."

"True."

Then Komyoji studied Saionji and said: "You don't mind my giving you some friendly advice, do you?"

"No. On what?"

"Don't think I'm drunk! I'm not, am I?" He wiped his face again.

"Huh, go ahead!"

"If you want to come and enjoy your evenings here, you must dress fashionably. You look like a tramp. Don't get angry, but you do! And—smell my handkerchief—do you get it? Use good perfume once in a while! Mademoiselle, don't you agree with me? I bet you do— but she doesn't know what I'm saying. Well, we'll leave her alone!"

She looked up sleepily and yawned.

"Let's exchange glasses, Komyoji-san."

"Do you get many letters from home?" Komyoji asked between hiccups.

"Yes, often."

"They make me more and more homesick. Ah, it's many thousand miles away—which way, east or west, Saionji-san?"

"Oh, it doesn't matter! What does matter is to get something worth-while for our people and for—"

"For the government authorities—"

"And for the Imperial Family! Let me tell you, Ko-Komyoji, my good friend, the government is nothing. Do you know that? I appreciated the fact that the Satsuma and Choshu men, some of whom are my benefactors and friends, have done a great deal for the restoration of the powers to the Imperial Family, but I am afraid they are going to usurp the Mikado's prerogatives or come between the Emperor and the people—"

"Don't slight our leaders. Who are you anyway? Saionji— Oh, are you that Commander-General of the Tamba Expedition, about whom my benefactor, Inouye, told me?"

"Maybe."

"Hu'm." Komyoji leaned over the table, hiccuping. "Don't slight them even if you are that *Okuge-sama* and drunk. I, I am from Choshu myself. Do you know I was actually baptized with cannon fire and blood?"

"Huh?"

"Do you remember in August 1864, when the seventeen British, French, Dutch and American warships bombarded our fortresses at Shimonoseki, in Choshu, and exacted a huge indemnity from us? I was fourteen years old. I volunteered under General Omura and, in the provincial army, fought the losing battle in defense of our shores. The foreigners praised our bravery and tactics, though we lost against their superior forces—"

"Huh, I remember that, I also was fourteen then."

"I met Inouye Kaoru during that conflict and have followed him ever since, particularly in our war in the next year against the Shogun who mobilized the whole nation against Choshu. What happened then? This time that *Dharma* General's strategy worked marvellously and the Choshu defeated the Tokugawa contingent in every sector. Our victory encouraged armed rebellion against the Feudal Regime. Well, although my father is a Buddhist priest, I was persuaded by my sponsor to study military science in this country, but now I'm taking up law—"

"Huh, so that's how you know Inouye. You know Kido, also of your province?"

"Do I? He's one of the biggest men in Nippon, though I think Inouye is a coming leader—I guess you know them too."

"Kido and General Omura are my sponsors."

"Do you know that Kido and the other big men are coming to Paris on their tours?"

Saionji, who stroked the sleeping girl's hair, mentally recounted the occurrences during his association with the Sat-cho leaders before the days of the 1868 civil strife.

"Waiter, fill our glasses! We'll go after this," said Saionji.

There wasn't another person in sight except the waiter pacing the aisle between the tables.

The three got to their feet with the glasses in their hands.

Said the eloquent Komyoji: "Here is to our future, our country—"

"Our Imperial Family!" Saionji finished; the girl smiled. They drank the wine in one gulp.

Komyoji tried to put his glass on the table like the others, but he staggered. Saionji tried to reach him. Komyoji's glass flew out of his hand, and hit the window. Saionji's companion gasped.

"Look, you broke it!" shouted the waiter, rushing towards them.

"What shall we do, Saionji-san?"

"Very sorry, waiter! He didn't mean it. It was a pure accident—"

"Accident? Nothing! You must pay for it or—"

"Or what?" The embarrassed Komyoji turned to him.

"Wait, Komyoji! So you demand that we should pay for it?"

"Certainly!"

"Very well! How much is it?"

The waiter went over to the manager and asked the cost, while Saionji whispered to Komyoji, who was grinning.

"This is for the bill and for the pane and your tip," he said when the waiter had returned.

"Thanks!" As he took the money they made ready to depart, coat and hat on one arm and the cane on the other.

"We paid for the window, too, didn't we?" Saionji asked.

"Yes!" The waiter was more than satisfied to get the money for the window without argument.

"Since we paid for it, Komyoji-san, it's ours. Is it not? Are you ready?" Saionji lifted his cane. "Step back farther!" he instructed his weary companion. Komyoji, too, held his stick tightly in his right hand.

"Go!" The canes of the young men flew at the large pane. The first blow, a second and a third blow crashed against the stained glass.

"Huh, it's ours—!"

Bang, bang, until the last piece of the pane fell from the window frame.

Leaving the dazed waiter behind, they went out into the street.

They were quite sober now.

"Do you know, to get the language, they say it is better to live with the people," said Komyoji, while they were waiting for a carriage.

"I think so," the other agreed with a smile.

Komyoji looked at him: "What do you mean? Are you snickering? What do you mean?"

"Oh, nothing!" Saionji eyed his pretty companion.

"You don't mean you are living with this *demoiselle*, do you?"

"Ha, ha, ha, not yet, but I might. How about it?" But the girl did not understand.

"Oh! You are a big fox! I give up. I go home this way. *Sayonara!* Meet you here again soon!"

"All right! See you soon and we'll drink to forget our troubles."

Saionji and the girl entered a carriage and drove towards the Rue de Bac.

It was in a cozy room in Saionji's Parisian boardinghouse. On his desk were French law texts and a few old volumes of Nipponese poetry.

One of his visitors was Matsuda Masahisa, an army lieutenant. He had grown an impressive mustache, his black hair fell over a high, square forehead, and his deep-set eyes under heavy eyebrows were brilliant. He was tall for a Nipponese.

"Monsieur Saionji, I have given up my intention of studying military science and am now in the field of law. I understand that you are too," he said in the accents of Southern Nippon.

"Huh, that's right, Matsuda-san. My intimate friend, Komyoji, is taking the same course."

"That stylish Choshu man—"

"Did he come here for military training, too?" asked a bespectacled scholar.

"That's right, Nakae-san. He is supposed to come here today. What are you interested in?" Saionji asked.

Nakae Chomin stroked his smooth, pointed chin. "I'm also a law student. At present, I am devoting my time to translating Rousseau's *Social Contract* into Nipponese."

"And you are translating a Nipponese play into French, aren't you?"

"Huh, I want to undertake some poems, too."

"What are you planning, Monsieur?" The scholar smiled in anticipation as Saionji cleared his desk.

"Nakae-san, when you and Matsuda-san are present, we never depart without 'solving' the country's problems and drying up several wine bottles." The host filled assorted glasses with wine.

"You are the senior among us, Matsuda-san. Will you take this glass?" He continued to serve his guests.

Komyoji came in, looking downcast.

"Ha, here's our best-dressed man!" Matsuda roared.

"Say, what's the matter with you, my friend? Take a drink. You'll get your spirit back!"

Komyoji wiped his face with the perfumed handkerchief after emptying a glass.

"Well, this may cheer me, Monsieur!" but his melancholy mood returned. The others ignored him.

Matsuda proposed a toast: "Let us drink to the new Nippon." All drank. "I wonder how Tokyo looks now, with telegraph, gas lights, mail service, jinrikisha and horse-carriages, national banks—what else—public schools, even a steam train between Yokohama and Tokyo. No more wearing of the two swords, no topknots, no more private revenge, no licensing of prostitutes—the lower classes are allowed to ride horseback—"

Saionji added: "Don't forget national currency, compulsory vaccination against smallpox—"

"And," Nakae interrupted, "conscript military service, the abolition of the local lords and their territorial possessions, the Gregorian calendar and so many other improvements have been made already. It won't seem like home when we get there."

He wiped his glasses and continued:

"You know, there are some amusing confusions. Sometime ago, my uncle gave me an account of an innocent mistake. A fellow in Tokyo wanted to know how his father in Yokohama was getting along. He had heard about the telegraph and its speedy communication, so he went to the near-by telegraph pole and shouted: 'How are you, Father?' and put his ear close to it to get his answer. He thought the hum of the wires was his father's snoring."

They laughed, and Saionji remarked:

"Mistakes of that nature and misunderstandings occur in such times, and the misunderstandings lead to discord and enmity. The conservatives, for instance, always oppose progressive measures of the new Government, no matter on what question. You know, my mentor, General Omura, was one of the victims of the reactionaries. He was fatally wounded at Kyoto before I left for France. I think there will be many more like him who will perish because of their progressive work during the period of transition.

"But at least there is now a closer union between the Mikado and the people. At that railway opening ceremony, for example, where the Emperor delivered an address—that was an epoch-making incident; there was no precedent for it. And another instance is His Majesty's participation in military manoeuvres. To think of his encamping with the soldiers in the fields, and in a heavy rainstorm, at that—"

"Who is really running the government?" someone asked.

"The Councillors of State, particularly those four leaders, Iwakura, Kido, Okubo, and Saigo. Don't you think so, Matsuda-san?"

"Yes."

"Do you think those great men will eventually grasp the power as the Tokugawas did?" Nakae was frowning.

"No, Nakae-san, I don't think so. First of all, they are unselfish, although they may have the ambition to keep their followers in important positions to carry out their programs. In that connection, I got a hint from Kido when the envoys were here. He said then he was interested in the British form of government, but he also said that he believed in a written pattern for the basic political organization so that it could not be altered by a few. After Kido reached home, he presented a memorandum to the Council of State for the adoption of a constitution."

"I never heard of that," Nakae said.

The streets were growing quiet. The second bottle of wine was empty.

"I guess Kido wants to expand what back in March 1868 the Emperor proclaimed as the 'Oath of the Five Articles,' the fundamental principles for the future political system of the country. Kido, who had written part of the document, seemed to think that it somewhat resembled the Magna Charta of the English, and he wanted to put more detail into the new document—like the constitution of the United States of America. He wants to define the division of powers."

"Say, who will be Kido's successor from the Choshu group?"

"Yamagata or Ito. Ito is very smàrt, and Kido's real protégé."

While the others talked, Komyoji went to Saionji's bookshelf. He smiled when he noticed the book of Nipponese poetry.

"Monsieur," Komyoji asked, "how soon will you be going back to Professor Gautier?" He looked hopefully at Saionji.

The host did not catch the question, but the lieutenant heard it and commented: "Well, Komyoji, I was told that our Monsieur and Madame Mendes are co-operating in the translation of plays and poems—"

Komyoji leaned towards Matsuda.

"Say, you are not interested in that young woman, are you?" Matsuda's teasing voice attracted the whole company. He went on: "I hope your case is not, as we say at home, 'one-sided love like a sea-ear shell'! Monsieur, you must help him out. How soon will you see her?"

"In a few days—"

"May I go with you?" Komyoji asked quietly.

"Huh, huh, why not?"

Saionji was at Professor Acollas'. He spoke earnestly.

"Following your kind advice, Professor Acollas, I'll leave the city shortly for my own country. Many, many thanks to you and your associates, like Milman and Georges Clemenceau, for your help during my stay here!"

"Monsieur Saionji, I'm glad to hear your decision. Your sojourn has been long and by your untiring efforts you completed the courses at our highest institution of learning. Although we like to have you here among us, your intimate friends want to see you go back to your home and contribute to the reconstruction of your country. Your knowledge and experience should be invaluable to Nippon."

"I'll try my best to live up to your expectations."

"What'll be your line of activity in the Far East?"

"I can't decide yet."

"You have an excellent background, we understand, in the political field."

"Well, Professor, I used to have some connections—"

"Some? Plenty, if you choose to look them up. Several years ago, when those envoys came, the leaders were very intimate with you and they spoke of you highly."

"Three of the best of the group have passed away. Kido is dead, and Okubo was murdered, and Saigo died on his own sword. Things have changed since I left the country in 1871. It is over nine years ago. I am inclined to fight for the 'people' against the autocratic government which is led by my acquaintances who are the successors to those past great leaders. These Satsuma and Choshu men are striving hard to get the power into their own hands, as we thought they would."

"I see. You are going back to a country in political turmoil."

"Professor, as you know, when the feudal regime was overthrown in 1868, in which I too had a humble part, the Sat-cho were the dynamic strength. Now we fear that they, too, will eventually usurp the sovereign powers of the Mikado. To me, our Emperor is the father of his beloved children. It is not his wish to treat them in a dictatorial manner." Saionji's face flushed.

"You realize how strange this sounds to my republican ears, but I understand the unique relationship between the Imperial Family and the people. So you'll fight for it."

"Yes."

"Capitalizing on your Western training?"

"That seems to me the only way, because I seem to have lost my prospects of getting a position since most of my senior friends are dead. There is already a political party headed by a former officer of the Imperial Army in the 1868 civil war. I know this man, Itagaki Taisuke, personally. Many of his followers were trained here in Europe. The party is getting strong. The government no longer can ignore the movement."

"And you will join him?"

"I'd like to. But one thing will be difficult for me. In my country, a politician can't say what he thinks, can't do what he says; occasionally he has to be a hypocrite and tell lies. This is very distressing to me!"

"You are fortunate if the politicians in your country can get along by lying only occasionally. In my country, everything, from top to bottom is a lie. There is no telling the truth. So don't quarrel with your destiny."

"Professor Acollas, this is farewell to you. I owe you so much since the days when you first tutored me in French law. In my excitement I have bored you with my political views!"

"I am delighted to hear your opinion, Monsieur Saionji. If you start now, when will you get there?"

"In the fall, the fall of the thirteenth year of Meiji, 1880. I'll travel with my friend, Komyoji."

"Good luck, Monsieur!"

"Farewell, Professor! I hope to be back to this country, my 'second home,' again!"

III

DIPLOMAT

what we advocated, but it doesn't seem like home. What confusion!"

"What, Monsieur?"

"Look at that young man," he said, gesturing towards a man on the sidewalk. "His cap, coat, necktie, trousers and shoes are all different in style, and probably of different origin, too. But huh—he seems proud to wear such clothes. And there are very few topknots left."

Saionji saw a few pretty girls strolling by. There were no changes in their costumes: Their hairdress, with the straight, long, lacquer-black hair fastened by a comb and a pin in flower design, was the same as always, and their kimonos of subdued striped stuff, covering even the ankle, had long sleeves, and the sashes around their chests were tied at the back. Their wooden clogs, striking the pavement with rhythmic sounds, made Saionji feel much at home. He studied the familiar profiles—from the forehead to the upper lip, an almost unbroken line.

While Saionji meditated, the driver's enthusiasm was overwhelming Komyoji: "*Dan-na*, since the *Go-Isshin* things have changed so fast and in every way. Now we can buy anything we want to, if we have the money to pay for it. Clothes, food, amusement-tickets, and hundreds of other things. We can go any place we want to—"

Komyoji too was eagerly studying the city. "Say, *bashaya*, are there any people that you know of who lost their jobs because of *Go-Isshin?* That is, after the government came into power."

"Yes, *Dan-na*, many people, but they got new jobs. Among us, the former *kagokaki* lost their palanquins, but they now have jinrikishas or horse-carriages. So it goes. Good times have come to Nippon. I remember when—"

He went on and on, explaining the situation, and frequently Komyoji remarked, "I see."

"Oh, *Dan-na*, there is another good thing. See, now even we can talk about politics. We even know of the fight between Councillor Okuma and the other Councillor of State. We get the news the day after it happens. It's very exciting."

Saionji heard Komyoji ask, "How is that?"

"We have newspapers. They tell us everything."

"Can you read the paper?"

"No, *Dan-na*."

He laughed aloud. Offended, the driver turned away.

Komyoji, laughing again, asked: "How can you understand it, if you can't read?"

"*Dan-na*, I have two eyes!" At that moment, the horse turned sharply to avoid another vehicle.

Saionji cautioned him: "Driver, be careful."

"Don't you see my eyes are just as good as yours?"

"I see, I see." Komyoji was slightly bored.

"*Dan-na*, you are slow. In these days of *Bummei-kaika* you don't need to read anything."

"You don't answer my question. How can anyone know what's in the paper if he can't read it? Does someone read it and tell the news to you?"

"I have two good eyes and see the pictures."

"What?"

"I buy the daily picture-paper. Don't you think when I see cartoons of Councillor Ito clenching his fists and Councillor Okuma putting his finger in his eye at him I know that there's something up? Besides, I have two good ears and hear my fares talk."

"Komyoji, it must be a pictorial newspaper that he's talking about. Well, at least it's a step forward from total ignorance."

"You are right, *Dan-na*," said the driver.

They came to the east end of the Ginza. The driver had to proceed more carefully, for the streets were narrow.

"Monsieur, are we going farther?"

"Yes."

Komyoji became drowsy, but Saionji was alert, studying the changed aspect of the capital.

The carriage went over more bridges. Every time the wheels and horses' hoofs pounded on the planks, Komyoji inquired as to the remaining distance. But when they crossed the last one, the Ryogoku bridge, he was fast asleep. Saionji continued to watch the scenes with keener interest.

Over ten years ago, he had taken a walk with Okiku on this street, as far as the Nihombashi. His recollection of that incident was vivid, as they approached their destination.

"*Dan-na*, are you going to the Nakamura-ro?"

"Yes, yes. Drive on!"

"This is the new *genkan*, *Dan-na*."

"Oh!"

"You didn't know the place has a big new annex?" the *bashaya* asked as he halted the carriage close to the receiving porch.

A maid was cleaning the veranda when Saionji alighted, followed by the still sleepy Komyoji.

Saionji paid the driver and turned to the clerk. "Is the *josho* at home?"

"Oh, oh, the Prince, the Prince! The Prince has come home!" The maid, screaming, a broom in her hand, jumped up and down on the veranda.

Then they heard the loud voice of the operator from inside the house: "What Prince? Who is it, Otake?"

" 'Re, ra, res' Prince! Here he is with another prince-like man."

"Well, well, what's this, in my humble living-quarters? What's on your mind?" Saionji had just come home from a public bathhouse, which he visited every evening following his lecture at the Meiji Law School, which later became Meiji University.

He had rented a small, flat frame house with modest furnishings. It had no garden space or *genkan*, the formal entrance to a Nipponese house, and was located behind one of the busiest Ginza blocks. His faithful governess, Sagami, frequently came to take care of his personal belongings.

Saionji greeted his visitors, Matsuda and his young companion. Matsuda had been in close contact with him since his student days in Paris. His comrade was about ten years younger than himself.

"Monsieur," Matsuda said, "this is my friend, and a very enterprising man. I would like to present Matsuzawa-kun to you!"

"With pleasure, Matsuzawa-kun."

"Professor Saionji, it certainly is a great honor to meet you. I have heard of your brilliant discourses on French liberalism in connection with your lectures on administrative laws at the Meiji Law School. Many students say that yours is one of the most lively and inspiring courses offered in the entire institution."

"Monsieur is considered a 'radical' there, are you not?" The older visitor smiled. Saionji grinned in response to their comments.

"Professor, we have a great project." The young man raised his right shoulder and lifted his chin. "We want you to join in it and spread your ideas throughout the country—"

"That's why we called upon you." Matsuda injected an apologetic note.

The young man continued: "We must fight, fight for the rights of

the people through publications along with lectures and political move-
ments. Talking to visible audiences is not enough, the appeal is limited. We want to have our own newspaper."

"What do you want me to do?"

"While the government and semi-official sources are said to be backing some conservative newspapers recently established, there is no
backer for this radical enterprise, so we must put up the funds and
contribute our time and energy to it." Matsuda explained.

"But is there such need of a newspaper, and any possibility of success?" The host turned to the older caller.

"The need is obvious, Monsieur, though its success depends entirely upon our efforts and the official attitude. You see, in the field
of journalism today, there are several able essayists, but they have very
little public confidence and respect because they are all former Tokugawa men. If they attack the Sat-cho bureaucracy in an editorial, for
instance, some people label it the expression of their personal grudge
and jealousy; if they uphold it, the writers are regarded as mercenary
traitors. Furthermore, their style is too much like that of a textbook."

"And they have no firm convictions. They are merely sentimental-
ists, without scholarship like yours, Professor." Matsuzawa emphasized
his argument with another shrug. "Moreover, their idea of the Man-
chester School of liberalism is obsolete. We must expound the French
concept through the newspaper."

"And my part?"

"President and editor."

"I, the president and editor?"

"Yes, that's your assignment, Monsieur."

"Who are the prospective associates, and what will they do?"

"Among them are Matsuda-san and another of your acquaintances,
Nakae-san. Matsuda-san will handle the business side of the venture and
Nakae-san has consented to do most of the writing. All the would-be
associates are expected here this evening. Well, I'll be the publisher
and assume all legal responsibilities. I am ready to be put behind the
bars every now and then. If the authorities continue the practice of
suppressing the opposing newspapers as they have since that time when
hundreds of editors and publishers were caught and punished in one
raid, several years ago, it won't be long before I'll find myself in jail.

"Anyway, we've got to strike at the corruption and bureaucracy of
the Sat-cho leaders. Professor, it is fortunate for you—"

"You mean for us," Matsuda corrected him.

"That's right. It is fortunate for us that you did not accept an official position."

"Anyway, your prestige alone will suffice to put this enterprise across." The would-be publisher turned to Saionji. "In addition to your editorial responsibility, we expect you to do one more thing, we want you to share in the investment. Each of us will contribute five hundred yen—"

"You expect me to contribute funds, too?" The host smiled.

"Yes, President. You are our leader and you are best situated, if you care to look up your influential friends and relatives, for instance. Since every one of us, though hard up, will put up that amount, will you endorse the cause with three thousand yen?"

"Do you plan to squeeze that sum from my empty purse? Six times as much—"

"Let's make it fifteen hundred. Your relatives will surely help you out, if you don't tell them where the money is going."

"You are a clever business man."

All laughed as Saionji and Matsuda eyed each other.

"Do you agree?" the young man persisted.

"Yes. What's the name of the paper? How about *Toyo Jiyu Shimbun*, the *Oriental Liberal Newspaper?*" the president suggested.

"That's settled," Matsuda said.

"Changing the subject, Monsieur, what progress have you made with that star geisha, Tama?"

"So far, none," Saionji sighed.

"Not hopeless though, with your masterly technique in the Parisian school of love-making and your determination—"

"A hunter must spot the game, otherwise he cannot fire at it. I can't meet her, how can I proceed? She avoids me. But I won't give up my attempt—"

"Oh, that Tama is literally besieged by men of power and wealth, they say. That's why she ignores invitations from an ordinary person or group."

They all laughed, for they knew the publisher's own vain efforts in that direction.

To lighten the air of defeatism, he, twisting his thick moustache, said: "Monsieur always wants the best. After the others come, may we all join in a sortie on your behalf?"

There were already signs of spring, and during the day the weather had been warm, but at night people put on mantles over their kimonos. The staff of the *Oriental Liberal Newspaper* went to the Nakamura-ro on foot through the gas-lighted narrow streets.

Time passed quickly at the teahouse. The party progressed in its making merry with several geishas. Everyone was drinking sake heavily.

Saionji leaned against the pillar separating the alcove and the recess, with his eyes half shut: "Say, my friends, where is Tama? Did you send for her? I knew you would back down on your promise."

It was the third time in an hour that he had said this.

"Oh, you poor college professor," said a vivacious geisha who overheard his remark, "you can't get her over. She is utterly beyond your reach. Forget her."

"That may be true. But you girls are not real entertainers. You can't even tune your instruments properly. Little girl, let me fix your samisen." He put out his hand.

"What do you know about it?"

"Give me that! Don't you know my Fujiwara heritage? For over thirty generations someone in my family has been a court musician in charge of the *biwa* music. I, too, am trained in the art—"

"Say," asked the same entertainer with a puzzled look, "say, Professor, are you citing a passage from *Tales of Genji?*"

Disregarding her remark, he took the samisen into his hands and sat down to manipulate the screws.

"Ah, listen to that! There is samisen music coming across the inner garden. That's real playing."

"That's Tama-san's."

Saionji leaped up: "Tama?"

"There are several big statesmen there at the party given by Councillor Inouye for his friend. They told me," said the geisha.

"Someone is singing a French song there. That's a familiar voice." Saionji, absorbed in the music, grinned.

The others heard it too. Nakae asked: "Monsieur, who would that be? Ah, now he's started '*la Marseillaise*' with excellent touch and accent."

Saionji smiled broadly and tapped a sake jug with a pair of chopsticks as he hummed the tune. He did not answer the query. Nakae, Matsuda and even their young followers and geisha girls joined in the singing.

Suddenly, he walked out onto the veranda and faced the other room across the garden. He saw the shadows on the paper screens and called: *"Monsieur, comment vous portez-vous?"* He was drowned out by the other noise. Saionji raised his voice and repeated the question, adding: "I smelled your perfume!"

From his associates behind him arose a roar of laughter.

The soloist across the way stopped. "Monsieur, Monsieur Saionji. Are you there? I'm coming."

Unsteady footsteps came along the veranda.

"Monsieur Komyoji!" Greetings were showered on him. "Have you heard from your French sweetheart?" someone asked.

Komyoji threw up his arms in response.

All arose and repeated the French national anthem. In the room opposite, a steady flow of the Nipponese songs and samisen music continued.

Komyoji, taking a seat next to Saionji, received a sake cup from him. "Too bad we can't get good French wine, isn't it?"

"Some day we'll have champagne," said Saionji hopefully.

"How did your friends get together tonight?"

"We have just decided through our own newspaper to dedicate our services to the country in defense of the people's rights against the arbitrary Sat-cho authorities."

"Like your friend, Monsieur Clemenceau, in France before we left there?"

"Precisely. What have you been doing? Who are your friends over there?"

"I just returned to the capital a few days ago, after I settled some family matters. Through my mentor, Councillor Inouye, I got a secretarial job in the government. He and his friends are there."

The young publisher frowned. He felt strongly about Komyoji's acceptance of an official position. Like the others, he became more outspoken than usual after a few drinks: "So you've sold yourself to the bureaucrats, eh?"

Komyoji bristled: "I have to earn my living some way. What's it to you, anyway?"

"Wait!" Saionji signalled to his younger friend. But Komyoji went on: "And it's Councillor Inouye's advice that I should gain a foothold and enter politics later. What's wrong with my taking the most logical course to get into the limelight eventually?"

"Well, it's one way, of course. But you play right into the hands of these politicians who are trying to get all the power for themselves, just like the Tokugawa! Well, what can one expect from a man who drenches himself with perfume?—Don't you think so?" Saionji asked the bored Matsuda.

"Each of us has his own views and circumstances," the latter replied tactfully.

"That's it." Komyoji thought he had found a sympathetic soul. At any rate, the party was once more in good humor.

After a while, Komyoji spoke to Saionji: "Monsieur, there are pretty girls in Nippon, too. The geisha named Tama is with us at Councillor Inouye's party there. She's pretty and charming. Her singing and dancing and her music are simply superb."

Saionji pricked up his ears.

"You can't say too much in praise of her, that's certain," said Matsuda.

Komyoji went on: "She has a very strong professional pride, besides, they say. Even my sponsor, with his wealth and prestige, had difficulty in getting her to come tonight. But you can't even touch her kimono sleeve."

"We sent for her, too, but she ignored our invitation altogether," the publisher consoled himself.

"Monsieur Saionji, she says she loves someone dearly, and for his sake she is endeavoring to perfect herself in her profession. My mentor told me no power or money can impress her and make her one's wife or mistress. As a matter of fact, one of the biggest business men is trying to get her by fair means or foul, but she won't listen."

Saionji became more and more agitated. He could hear the sound of his own heartbeat.

He murmured: "What if I told you I know that girl?"

"What? Do you know her?"

"Perhaps. What would you say if I win her for myself?"

All sat up and stared at Saionji.

The publisher spoke: "Say, President, you could not mean anything to a woman in that trade. You have no money and no political title. She won't look at you."

"When did you get acquainted with her?" Komyoji asked.

"Before I left for France."

"What? Is it you then whom Tama is thinking about so much?"

"Maybe. Her real name is Okiku. I didn't know that I was anything but a title to her then."

"How are you going to win her?"

"There is only one way. She scorns money and prestige. The means left is—" Matsuda began.

"Love and affection," said Saionji firmly. Komyoji nodded to himself.

"Tell me about this secret romance," Nakae teased.

"She was largely responsible over ten years ago for my awakening to the reality of life. At that time she was a very young girl, just admitted as a full-fledged geisha. You know her career better than I do."

"Hur-rah!" the publisher shrieked. "A great statesman in the making. Almost every one of the great men married a famous geisha. Now our leader is about to follow suit. Let's drink to the success of his private project."

And Saionji, who in France had almost forgotten Okiku, resolved to have Tama for himself.

"Our paper is causing a great sensation among the people, Matsuda-kun," the bespectacled Nakae said to his colleague across the table, in the dingy editorial room of the *Toyo Jiyu Shimbun*. The two were writing, their brushes moving busily up and down the page.

The young publisher, who occupied another corner, broke in: "Every day we're sold out. Say, we must write some articles about how the government has begun to interfere. Our public will realize that we're getting recognition. Watch the circulation go up."

Nakae resumed: "It will drive the Sat-cho bureaucrats mad, and finally bring them to their knees before us—"

"Because"—the publisher was jubilant—"because we have prestige, brains, conviction and courage," he said, counting on his fingers. "No other paper can come up to our standard."

"By the way, where is our president today? Did you hear the latest development in Saionji-kun's verbal battles with his relatives and some of the high dignitaries?" Nakae was worried.

"He is putting up a great fight. He is surely worthy to be our head. You know, Nakae-kun, he contradicted his brother, Tokudaiji Sane-nori, the one who's the Lord Chamberlain. He flatly refused to listen to the Minister of the Right, Iwakura, and Premier Sanjyo."

After a short silence, Nakae remarked: "If our president had a little more tenacity and fire, we would be able to smash the Sat-cho. But maybe he is a philosopher."

"Ah, there he comes!" the publisher shouted as Saionji entered the room.

"Monsieur President, what's happened?" Nakae asked.

Saionji came to his desk. "Huh, my brother and Premier Sanjyo sent for me again. I knew it was the same old argument. It's really disgusting. Why can't I live my own life?"

"You refused again?"

"I'll refuse a thousand times."

"Great!" The publisher lifted his chin. "Do you foresee any more interference?"

"Nakae-kun, I do. I insisted that I should be allowed to have an audience with His Majesty to whom I'll make a direct appeal. But they declined my request, so I left with them a petition to the Mikado explaining my purpose in this venture. They were very polite, but they can't allow me an audience. I know they can't act independently of the Sat-cho influence." He sighed. "If it were only like it used to be when I was a boy and almost ran in and out of the Imperial Court."

"Pardon me, President, someone is knocking." The publisher went to the door. "A messenger from the Lord Chamberlain, sir." He made a mock bow and gave Saionji the folded paper.

"What? From my brother Tokudaiji?"

Saionji received and hastily opened the paper, finding his petition to the Emperor enclosed with his brother's note. "Cowards! They returned my petition without presenting it."

"What, Monsieur?" Nakae and Matsuda looked over his shoulder. Saionji read his brother's message: "Regarding your Presidency of the recently established *Toyo Jiyu Shimbun,* since it is His Majesty's wish that you should resign from the post, hereby I, Tokudaiji Sanenori, the Lord Chamberlain, unofficially notify you as to the Imperial Command. Tokudaiji Sanenori to Saionji Kimmochi-dono."

As he finished reading, he placed the note on his desk. His anger broke. "What tyranny! I don't believe they ever mentioned it to His Majesty. It is one's inalienable right to choose his own profession. Even under the tyranny of the Czarist Russia, no attempt is made to interfere in the choice of a man's trade. Now they are forcing me to surrender my chosen calling. What tyranny, what an outrage!"

It was already sundown of the long cherryblossom day. Matsuda called together all the staff members into the editorial room. Saionji spoke:

"Well, my friends, I must take leave of you. I can not disobey the Imperial Command."

It was the last part of September 1881. Councillor Ito was talking to Saionji at the latter's modest living-quarters.

"So you won't accept any position in the Government?" the thin-bearded visitor inquired.

"I will not!" Saionji's flat refusal made Ito more polite and persuasive.

"You are very active in politics these days, as I see in the newspapers. You joined the Itagaki liberals' dinner party last night at the Seiyoken in Uyeno Park, didn't you? They're the original windbags."

"I am fully convinced that the only hope for the healthy growth of social and political Nippon is to encourage their activities," Saionji responded coldly.

"Their idle talk on liberty and freedom—French imitation—"

"Councillor Ito, you and Okuma were once 'liberals,' weren't you?"

"Well—"

"You didn't know the meaning of liberty, I'm afraid."

"Well, that's another matter—"

"That's the fundamental issue which I attempted to explain to the public through the *Oriental Liberal Newspaper*. You, through my brother and others, put me out of it and wiped out the paper." There was bitter accusation in his voice.

"What was the chief topic of the discussion at the Seiyoken party? Is it a secret?" asked Ito.

"There is no secrecy in our group. It's all open. The main issue was the advisability of reviving Itagaki's Liberal Party on a sounder and more permanent basis than before."

"I thought you were going to unite all the 'outs' against us because of the Overseas Minister Kuroda scandal in connection with the Government's plans to develop Hokkaido," Ito said smoothly.

"That's only a side issue, though it will interest the people in the prospective party. But that corrupt practice is typical of the evil consequences of a dictatorial regime like yours. You stifle any criticism of the authorities. I think the Tokugawa weren't any worse than you. Without constructive and constant deliberation, it is only natural that leaders will eventually become arrogant and despotic. That's what brought every government, here and in the West, to its grave. The best examples are the very Tokugawa that you put out."

"But you helped us."

"I didn't expect this result," was Saionji's scornful reply.

Ito had not dreamed of meeting such a cold reception. His lips under the moustache quivered, but he still managed to control himself. Saionji was calm.

"Saionji-san, I understand your position. But let me tell you a few things."

"Go ahead. More justification of your bureaucratic conduct, I suppose."

"You know that the permanent irreconcilables have made unjust criticisms. It is no secret that on one hand we discriminate even against our own former associates. But on the other hand, we have admitted to our circles the leaders of the defunct Tokugawa camp—for instance, Katsu Awa, who negotiated the surrender of Edo, and Enomoto Buyo, the Tokugawa's Western-trained admiral and the last convert to the Imperial Government."

Saionji nodded cynically.

"We have done our best in domestic improvements. Here in Tokyo, following European examples, many parks have been established and improved, the Metropolitan Police Headquarters created—"

Saionji snapped at Ito: "I heard, also, that you manned the police forces by all the former *samurai* of Satsuma and Choshu, to check and suppress any opposition to you—"

"That's true, too, but that is incidental and is, after all, one of the vital means to preserve law and order. Last year we called the third conference of the Prefects which the late Kido began for future parliamental practice. You know he presided over the first one before his death. The Supreme Court and the Genro-in have been functioning for some time. We established stock exchanges, public schools, and more railways, and also national banks. We put an end to the custom of exposing the heads of notorious criminals in public squares."

Ito knew that he was telling his host nothing new, but he hoped that something might catch Saionji's fancy. One after another, he put his feelers forward.

"What if Kido knew how you are turning his ideas and efforts to your own advantage?" Saionji asked, but Ito ignored the question.

"We successfully persuaded Britain and France to withdraw their marines stationed in Yokohama—"

"That caused many comical situations."

Ito wondered if Saionji were ridiculing him. He faced the strong headwind of indifference. But he could not retreat. His reticent host now even took the initiative.

"In diplomacy, you didn't fare too well in the exchanging of Saghalien Island for the uninhabitable Kurils, did you? The bravery of your Sat-cho puffed away when the Russian Bear snarled at you, and you quickly consented to give up, ha, ha!"

The visitor took time to light his cigar: "I should like to leave with you a few thoughts regarding our future programs. Of course, in these days as in the past, we, the leaders, have received some benefits from our leadership, but that is as it should be. If it weren't the Satcho, it would be someone else. Don't let your rebel mind forget that!" Ito took a deep breath and smiled again. "And we have modified the policies to suit the need of the times. You see, politics is a living thing that you can't learn from your textbooks."

"Haven't you told me enough?"

Ito hid his irritation behind his cigar smoke. "Listen a while longer. I would like to carry through some plans to which you and your political and journalist friends would agree, I think."

"Due to public resentment and pressure against your tyranny?"

"No, not necessarily. I am speaking of the adoption of an Imperial Constitution. Our Choshu leader, Kido, paved the way for it. To me, it is now only a matter of time."

"What? *You* are in favor of a constitution? I am amazed. I see. I see. So you're going to steal Kido's thunder, and the ideas of Itagaki and Goto and Okuma, and put up a constitution before someone else does, so that you will be secure in power. You're a traitor, Ito Hirobumi!" Saionji's eyes flashed.

Ito restrained his anger. "That is your interpretation. But the Sat-cho who rescued Nippon from the Tokugawa Shogun should guide the nation through these reconstruction days."

Saionji sighed deeply. "Why do you waste your time and mine? Why are you so interested in my personal affairs? It is my privilege to do whatever I choose to do. You have numerous clannish followers, you can elevate them to any post among your Sat-cho contingents, like a puppet showman handling his dolls."

"Well, because—" Ito hesitated. "You see, your elder brother Tokudaiji, Premier Sanjyo and Right Minister Iwakura, for instance, have co-operated with us, since the early days of the Restoration. We would like to have you, too."

"I see. You have them under your thumb, and now you want to

get me in line, to exploit whatever antiquated prestige is associated with my family name, and"—his voice cut the air like a knife—"whatever affection you think the Mikado might have for my person." His eyes bored into Ito's, then he gave a short bitter laugh. "You think it would be safer to have me as a friend than as an enemy of your machinations."

Ito saw that the young liberal trained abroad was not to be caught in his net. He was exasperated, and only with difficulty kept from showing his contempt for what he considered the callowness of youth. Suddenly his confident smile returned.

"Saionji-san, you want to improve national unity and restrengthen the foundations of the Imperial House, don't you?" he said after a lingering puff of smoke.

"What has that to do with my joining you?"

"Your attitude confused me. I sincerely wish to promote national integrity and to perpetuate the Emperor's prerogatives. Therefore I am in favor of a constitution. That basic document will grant the organization of a parliament which will have limited power. It will foster all modern political institutions. That means a cabinet system which will formulate and execute the national policies more efficiently."

"You want to sit there and dominate the nation, huh?" Saionji was still sarcastic, then he asked: "You really favor a constitution?"

"Yes, but we need discipline in the country. I want to see our Sat-cho men continue to occupy the key positions."

"Huh."

"But the point is"—Ito became emphatic—"that we are willing to listen to important proposals from the opposition." He lost his air of belligerence and his whiskered face became almost distinguished.

Saionji felt the contagion of his words. "Huh—the constitution, administrative reforms—" he murmured.

Ito, regaining his confidence, measured the young man's shift of sentiment. He knew that his remarks had struck home: "Anyway, I shall leave the proposition with you. On that basis, can you join us? Give me your answer later. But we must move fast, and yet make watertight preparations, and keep it all a secret."

"Must I decide soon? If I were to accept," Saionji spoke hesitantly, "it would only be because I feel that your strong Sat-cho organization would guarantee speedier action in adopting a constitution than could any organization of mixed opposition groups. But I don't know—"

Ito showed no sign of his victory. He merely changed the subject:

"Say, will you do me honor tonight by accepting my invitation to a teahouse party? You must have been spending rather dull days after that newspaper incident. Let's forget business. Can we now be friends?"

"Well—" His hesitation was not entirely because of his political relationship with Ito, but because his repeated failures to regain Tama's attention had made him avoid the gay quarters altogether. Several times he had sent her notes, but they had been returned unopened. His endeavor to see her was also futile. The fact that she was in such popular demand served to fan his ardor, and he had withdrawn to temporary brooding.

Ito knew Saionji's personal affairs. He was fortified with detailed information about the private lives of politicians, particularly in the geisha districts and with the entertainers.

"A man of your calibre and prestige, Saionji-san, must aim at the best. The Shimbashi is a popular quarter, but the Koto is just as good. Do you know that geisha named Tama, who is the best all-round entertainer, and very beautiful, too? I have sent word to one of my favorite houses, the Nakamura-ro, to make arrangements with her." He sighed in anticipation. "Sober, we command national affairs; drunk, we lay our heads in the beauty's lap. How's that? Some call us 'teahouse politicians' and all that, but it's merely jealousy. It's strange that at present the teahouse is the best place to discuss even the major problems of state, just as it was in the early days when we Sat-cho laid our plans against the Tokugawa. Farther back, brothels in the Yoshiwara served the same purpose. Nobody listens in on you, you're not interrupted, whatever the girls hear doesn't mean much to them. Even Yamagata of Choshu, the army chief, and once your own chief of staff, I believe, when you commanded the army on the Echigo front in 1868, goes there. So do Kuroda, who was Yamagata's colleague under you; Matsukata, of Satsuma, who is in charge of financial affairs; Okuma, Senior Councillor of State, and Katsura, also of Choshu. Not a single one of them ever thought that meetings in geisha houses were improper. Of course, brothels are different. Well, are you coming?"

"Yes, I'll accompany you. Thanks for your invitation. Do you think you can really get Tama to the party?" Saionji could not keep from asking. "I heard that some big business man is on her trail."

"Many of them, Saionji-san, many of them." Ito grinned like a mischievous boy. "But be at ease and take my word for her coming. The agreement was made with the *kemban* to which she now belongs, that at any time I put in a call, she is to cancel all her engagements and be with me, no matter where I have my merrymaking. So far she has never failed me." Seeing the look of dismay in Saionji's face, he added: "She's difficult. Won't go any further than the ordinary duties of entertainment. She'd give a man a real chase. Well, it's the best season for a little relaxation."

"The shining stars in the high greenish sky mark the time of the chrysanthemum and the seven autumnal flowers," Saionji murmured to himself.

They drove through the gas-lighted Ginza towards the Koto.

"Where is Tama? Bring her along. Where is the *josho?* Oh, there you are. Who do you think you are, anyway? If you don't carry out my order at once, I can have your business suspended or revoke your license, or even wipe out this entire gay quarter. Don't you know that?"

Councillor Ito had lost his cloak of courtesy. Under the influence of drink, he was revealing his lust for power.

A score of girls and *hokan* retreated fearfully.

"Didn't I make it clear to you that Tama should be invited to my parties regardless of other calls? Where is she?"

The *josho* was clever. She politely, but in no uncertain terms, said: "Your Honor, there is nothing I can say except to repeat my former reply that Tama is coming as soon as her previous engagement is completed—"

"So she did accept others, though she knew I was coming." His pride was hurt. "Neither you nor the *kemban* nor Tama respect my command."

"Your Honor, it is cruel and unfair for you to say that." She was determined to calm her important customer. "I have no authority over her since the registry house manages her affairs; she is busy every minute even though she fills only a small portion of the daily requests for her presence from all over town. And after all, she has to glean while the gathering is good—"

"How much does she want for her exclusive appearance for my guests? I have the nation's treasury behind me—" Ito emptied several sake cups in succession.

"Your customary teasing, sir. And furthermore, you officially—"

The heretofore silent Saionji took over the argument. "Officially he encourages the people to work as hard as they can, huh?"

"Still the rebellious *Okuge-sama*, ha, ha."

"Now, now, *josho*." With a more amicable gesture he beckoned to her. "Now, send your messenger once more to Tama and tell her that I have a young friend—"

"Why don't you say Monsieur Saionji?" a giggling geisha interrupted.

"All right. Monsieur Saionji, with me tonight—I want her to meet him and entertain him."

The giggling began again.

"What's the matter, children?" Ito beamed at them.

"Who doesn't know that Tama-san is always talking about Monsieur?"

"What?" Another shout frightened the girls.

"Why didn't you tell me before? You get out, all of you, and stay out until I call you again."

Like the ears of rice bending backwards in a heavy autumn wind, they fled from the room.

"Well, Saionji-san, this is a little harmless mischief after a hard day's work on tremendous national affairs," the half-drunken Ito continued when they were alone. "And now, have you made up your mind?"

"About what?"

Ito smiled. The master of political strategy changed from direct attack to a flanking manoeuvre behind the smoke screen of amatory interests.

"Well, of course, about Tama. After hearing what I did, I guess you have won her." Malice and triumph were in his voice. He drew out a pair of imported cigars, one for himself, and the other for his friend.

"Huh, I thought you meant your proposal."

The Councillor smiled again.

Iron was to be hammered into a mould while it was hot—but carefully.

"Oh, let's have more sake." He poured liquor into Saionji's cup and then into his own. "By the way, from your academic point of view on a constitution, if we should, as I hinted, adopt one right away, what model would you recommend?"

Saionji felt the pall of subtle flattery descend on him, but he seemed helpless: "I can't recommend any basic law without some modification. A constitution is the outgrowth of political traditions of any particular people. Therefore, many things must be considered, and we must study some model instrument thoroughly. But there are some which we can copy to a great extent—"

"I would like to discuss the subject with you some other time."

"So you are quite serious about what you said at my place this afternoon, are you?"

"Certainly. I have a grave decision to make in a few weeks." He watched Saionji's reaction. "We must stage a coup to regain the power of the Sat-cho for the sake of the country's progress. I want to save the country from the wreckage of dissension. You may call me an opportunist, but I would risk my life for the integrity of Nippon."

Saionji realized that Ito was essentially honest. Beneath all the scheming was a real faith in the need of national integrity.

"I and a few colleagues are enlisting a dependable few. We want a nucleus for our action to save His Majesty's country." Looking straight into Saionji's face, he said in a heavy whisper: "We have talked of you. Will you join us?"

His listener said nothing.

Ito went on: "Assuming that you are willing to lend us your hand as you did in the Restoration Wars, I would like to confide to you briefly our immediate objectives and procedure." The two foreheads were close together over a charcoal brazier. "Am I right in assuming that you are in absolute sympathy with us in our Imperial cause?"

Saionji nodded. Ito still whispered: "Wonderful, we are together again. The immediate step is to eliminate all the non-Sat-cho men from the Government—"

"Including Senior Councillor Okuma?" Saionji was astonished.

"Yes, he is a 'wen on the eyes.' His growing political influence may soon overshadow us unless we remove him now. Furthermore, he and his British parliamentary system—" Ito curled his lower lip, forcing his thin beard down.

"How are you going to deal with him? Any misconduct? That's the most popular charge." Saionji was cynical again. He felt trapped, and yet the time had come for him to take a definite stand.

"No, we simply will force him to submit his resignation when he reaches Tokyo the middle of next month with His Majesty's North-eastern inspection party."

"If he refuses?"

Ito thrust out his right hand, his finger pointing. "This is the only way then," he said, intimating that he was ready to have Okuma cut down by his henchmen. "We'll make arrangements with Sanjyo and

Iwakura so that they will accept if he presents his resignation. We will complete our program, including the Edict, on the date for proclaiming a constitution. Thus we can reconsolidate the political power in the hands of the Sat-cho and we can snap our fingers at the so-called party men. Their leaders, Itagaki and Goto, in their campaign for a French Republican political system in Nippon, would temporarily lessen the powers of the Imperial House. If the opposing factions all get together, we'll lose out entirely, we're afraid."

"I suppose the Prussian system of centralization would be more to your taste."

"I haven't decided yet." Ito closed his lips firmly.

"What do you want me to do?"

They heard the entertainers who were coming along the veranda.

"When this coup has materialized, I have a few jobs that you can do better than anybody else—"

"Tama-san is here at last. May we come in?" A bevy of girls broke into the room, and surrounded the star geisha.

Tama was playing on her samisen.

Saionji listened raptly.

Her years of waiting were crowned with triumph. Before Saionji's Paris sojourn, she had suffered deeply from his indifference. Though she was then very young she had realized that in his conversation he had expressed the thoughts of a bewildered rather than of a mature mind.

During the intervening years, while he had had his studies and his career, she had concentrated all her efforts on the perfecting of her music, so that her success would be a silent tribute to her love.

When he came back to Nippon, her impulse had been to rush to his side. But she could not return to those hurt moments when his eyes had been unaware of her. She would not again be a suppliant.

Although she kept herself informed of his every movement, she stayed aloof from him. When his notes came, her heart beat fast and her hands trembled, but she returned them unopened. Either her apparent indifference would enflame him, or the new hope had better be quenched at once. Gradually, hearing from various sources of his interest in her, she became more certain of herself. Some night they would meet and her music would enmesh him so that he could not escape.

Now he was in her audience.

Tama tried to ignore him, but under the influence of sake, she looked his way from time to time. To the great delight of the other geisha, she entirely forgot Ito's presence. In disgust, the councillor smoked and drank constantly.

She came close to Saionji. She sang light, popular songs, then classical tunes; her delicate fingers drummed on the tabors, one on her shoulder, the other in her lap. Her melodious voice, perfect rhythm, enunciation and control enchanted her listeners and transported them to other scenes.

Tama saw that Saionji's head was bowed; he was lost in her music. At the conclusion of every song, Saionji and Tama drank together.

Saionji awoke with a heavy head and found the star geisha lying beside him. Someone had put their *haori* on the clothes hanger. Two pillows stood undisturbed near by. He reached for the water pitcher on the lacquer tray. Tama woke up too.

"Oh!"

"Huh, we're alone." He smiled at her.

Tama's face became radiant under the light from a small kerosene lamp in the recess.

He sat up on the mat; the geisha was still on her side. Her face clouded. "I have never rested with any man. No matter how drunk I was as part of my entertaining patrons at this house—"

"Or any other place, huh?"

She tried to get up: "Oh, my arm! You slept on my arm— My!"

She gently rubbed her upper arm.

"Are you sorry?"

"No! But—" She adjusted her kimono collar as she sat up. Saionji pulled the charcoal brazier with its tiny fire and the water pitcher close to them. Tama filled one glass and offered it to Saionji. She took another for herself.

"It's good. Will you give me another one?"

"Gladly, Prince."

"Would you care for a cigarette?"

"How you've changed, Prince!"

"Why? Do I look old?"

"No, but you lit my cigarette for me. How wonderful! Do European people do that? Here everybody expects the geisha to do the lighting—"

They heard the horn of the horse-carriage calling for fares.

"Ah, I must be going back to the *kemban*. It's very late, I think."
She got up.

"Wait! Why do you go so soon?"

"Prince, do you really want me to be with you?"

She lighted the gas lamp, and as she returned to her seat, she repeated: "Prince, do you really want me to be with you?"

Smiling, their eyes met.

"Tama!"

She shivered and her eyes traced the weave of the mats on the floor.

"Why didn't you come to the parties I was at before?"

"Prince—"

"Prince?" Saionji scowled. "That title is abolished."

"May I say Prince when we are alone? I called you that before you
left for Europe. May I?"

Saionji smiled in assent.

"And will you call me Okiku? That is my real name and you used
to use it, do you remember?"

Quickly he agreed to do so.

"Did you ever think of me while you were away?" she asked, and
immediately shook her head because she had not meant to ask that
question.

"To be frank—you don't mind, do you?—I forgot all about you in
the beginning, for I was too busy with my studies. And I did not know
you were thinking of me at all, because before I left you were just a
girl to me. But later, when I was depressed, for some reason, I began
to think of you."

"Oh, I longed for news day and night." She shook her head again.
Tears started in her eyes. Her tongue was undoing the work of ten
years.

"But after I came back a year ago you refused to see me. So I concluded that you were merely mercenary."

"You are wrong, Prince."

"How?"

"I saw you practically every day." She let her emotions have their
way.

"What?"

"I did. I asked all my geisha friends and acquaintances about you. I
watched you going to teach at the Law School or walking to the newspaper office. Once I almost jumped in your way."

"Why, Okiku!"

"I didn't want you to see me. I didn't want you to find out I was thinking of you. So I had my jinrikishaman put the hood on the carriage and place the car as if it were waiting for a fare near the corner of the Ginza where you passed daily. I waited in the covered jinrikisha every day. When you approached I peeped out from behind the blind. When I missed you there, I came near your home or your newspaper office and did the same thing. Anyway, I followed you no matter how busy I was, for I couldn't sleep without a glimpse of you."

"Why didn't you speak to me?"

"Because I thought you did not love me. And I wanted to surprise you with my music and dancing. But tonight I wished to give a lesson to that conceited Sat-cho leader. He thinks he can do anything with anybody. He does everything to satisfy his greed. He may be a good politician, but after all, we are not prostitutes in the Yoshiwara, and we have a certain professional pride. At least I do. When he starts to chase anyone, she couldn't displease him for fear of reprisal."

"Do you mean Councillor Ito?"

"Yes."

"Well, you still have plenty of fire, haven't you?"

"I was so glad tonight when they told me that Ito was here with you. I was first thinking of making him miserable, but soon I forgot it and played only for you."

"But let's not talk of Ito."

"I was so filled with emotion, I could have danced and sung all night. Oh, Prince, I am so happy." She leaned over to Saionji, and continued: "I never felt as I did tonight in all my life—"

"In Paris I attended many performances of internationally known players and operas, but something was always lacking. Tonight when I saw your dances and listened to your songs and samisen music, I felt that every gesture of yours touched the very tips of my nerves, sometimes driving me to grief, and at other times to overwhelming joy."

"Oh, such compliments, Prince. Thank you."

Saionji took Okiku's hand when she touched his on the edge of the brazier.

"Not compliments. Merely that your hard work has been rewarded. You have triumphed, although your love was for a while one-sided— or perhaps I loved you and did not know it."

She put her head in Saionji's lap. He was softly patting her side-loops and watching her profile under the gas light.

"Your pretty face."

"Do you think so? You look so distinguished. Some day I want you to be like those big men in the Government. I am sure you will be."

"Hero-worshipper!"

"I don't care what you call me."

A long silence followed.

"They say you won't listen to any proposals to take you out of your profession. I haven't even as much to offer you as that big business executive who is supposed to be after you, but—"

"But what?"

"But all I have in me is yours."

Saionji removed her hand from her face.

In the month of October 1881, the Sat-cho politicians executed their plot with precision. Their victory was decisive, as Ito had prophesied to Saionji about three weeks earlier.

On the eleventh, Okuma was forced to relinquish his post as Senior Councillor of State under their threat.—His promising followers, who had occupied positions of secondary importance, also had to leave. On the following day, the Emperor's edict proclaimed that the Imperial Diet would be opened in 1890.

Political agitation against the Sat-cho men spread throughout the country and penetrated all walks of life under the leadership of Itagaki and later of Okuma, who had been the chief victim of the October coup. Itagaki's Liberal Party was revived on October 29th of the same year, and Okuma's Constitutional Imperialist Party was born in March 1882.

Thirteen days after this memorable political change, on October 24th, Saionji was appointed associate councillor to a newly-created Advisory Council headed by Ito, the chief function of which was to prepare the constitution and the opening of the Diet according to the late Imperial decree. Thus, Saionji was now irrevocably with the Sat-cho party, which had originally brought him into the national limelight in 1868, and from which he had held aloof for more than ten years.

This new contact with the Sat-cho paved the way for his eventual rise to the highest political office in Nippon. But twelve years were to pass before his name was again in the public mind. Not until the time of the Sino-Nipponese War did he take up his first ministerial portfolio.

During the New Year's season the Saionji household was once more assembled—this time in a mansion owned by Lord I-i in the shadow of the Imperial Palace, the former Tokugawa's Edo Castle. Although Saionji cared little for formalities, he had paid his New Year's respects to the Imperial Family, and had called upon relatives and friends. Now he was at home.

His governess, Sagami, was with him. She no longer did mending at night by the wick-light of vegetable oil. Kerosene lamps and gas light had taken its place some years ago, about the time topknots disappeared. The past decade had left its mark on her. She looked older, her hair was already grizzled. Her semi-court garb of bluish hemp fibre harmonized with her nature, and her spirit, conduct and attire had been unaffected by Western influences.

But certainly her master had changed in the thirty years since the two-year-old boy was first brought to the house. She had followed his progress with breathless pride. Her unshaken faith in him was contagious and comfortable, and her presence imbued him with a feeling of self-assurance.

He was looking over a few of his antiques when Sagami politely knelt a few feet away. "My Master," she said, bowing low to Saionji, who smilingly acknowledged her greeting, "my Master, this is the most auspicious and joyous New Year since the one when you took command of the Tamba expeditionary forces for the Mikado, exactly fourteen years ago. Those were turbulent days and this is the time of calm and hope."

"Yes, Sagami. But there are still many things to be done. The adoption of the constitution is our most important task. An inquiry committee under Councillor Ito will be especially sent to Europe to investigate the forms, the application and the results of the basic law of European countries. I have been assigned to this party. We may be leaving sometime this spring. During my absence I want you and the others to stay with my brother's household again."

"We are grateful for another honor, Master." She was silent for a moment. Then she said hesitantly: "I met your favorite geisha, Tama, the other day and found her a woman worthy to be your mate, with her appearance, intelligence, and her intense love for you." Sagami smiled and looked into his shining eyes. "I heard that her jinrikisha faithfully follows wherever you go. I made inquiries at the Naka-mura-ro. I learned that she was the daughter of a *hatamoto* of high standing. Although I would rather see you with a lady of noble birth like yourself, she is your own choice, and in this changing time, many men of distinction choose women among the geisha. There is no longer so much prejudice against that occupation, I must think of her in terms of personality and character." She sighed nevertheless.

"Do you believe she would make a good companion?"

"I haven't the slightest doubt of it. But do you expect to register her as your lady or your mistress?"

"It doesn't matter, does it? Huh, Sagami?" He laughed.

She plucked at her obi.

"You see, Master—I—I have something to tell you. You may disregard it entirely, but I would fail in my duty—"

"Go on."

She began by reminiscing.

"Ah, I remember when you were a little boy and your real father, Tokudaiji, tried to keep you at your *biwa* lessons, and you much preferred books—"

"Huh."

"Well, it's very difficult—you see, when you were adopted into the Saionji household, you inherited all its traditions."

"Huh."

"And one of them concerns this *biwa* instrument. Some of your ancestors ignored the legend and they died young, like your foster parents, or were otherwise overcome by misfortunes. I do not say that harm will really come—"

"Yes, yes, I understand."

"Many centuries ago, when the Saionji household was already dedicated to the especial worship of the goddess of *biwa* music, one of your ancestors had a beautiful wife whom he loved dearly. On a clear autumn night he was playing to her on his *biwa* near the veranda. The paper screens were open onto the garden. Suddenly there was a blinding flash of light. When the player recovered, his beloved wife was lying dead and his instrument was broken. The sages interpreted this incident to mean that this jealous goddess does not want the master of this house to marry. She whom a Saionji weds shall die a sudden death. Thus, Master."

Saionji laughed softly. "Well, it's a pleasant fancy, and one could always refer to it in case one did not want to be too tied down, huh, Sagami? At any rate, we shall live together after I come back from Europe. I trust you as our sole go-between."

Before Saionji's departure, the members of the Ito Committee were received in audience by His Majesty at the Akasaka Detached Palace.

On his return home, he called on his father, Tokudaiji, who had retired from public life and was living with Saionji's elder brother, Sanenori.

The old man was sunning himself in the front garden of the residence. At first he did not recognize the smartly dressed gentleman coming through the gate. The visitor removed his hat.

"Father, I came to say farewell before I leave with Councillor Ito for Europe."

Tokudaiji arose from the bench.

"Ah, I am glad of your wise decision. I heard it from Sanenori. In my advanced age my only worry was your future. Well, Sanenori too will be back from the palace soon. You must have seen him there. And Takamaro is coming home early from school. He hoped you would come. Let us go into the house."

As they walked slowly side by side, the father continued: "Since you are now leaving for an important service, I imagine you'll do your share for the Mikado."

"Yes, Father."

Tokudaiji hesitated, and then with a smile said: "Kimmochi, I used to worry about you. But I see that the young rebel will some day be a great statesman and a patriot. I have been proud of you for many years. And now—when will you take a bride? I hope it will be on your return from Europe, eh?"

The sound of a horse-carriage spared Saionji the trouble of answering.

When Lord Chamberlain Sanenori alighted from the carriage, Takamaro was already coming down the path.

The jubilant father gathered his three sons to him, saying: "Kimmochi has come! My children, this is the happiest day in my life."

Councillor Ito's party completed their fact-finding sojourn in Europe. On August 8, 1883, they returned home laden with material and accompanied by German educators and authorities on drafting legal documents.

Saionji came home with them. In December he was promoted to the full councillorship of the same Advisory Council and transferred to its legislative division.

In that year Tokudaiji Kinzumi died.

In the following fall, the new peerage was created in continental form, and Saionji and his brother, Sanenori, were made marquis, while most political leaders, including Ito, received the title of count.

On February 14, 1885, Marquis Saionji was appointed by His Majesty's Government as Nipponese Minister Extraordinary and Plenipotentiary and was accredited to the Austrian Court in Vienna. He left Nippon on February 18, and returned home on leave on June 5, 1886.

"Okiku, my dear!"

"Yes, Prince—"

"How do you like our new life?" He laid a small French book on the mat.

"How do *you* like it, Prince?"

"Huh, it was worth waiting and longing for. I am contented when I am with you."

Okiku stopped her fanning and smiled back at him. "I feel the same way. When you came back from France I thought you would never leave Nippon again, but you went to Germany with Genro Ito and his party, and again to Austria as the Nipponese Minister. I hope you don't have to leave me any more."

"I hope not. Sagami also thought the days of my absence were over. Do you like her?"

"Yes, Prince, she's very kind to me. I hope we'll get along like this for ever—"

"I'd like to take you over with me, but Sagami wouldn't allow it. Besides, the diplomatic job is uncertain. Every few years we are shifted from one place to the other. If it were steady, that is, if I could stay at one capital several years, I would take you along at all cost. And I'd like to take you around in Nippon, too—"

"But that's the way everybody is promoted, I suppose, Prince."

"That's right, Okiku."

"Well, then if you have to leave me here, I'll be patient with Sagami at home and will wait for your return. If I had a baby I could spend my time with something of you—"

Saionji beamed again.

"Prince, what did Councillor Ito say about your work at Vienna?"

"Huh, he was quite satisfied with me and with himself, you know, Okiku. Now he's the first *Soridaijin* in the so-called cabinet installed in December 1885. In the following April he annexed the office of Foreign

Minister, too, after Inouye resigned. He was forty-four years old when he took up the Premiership."

"So you think he'll send you abroad again because you have done a good job?"

"Huh, possibly. I came home on leave of absence from Austria, you know—"

"Why?"

"Well! Well, I wanted to—"

"To be with me?"

"Yes!"

Saionji patted her shoulder and began. "Do you know, Ito enjoyed it very much when I told him of an incident that occurred in Vienna?"

"What was it, Prince?"

"Huh, at the Foreign Office in Vienna, the representatives of different countries became personally acquainted with each other and often did a lot of gossiping, especially about their seniors and superiors—"

"Like housewives—"

"Yes. Once a Russian diplomat who was a very jolly person told us how his former chief at the Russian Embassy in London was stingy. All suddenly burst into laughter when a man left the room. I was told later that the ambassador who made his quick exit was also well known for his extreme parsimony."

"Oh, Prince, someone's at the door. I'll see—"

"Is Monsieur Saionji here?"

"Oh, Komyoji!" Saionji shouted before Okiku could reply.

"Come right in!"

Saionji rushed to welcome his old friend.

"Your Excellency, the Minister Plenipotentiary—" Komyoji began formally. The next minute the host and the visitor were patting each other's backs, and laughing.

"Well, how was your first job? Did you get to the 'city' often?"

"Nothing very exciting, but I got used to it all right. To them our country is still non-existent, as you know. I returned to Paris a few times."

"On your visit to Europe with Premier Ito and those others?"

"That was a hard task, every minute of our stay. I spent most of my time in London where I was conducted through Buckingham and Windsor Palaces, besides making many inquiries concerning Parliament. Great Britain under Queen Victoria is now in the zenith of her glory—everything is magnificent. For that matter, Prussia, too, is coming on. Kaiser Wilhelm I is an ambitious-looking monarch backed by the Iron Chancellor—"

"You're actually launched on the diplomatic career we used to talk about." Komyoji was suddenly dismayed. "I'm disappointed in you, Monsieur, I mean, Marquis Saionji."

"Huh?"

"It's true that I aligned myself with the bureaucrats, but I thought you would stand aloof, Monsieur."

"You thought I would be the peace offering for the political compromise of you others?"

"Yes, yes." Komyoji spoke eagerly. "It was too much to ask of you—"

"Say, Komyoji, by the way, meet my wife!"

Komyoji quickly resumed his European manner. He bent down and kissed Okiku's hand.

"Well, Monsieur, my heartiest congratulations to you and Madame, I am terribly proud of you both. In this, I take my hat off to you and bow to the ground. The victory of love— What could give greater satisfaction than this? Madame, I met you many times before. You stuck to your guns to win Monsieur. Don't they say 'a woman's determination penetrates even a rock'? Monsieur, you reciprocated. Now at last the lovers are together peacefully and triumphantly under one roof!"

Komyoji's vehement gestures and perfume almost overpowered the Saionjis.

"Well, glad to see you anyway, Komyoji. What has brought you over? I have good news to—"

"Monsieur, I have bad news, very contrary to the happy outcome of your romance," Komyoji said as they sat on the mat.

"What and how? Tell me about—"

"You must listen to me—disappointed in love!"

"What, again?"

The contrast between Komyoji's previous cheerfulness and his saddened mood was striking. Saionji and Okiku glanced at each other.

"Tell me more, if we can help you in any way—"

"In my case, Monsieur, love seems to be all one-sided, as you once said. A woman's promises and sweet words don't amount to a whiff." He again pulled out his perfumed handkerchief and touched his face.

"What do you mean?"

"Here and abroad it's the same story. One day I was perfectly happy and fascinated by sweet whispers and the next day there is nothing from her. The only thing I hear is my creditors' complaints."

"Komyoji, wait! I want to show you something—"

Saionji reached towards his desk and took the French book he had been reading.

"Do you recognize this?" he asked, handing it to Komyoji. "To whom is this lovely poetry dedicated? The Nipponese poems I translated in collaboration with her—"

Komyoji's fingers ran through the pages.

"Ah, I remember you did this translation with Madame Mendes before we left France. She broke my heart by her complete silence. Oh, it's entitled to 'The Dragon-fly.' *Poèmes de la Libellule.* Ah, Monsieur, your title is *Conseiller d'etat de S. M. L'Empereur du Japon.* Ah, she betrayed me—" He shook his head sadly, and turned to the following page.

"Oh, here, what is this?" He read:

> Je t'offre ces fleurs
> De tes îles bien-aimées.
> Sous nos ciels en pleurs,
> Reconnais-tu leurs couleurs
> Et leurs âmes parfumées?

He kissed the page and repeated the line: " 'Sous nos ciels en pleurs!' Oh, my dearest!"

He swung the book over his head in excitement. Tears rolled from his eyes.

"Tell, tell me, Monsieur, help me to get back to the 'city'! I have no savings. I must go back to her and see my sweetheart in Paris once more—"

The sympathetic host said: "Huh, if you don't mind, how about applying for a secretarial post in the Nipponese legation in Paris? There's an opening. Maybe too unimportant for you, though—"

"It doesn't matter, Monsieur, as long as I can return to Paris just once more to take her loving hand in the clear moonlight on the bank of the Seine—"

"So you go back to our old home?"

"Immediately." He was already up. "I'll put in my application and get the help of all my acquaintances—

"Well, Monsieur, see you in Paris. Good-day!"

"Hah, hah, Saionji-san, I have something to tell you." Premier Ito, who was also Foreign Minister, was at his official residence in conference with Saionji.

"I see your ministers are all from Satsuma and Choshu."

"In the ten posts including my own, we have one non-Sat-cho man, Enomoto, the Minister of Communications whose department is at present inactive. But he is a 'convert' to the Sat-cho. I mentioned this to you some time ago. Our clans have enough talent to fill the portfolios and we don't want to have others in the administration. We keep them out as long as possible.

"One of the most threatening and difficult problems of the Foreign Department came up in that incident at Nagasaki, where last August Chinese sailors from the Chinese Oriental Squadron, commanded by Admiral Ting Ju Ch'ang, went on a rampage. They molested and injured our local police and the people. We couldn't do a thing against our strong neighbor."

Saionji leaned forward, listening, and said: "I followed that affair with great interest. What was the real cause of this international incident, Premier Ito?"

"Well, briefly, this: On August 13, the mighty Chinese squadron headed by the new sea monsters, the *Ting-Yuan* and the *Chen Yuan*, the sister battleships, anchored in Nagasaki harbor on their way from Vladivostok. Five bluejackets who visited the red-light district there started the riots. They not only ate and drank and refused to pay, but also smashed the furniture. The local police subdued them with difficulty and took them to the Chinese Consulate—"

"Huh."

"That was only the beginning. Two days later, over four hundred sailors from the four men-of-war in the harbor landed, presumably with fixed intentions of doing further violence. They raided the city and the police were helpless, and finally they even attacked police headquarters. The citizens at last rose in self-defence and the Chinese retreated to the warships, leaving the wreckage and the wounded behind them."

"What a pity!"

"Yes. That's it. See, China, like the Western Powers, has all diplomatic advantages over us, including the right of extraterritoriality. As usual, in this particular instance, too, we were not even allowed to bring the Chinese rascals before our own tribunal—"

"What was the final settlement?"

"Nothing came of it. The loss was ours of course. What can we do against that mighty nation backed by her great sea power? Furthermore, they had no intentions of adjudicating the affair at all. We dispatched officials from here with the foreign experts of the Department, Dennison and others, to negotiate the case with the Chinese representatives on the spot. The Chinese killed time and did nothing until the middle of November when the negotiations were temporarily terminated. Now we're about to reopen the case here in Tokyo, but I don't know what'll come of it." Ito spread his hands on the table in a helpless gesture, and went on: "You see, the Peking Government is so powerful, we are afraid to press the issue too much. We don't know what will happen if we do. We gnash our teeth, and that's all.

"There is a great deal of resentment. In some respects China and Nippon today are something like a monstrous dragon and a tiny mouse. We have no chance. Should those new Chinese battleships level their big cannon against our cities, for instance, any one of them could be reduced to ashes in a few hours."

"That was a really unfortunate incident. And we shall not be able to match China in diplomacy until our military strength is increased, as General Omura often said."

Both sighed.

"In addition to that, Saionji-san, I see a troubled sky over the Korean Peninsula. Things have seemed relatively calm there ever since the withdrawal in January 1885 of the Chinese and Nipponese troops from that country in accordance with the terms of the Tientsin Treaty which Li Hung-chang and I concluded that year. We must prevent China from dominating Korea which is our stepping-stone to the Asiatic Continent, for soon there'll be a great over-crowding of population in our country. It is we who must begin to work on the problem now. If Korea is allowed to go to China or Russia, posterity will blame us. That brewing trouble may break into a tempestuous storm which may easily throw us into a headlong collision—"

"With China?" Saionji anxiously inquired.

"Yes, with China. Or with Russia or perhaps with both against us. With our limited resources and revenues, what can we do against either one of them?"

"It seems we're certainly heading for trouble, but we can't avoid it, can we?"

"No, I am afraid not. Don't you remember Kido and Omura used to predict this unhappy development?" Ito threw his head back with his weary eyes shut for a moment.

"I do very vividly. Even twenty years ago General Omura was anxious to execute Councillor Kido's Korean colonization plans," Saionji remarked. "Huh, we shall do our best."

"True. Oh, well, if I could settle in our favor this future life-and-death problem of our country and people, I could die peacefully on my bed or in the field.—Ah, I have spent much time and worry on the subject. Do you have any other official reports to make besides those we received from you while you were in Vienna?"

"No, Your Excellency—"

"*Excellency*, Saionji-san? Are you teasing me? Of course from lesser people— But no formalities are necessary, now."

"Ha, ha, Premier Ito, I've got the habit in these last years."

"Well, until I give you your next assignment abroad, I want you to help that Law Investigation Commission as the vice-chairman. That's what I wanted to tell you. That's all—"

It was a quiet afternoon.

The governess with a short sleeveless kimono covering her ordinary attire was trotting in and out and often looking towards the gate.

In the Saionji house people moved around on tiptoe. A large, soft, linen-covered mattress wadded with chopped straw, a new wooden tub and linen were brought in. A midwife had already arrived. From the kitchen chimney rose a column of smoke, and water was boiling on the clay stove.

Through the modest gate a jinrikisha rushed in. Saionji had returned from the office of the Law Investigation Commission.

"Sagami!"

When he saw the governess he dropped his voice: "Sagami!"

"Oh, Master!"

"How is she? How's Okiku?"

A faint groaning came from the rear room.

"Shall I call a doctor, Sagami?"

"Well, that midwife is supposed to be very good, never lost a child or mother—"

Saionji asked again: "Is Okiku all right? Can I see her?"

Sagami held out her hand to bar her master from advancing past the partly open screen. He saw the midwife and a few neighbors busy around Okiku who lay on the mattress.

Another groan made Saionji frown: "Can I see her? Is she all right?"
He was perspiring.

"Master, just another few moments, they say. Everything is all
right—"

"Now, now, *Okusama*, sit up a little! Will you hold her from behind?" came a commanding voice. The groaning began again. "Once
more, press hard! There, there!"

Sagami held her breasts tightly; Saionji's fists shook.

"Don't loosen! There, there! Ah, it's all over—a pretty girl baby!"

"Master, a Princess!" The governess held her master's hands in hers
and whispered tearfully.

As the new-born baby's cries became louder, Saionji's worried look
gradually changed to a broad smile: "Sagami! A daughter— Okiku's
well!"

"Okiku, let me hold Shinko for a while. You are getting your complexion back, huh?"

"Yes, Prince, I feel very fine."

"Do you think she'll begin to smile before I go to Germany? I hate
to leave you here—I'll really feel homesick for you and Shinko—"

"You didn't tell me that you were going to Europe again, Prince."

"Huh, I had the order from the Foreign Office on the day Shinko
was born, but I didn't tell you because I didn't want you to get excited.
I am transferred from Vienna to Berlin as Minister to Germany and
also Belgium. I asked for an extension of my leave until you got well—"

"Oh?"

"It'll soon be the *Girls' Festival*. I sent for a set of dolls from Kyoto.
Will you arrange them for Shinko, since I can't stay that long?"

"That's wonderful, Prince! I thought of it, but since you seemed
indifferent about traditional observances I thought you might not care
for the March Festival."

"Huh, in theory, but in practice things are different, especially with
Shinko. Look, Okiku, the baby is smiling!"

"Prince, they say it's not a real smile."

But Okiku, too, looked joyfully down over Saionji's shoulder.

"I don't care what they say—I'm sure she smiled at me."

"I must congratulate you and your family." Ito smiled at Saionji.
"It is great news. To manage the affairs of a nation is one thing, and

to have a family and particularly a child is another kind of joy and satisfaction. Are the mother and child doing well?"

"Yes, thanks! They are."

"Boy or girl?"

"Girl."

"She'll be beautiful and talented, for the parents are exceptionally handsome and intelligent. I suppose you'll want a boy next. How does it feel to be a father?"

"I can't explain in words. As you said, a sense of joy, satisfaction and new responsibility, together with anxieties, come over me at the same time."

"Are you going to bring her up as a princess in your ancestral Fujiwara fashion?"

"No. I want my child to be a well-rounded human being. I'll send her to the public schools, a girls' high school and a college to prepare her for family life. But my old governess favors the traditional ways."

"You have a really democratic soul. Look at the many titled people, especially those newly-elevated ones, who are anxious to do things in a 'princely' way for their children. Here everything is at your command, but you don't care to take advantage of your privilege."

"Premier Ito, it may be stubbornness, it may be ignorance—but I think the best parents can do for their child is to teach her the world of facts instead of giving her a false notion of life and society."

"Well, Saionji-san, that's beyond me."

"It's the result of my own experience. I think I enjoyed life so much because I abandoned the traditions which clustered about and fossilized us courtiers while the world was moving constantly forward. It was what those new scientists call the process of evolution."

"That sounds very logical, doesn't it?"

"Huh, we were discussing—" Saionji's laugh was characteristically soft.

"Well, you can't keep a new father to an impersonal subject very long." Ito laughed too. After a few moments he continued: "This time it will be hard work for you because we want you to concentrate on the revision of our treaty with Germany. On the other hand, the outlook is bright because Prince Bismarck, whom we met when we investigated the constitutional affairs, is there. And he is, like myself, both Chancellor and Foreign Minister."

"Now that my wife and child are doing well, if you want me to, I can leave for Germany at any time."

"That's fine. Oh, one more thing. The Government wants you to pay respect to the Papal Court at Rome on your way. All your papers and credentials will be ready for you."

In 1887, Marquis Saionji, as Nipponese Minister to Germany and Belgium, left Yokohama for his post.

He sailed on a liner owned and operated between Yokohama and Shanghai by the recently-organized Nippon Yusen Kaisha. From Shanghai, the Minister proceeded on a European steamer by way of Hongkong, Singapore, Calcutta, Bombay, Columbo, the Suez Canal, and finally reached Naples. He discharged his official mission at the Papal Court, and started for Berlin.

Some time after he had presented his credentials to the German Government, he was dining at Chancellor Bismarck's official residence. The elaborate meal was over and the host and his guest relaxed over coffee and cigars.

"Your Excellency, I hear that your country has adopted many things of the West since you were here last in 1883. Is that right?"

"Yes, Your Excellency, that is correct. I am sure you have been given a good deal of information by those German scholars, who acted as technical and scientific assistants to our Government. Almost every branch of our national defence, and of our political and social systems has been modified in the light of your dictum of 'order and efficiency.' In 1884 we created a new peerage with five classes, covering more than 400 families; we installed a cabinet system in December 1885, headed by Count Ito—"

"The leader on your former visit?"

"Yes. We are completing the Imperial Constitution and we expect great things of it and of the opening of the Imperial Diet."

"When will your constitution be promulgated?"

"On February 11, 1889. February 11 is our Founder's Day, by the way. And the first session of the Diet will be convened the following November, after the first general election that summer."

"That seems excellent."

"Six modern army divisions were created in January 1886, and sometime before I left home, Tokyo, our capital, saw the first electric lamp used!"

"That all goes to show that you Oriental people, too, can learn our Western techniques. Your remarks about the military expansion made me recall the visit of your War Minister. What was his name—and the young colonel on his staff? That was in 1884."

"I presume that the War Minister was General Oyama Iwao, and the colonel you mentioned was Katsura Taro. The latter studied here and came back as our military attaché in 1875. He originally intended to study in France where I stayed from 1871 to 1880. But your army's siege of Paris so impressed him that he came to Your Excellency's country instead."

"H'm, that siege was nothing." With this remark the Chancellor suddenly sat up, his chest bulging and his broad shoulders back. "H'm, he made a very wise decision. Your Excellency should have acted likewise." His eyes were like bright stars. "But speaking of the siege, my really exciting days came much later."

Saionji knew what was coming, for he had frequently heard the account from Bismarck's lips. He assumed a look of rapt attention while Bismarck went on: "Although my career dates back to the 1840's," he said, "I presided at that epoch-making Berlin Conference in 1878 attended by the outstanding diplomats and statesmen of Europe—"

Saionji became drowsy in spite of himself. And when the Chancellor pounded the table with his fist, he started up, blinking.

With another bang on the table, Bismarck continued: "I presided at the revising of the Treaty of San Stefano. You knew that, didn't you?"

"Yes—I mean no, Your Excellency. I have only read about it," was his confused reply.

"Well, these are the facts about that conference." The Chancellor went on at great length again and traced his entire career.

"That's how we revised that treaty." This time the word 'treaty' was a clanging bell in Saionji's consciousness. "Yes, Your Excellency, the treaty revision. I would like to know your attitude—"

Bismarck stared at him. "What does Your Excellency mean? I was just—" Suddenly light broke on his face. After a heavy moment both of them began to laugh.

Saionji apologized. "I am very sorry, Your Excellency. I was thinking of the treaty revision which my Government urged me to bring to your attention once more."

"Ah, yes—that. Yes. We must speak of it. But it will be satisfactory to all." Bismarck looked like a genial tiger.

"There will be a reduction of tariffs?"

"Perhaps, and on the other hand, we will deal with the naturalization of Germans and others in your country. Well, it doubtless can be arranged. How soon do you want it negotiated?"

"As soon as possible, Your Excellency."

"Leave it to me."

The aged tiger and the little cat nodded in agreement.

Saionji was among the official guests at the annual theatre party given to diplomatic corps by Wilhelm II. During one of the intermissions he went into the lobby. There he saw the young German Emperor with his attendants coming towards him:

"How is Your Excellency faring these days?" The towering Wilhelm looked down upon the smooth-faced Saionji and continued amiably: "You look very young. You are about my age, are you not?"

"Your Majesty, with your permission—"

"How old are you?"

"Your Majesty, I am ten years older than Your Majesty."

"Ten years older?" the Emperor said in surprise, looking up and down the faultlessly attired Oriental representative. "And is it true that your parliament building burned down in Tokyo?"

"Your Majesty, it is true. I received a cable message to that effect last night."

"How can a parliament building burn to the ground? It doesn't sound plausible to me."

"With Your Majesty's permission—fire burns wood. The structure was a two-story temporary frame house—"

"Ah, ah—"

"We do not use much of stone and bricks for building in my country, Your Majesty."

"Saionji-san, your service in Germany and Belgium pleased all of us. When you completed the treaty revision with Prince Bismarck in June 1889, Okuma, who was then Foreign Minister, was very appreciative, although he later paid the price of a leg for it and the ratification of the treaty was postponed."

"Huh, yes, Genro Ito. I was first of all amazed to find that you and that clever Okuma had come to terms."

"Well, I don't know that he's so clever, but of course we had to break up the Itagaki-Okuma opposition, so we took him over." He touched his thin beard confidently and added happily: "Did you call me *Genro?*"

"You deserve it. But how was it about Okuma's losing his leg? There were various reports. They said he was almost murdered."

"A young reactionary of the opposition threw a bomb at him, thinking he was responsible for the treaty clause which permitted the naturalization of foreigners. Oh, yes, there was another sacrifice in the cause of the nation's progress. Mori, the Minister of Education, was assassinated on February 11, 1889, because he was too liberal. That was the day the Constitution was proclaimed in the *Seiden* of the new Imperial Palace."

"The country advances at great personal sacrifice—but it moves on. The opening of our Diet made a good impression on the West, by the way." Saionji smiled gently. "Well, it's good to be home, and to be back with my family. Okiku and Shinko will come to greet you soon. We started out together.—"

"Your daughter is four years old now, isn't she? She is a lovely child.—Now regarding your future official station, I want you to help us at home. Will you accept the presidency of the Bureau of Decorations? The appointment will be announced by the proper authorities but that's a matter of formality. There you can rest awhile. Then in case I find a vacancy in my next Cabinet, I want your assistance. If the present Satsuma ministry fails, we Choshu men will form the Cabinet. Yamagata tried, but of course in vain, and next time it's my turn again. Now, tell me what happened at Rome?"

"I enjoyed my mission very much. Pope Leo XIII, who, strangely enough, resembled a bust of Voltaire, was an elderly, peaceful man of undeniable dignity, a good conversationalist, a good listener."

"They observe formalities, do they?"

"It was relatively easy for me after all the tasks you have assigned me. I was told that everyone received in audience by His Holiness must remove his headgear and all decorations. But since I was to be interviewed in full dress, I inquired whether I should remove my hat, sword and gloves. The official told me to keep my sword."

"Hu'm."

"Not only His Holiness, but the Papal Secretary, Cardinal Rampolla, was a likeable individual. I called on him, too. He was a man in his thirties, who looked intelligent. After the audience I was entertained by the Cardinal at a dinner there. I have never tasted such luxurious, yet well-balanced feasts anywhere. He was pleased at my liking the food."

"You don't mean your big appetite?"

"Anyway, I enjoyed my visit with the Cardinal. When I commented on the abundant supplies of good wines and tobaccos, he jokingly whispered to me: 'These two articles are officially forbidden at the Papal Court, but forbidden fruits are sweet, you know.'"

"That's interesting. Well, Saionji-san, after your rest I want you to tell me more about Europe, especially about the Triple Alliance against Russia and France."

"Certainly, Genro Ito. By the way, how is the Imperial Constitution working?"

"Splendid!" He sat up and continued: "See, I framed it—you did your small share, too—I either apply it directly as the Premier or closely watch its application by other people."

Saionji was not listening. Through the shrubs in the garden he saw Okiku and Shinko coming to the Genro's residence. Ito kept on talking.

On her slender figure Okiku wore a *yukata* of variegated stuff with a sash to match; her hair was in the becoming *marumage* style with plain hairpins; she used little make-up now over her fair complexion. In her hand was a small folding fan and with her white *tabi* she wore light clogs.

She had her daughter by the other hand. Shinko's black hair and her face closely resembled her mother's. Her hair was bobbed.

"Oh, here is your family!"

Ito took Shinko's hand in his. The girl bowed to him as she said: "Uncle Ito, *kon-nichi-wa!*"

The statesman responded affectionately to the cheerful greeting and remarked: "Saionji-san, I envy you. You have such a lovely child."

"Shinko-chan, let Uncle Ito hold you."

He continued: "I and my wife regret intensely that we don't have a child of our own. Our adopted son is, as you will agree, a good young man, but after all, 'blood is thicker than water.'" The lines on Ito's bearded face had deepened.

Returning Shinko to Okiku, he added cheerfully: "Well, we say 'a child is worth more than ten thousand treasure houses.' She is your fortune—the fortune of real family life."

IV

CABINET MINISTER

CHAPTER IV

CABINET MINISTER

"Okiku, shall we take a little walk? it's a nice day. Let's go up to the Yasukuni shrine on the Kudanzaka where the bronze statue was dedicated to the late General Omura in commemoration of his services to the early development of our military system. You remember him?"

"Yes, Prince. Let's take Shinko along."

"How about her wearing one of those costumes just arrived from Paris?"

"They look adorable on her, but—"

"But what? Don't you like them?"

"Yes, I do. But Sagami criticizes my putting them on Shinko, and it's so much bother—"

"Huh, that's it. Sagami and you, too, don't like them because you don't know how to handle them. Bring the spring outfit, I'll show you how. You must get used to it."

Okiku went to the closet.

"Shinko, where are you? Come, come, we'll take you out."

"Yes, Daddy, I'm coming." A doll-like girl of five in a neat kimono ran up to him. Embracing his knees, she looked up. "Daddy, why don't you get a pretty Parisian dress for Mommy, too? Lots of ladies wear them."

"Yes, Shinko. Don't tell Mama yet, but Daddy ordered some for her, too. They will come by the next boat." His brown eyes twinkled into her merry ones.

"Now take the kimono off and put this underwear on first, and then—" He turned to Okiku who was doubtfully watching the proceeding. "Although you ladies need a few more things than Shinko, the principle of dress is the same. You see, first this underwear, then stockings—" He went on explaining as he put them on one by one.

"You told me something about it, but I never realized you knew so much about women's clothes—"

"Oh, you misjudged me, huh?" he said with a pleasant smile.

"But I have no use for it myself. I am satisfied with the kimono and my hair in *marumage*, the real Nipponese style, Prince."

"No, you are not, and I want you to try the Western fashions."

Beaming with joy, she said: "Do you?"

"See, Mommy, Daddy is going to buy some for you, too."

Saionji smiled to see his wife and daughter putting their cheeks together with delight.

"See, Daddy, Mommy's so glad."

"Prince, you never told me that I could have Western dresses. The wives of the big statesmen wear them and now some girl students, too."

"Okiku, not that kind. They don't know anything about it. It's painful to look at them, for their outfits are a bad mix-up of styles. Usually no two parts of their wearing apparel match. Though it's an extreme case, I saw a lady in the Ginza the other day who wore a daytime hat, peasant shoes from Germany, a tailored evening gown, and she carried a parasol of striking color that was popular among the women of the red-light districts in Europe when I was in Paris almost twenty years ago."

"That must have been strange in your eyes, but the average woman thinks it's just perfect. And when those odd-looking ladies have a dance-party, the whole country envies them. But why does high society encourage that, Prince?"

"Well, they think they can please the Westerners by imitating everything. But thoughtful foreigners laugh at them. It's too superficial. That's why some people are already protesting against Westernization."

"Where can I get those dresses?"

"Oh, don't you worry, they will arrive soon. I had them made in Paris on my way home from Berlin this time."

"Really!"

"You see, when I came home from Vienna I was so hurried, I forgot to buy them and at home I was too busy. Then after Shinko came I had to leave right away for the West again. We haven't had much time to ourselves since we've been together. Now my present office is more honorary than real and I have plenty of leisure. So, belatedly, I want to take you to different places in good clothes. We can leave Shinko at home with Sagami."

Okiku's face clouded suddenly. "What will Sagami say if I dress that way?"

"Huh, you women are very sensitive to what others might say. Forget it."

"Daddy, Mommy, aren't we going out?"

Shinko, who had run to the veranda, came back and pulled at their kimono sleeves.

"All right, Shinko. Now you must have shoes. But you mustn't wear them on the matted floor. When you come home, you take them off, like I do, before you come in."

As Saionji put the shoes on her tiny feet, Shinko said: "See, Daddy, a little skylark came up from the Hibiya parade ground over Shinko's house-top and went singing up, up, and up into the sky and is gone. Will she come down again, Daddy?"

"Yes, she will. Now let's go."

Saionji was at home, reading.

A student carrying German law textbooks under his arm came through the gate and entered the house.

"Huh, Takamaro, glad you came. What's the matter? You look pale. What is it? Brother Tokudaiji told me some time ago that since your good friend, young Sumitomo died, you didn't seem yourself."

Gently laying down his books and taking his shoes off, Saionji's younger brother said: "Yes, I am awfully lonesome. It's impossible to find such a good friend again. Sometimes I hate this student life without him."

"I understand, but that mustn't interfere with your health."

"Thanks. I'd like to talk to you. I hesitate to tell my brother at home."

"Come, come. Tell me, what is it? I know you are in love with some pretty girl. Probably that and the death of your best friend make you look so wan."

"Yes, the affair is related to him."

"Who is the girl?"

"His younger sister."

"It's very natural."

"But, Brother—" Takamaro raised his face and went on—"there is a problem connected with it. The family wants me to be the heir to the Sumitomo fortune if I marry her, since there are no other sons in the family—"

"Huh, that's splendid. Brother Tokudaiji wrote me about it when I was still in Germany. Didn't his eldest daughter marry a member of the powerful Mitsui family? I did not pay much attention because the traditional formula of marriage was often devoid of human happiness for the couple concerned. But the problem is different if you know and love the lady and the lady reciprocates."

"Yes, but—"

"What's the trouble?"

"The Sumitomo family presented its formal proposal to him long ago, but he has done nothing about it. You know how he is. And she says—" his voice trembled—"she says that the family is still anxious to see it through. I'm afraid if Elder Brother delays any longer—"

"Come, we will see him at once. Wait, he's coming up the walk. A gentleman is with him."

Tokudaiji, recently elevated from Grand Chamberlain to Lord Keeper of the Privy Seal, called through the open screen: "Kimmochi home?"

"Yes. Come in!"

"Hirose-san, this is my brother Kimmochi and my brother Taka-maro."

"It is a great pleasure to meet you, Marquis Saionji."

"The pleasure is mine, Hirose-san!"

They bowed to each other.

"Kimmochi, Hirose-san is the manager of the Sumitomo house of Osaka, and today he is their sole representative. He previously sounded out our attitude towards the proposal of marriage between the daughter of the late Sumitomo and Takamaro here. Should we agree, he will see to it that the proper *nakaudo* handle the formalities and we shall do likewise."

"Marquis Saionji, my appealing to you and your brother directly is very informal, but I can explain. A few years ago, the master died and immediately thereafter, the young heir, who was the only son, also passed away. The family and we employees were stricken with sorrow."

Hirose turned towards Takamaro and continued: "The family, particularly the widow, knows Takamaro-san well. He had been her dead son's best friend from their early school days. She wishes him to be the husband of her daughter who, we think, is an accomplished young lady. In line with this thought, we sent our *nakaudo* to Marquis Tokudaiji some time ago but they accomplished nothing. Any negotiations through them are customarily very slow, and the grief-stricken, masterless family can not wait any longer without definite word. That is why the widow instructed me to come directly to you."

Tokudaiji said seriously, "As I wrote you, Kimmochi, I was unable to refuse or accept the proposal before your return from Europe and so I delayed answering. I must apologize to Hirose-san and the Sumitomo house and their formal representatives."

Saionji smiled. "Brother Tokudaiji, how do you answer Hirose-san now?"

"Shall we ask him to wait for a few days more for the family conference? I want no dissenting voice from you or any other of our relatives."

Saionji, looking at his brother's stern face, said in a low voice: "As you know, the only important thing is Takamaro's consent, but—"

Takamaro looked up affectionately at Saionji.

"But that will be easy, eh?" said Tokudaiji, shrugging his shoulders. Then he too smiled.

Okiku had gone to a hairdresser. Saionji was at home, talking to his visitor, Mutsu Munemitsu, Minister of Agriculture and Commerce. He was a man of fifty with full whiskers, moustache and beard, impressive features and bright eyes.

"So, Minister Mutsu, you do not approve of your colleagues' way of handling the last general elections? There were many casualties."

"No. Absolutely not, Marquis Saionji. Home Minister Shinagawa Yajiro, who was chiefly responsible for the atrocities, reported at the cabinet meeting that there were twenty-five dead and three hundred and eighty-eight wounded during the campaign. I don't know how many more there would be if all the sufferers were counted."

"Is it true that you will resign in protest from your post?"

"Yes. Those barbarians are too much for me. I did my part in the Meiji Restoration, but the results were disappointing. I attempted to raise an army in 1877 for the Saigo Rebellion against the new Government of the Sat-cho despot. My attempt failed, and the Saigo group was defeated. I served five years in prison. But after the Imperial Edict of 1881 proclaimed the adoption of a constitution for 1889 and the Diet for 1890, I became somewhat reconciled to the Sat-cho. But this new arrogance—" He shook his head.

"Confidentially, Minister Mutsu, I have felt much as you do."

"My chief hope was to play a fair game of politics under new rules laid down by the Imperial Constitution. If the people back the Liberals, give them a chance to steer the ship of state, let them try it. That's my idea. But now my Sat-cho colleagues regard the liberal opposition as rebellion. They have even mobilized army units to suppress them in the general elections. They think that the government is their private affair."

"They are defeating their own ends, aren't they?"

"But some of the clansmen don't realize it, Marquis."

"I haven't talked to anybody since the election. Are the Sat-cho leaders all accepting Home Minister Shinagawa's explanation for the act?"

"They are divided, Marquis Saionji. President of the Privy Council Ito, who during the campaign had cautioned the cabinet against relentless suppression, is furious. He was incensed at the disgraceful human casualties, and then at the loss of 'face' of the Sat-cho. Despite that interference, the government supporters were defeated one hundred and sixty-three to one hundred and thirty-seven in favor of the opposition. But I suppose you know that. Last night the Premier, Matsukata Masayoshi, attempted to pacify Ito and other leaders. I don't know the outcome. Ito's feeling was high because he took the cabinet's indifference to his warning as a personal insult."

"I beg your pardon. Prince, Marquis Ito wishes to speak to you on the telephone." Okiku announced, bowing as she opened the paper screen. "It is very urgent, he says."

"Huh, are you back from the hairdresser? All right, Okiku. I will come. I beg your pardon," he said to his guest.

Mutsu nodded, and, turning to Okiku as Saionji left the room, said: "Madame, I haven't greeted you yet."

Okiku answered: "I am sorry, sir, that I wasn't in this afternoon. And I haven't paid my respects to you since your return from America. You must have seen many interesting things abroad—"

"Yes, Madame. I want you to see my *talking-machine*. It's called a phonograph. I play songs and music on it. Mine is the second one brought into Nippon."

The Minister suddenly stared at her.

"Oh, what has happened to your hair? Your lovely *marumage* has turned into the fashionable Western style, *sokuhatsu*."

She was embarrassed.

"Well, Prince wants me to do this."

"H'm." He studied it for a while. "How do you like it? Is it better than the traditional hairdressing?"

"I just had it done, so I can't say much. But this is certainly light, so light and loose in comparison with our way that I feel as if my hair would fall off any minute. Every time I move, these wire hairpins come away. In our old system, the hairdresser uses plenty of camellia oil, puts extra false hair in the loops and a paper-made mold in the semi-oval loop at the top and ties the hair many times with strong thread made of paper, and also puts in two or three kinds of coiffure pieces. Then she puts in more greasy stuff as she finishes. All these make the hairdress as solid as if it were directly planted on the skull."

Mutsu nodded and then was lost in thought.

Saionji came back to the room and as he sat down he said to Mutsu: "You were right. Ito was disgusted and in protest he resigned from his office and is leaving for his Oiso villa."

"Ah, he was not satisfied with Premier Matsukata's explanation last night, I presume. Well, Marquis, the Matsukata Cabinet will break down soon because it aroused the anger of the elder statesmen. Before he emerges from his retreat, Ito will try a thing or two. He eventually will take up the premiership for a second time. In my opinion he is the ablest and most fair-minded among the Sat-cho elders."

Saionji nodded his agreement.

"In Nippon the cabinet remains intact even if it loses in the general election," Mutsu remarked, "but it goes out when it gets a scolding from the Sat-cho leaders among whom the premiership is rotated. Three years ago, when I was at Washington as Minister, a presidential election took place. Benjamin Harrison, a Republican, was chosen over the incumbent Democratic President Grover Cleveland on clear-cut issues. Just before I left for home, the new President and his supporters completely replaced the former. I thought it was an extreme sort of practice.

"In contrast to our system, in the United States, the people really vote for their Chief Executive, while here the Sat-cho men take turns at the political helm, disregarding the expression of the electorates.

"We have a long way to go, haven't we?"

"Yes." Saionji sighed.

"Marquis Saionji, one of these days I want you to allow me to present one of my young friends to you.

"His name is Takekoshi Yosaburo. A very talented and likeable fellow Takekoshi is. I want him to have a good friend and councillor. He is quite literary and pretty much of a man about town."

Saionji and Okiku came into their modest garden, Okiku wearing her new European clothes for the first time.

"Are your clothes too tight?"

She looked reflectively at the strange sight of her feet in pointed shoes.

"I am not used to them. I don't know what it is, the belt or the corset or the shoes. My legs have been asleep for some time. May I just take off my shoes? Nipponese dress is, after all, more comfortable and convenient."

"So you are tired of it so soon? I don't blame you. It can't be done in Europe, but a foreign-dressed Nipponese often takes off her shoes."

With Saionji's assistance, Okiku removed them and sat on the newly purchased garden chair: "Oh, such a relief. I'd like to loosen this collar, too. It chokes me."

"Now what else?" His eyes were amused, but there was impatience in his voice.

"This body-protector sort of thing pushes up my breasts and makes me feel stuffy. A tight sash around the breast is much better than this."

"I imagine you'll wear your kimono tomorrow."

"Are you disappointed in me because I can't wear this costly outfit with ease?"

He was silent.

"I'll wear this tomorrow and day after day until I get used to it. I can't bear to have you think I don't appreciate your loving present. Other women are so proud of having such a costume even if unmatched and out of date."

He turned to her.

"I was meditating. I remember my first experience like yours, exactly twenty-four years ago. Do you remember—soon after you and I got acquainted with each other?"

"Yes, Prince." Okiku raised her face.

"How hard it was to wear my new outfit! I resolved never to bother with it, for it was miserably stiff and tight. Since that time I lived in Paris for ten years, and in Vienna and Berlin a number of years. Still, I wear a kimono at home, don't I?"

"Yes, Prince." Okiku was much relieved by his sympathy.

"I think Councillor Kido was right when he said that the problem was how to adjust this type of clothing, like all other things of the West, to our mode of living. Anyway, I like these Western clothes on your slender figure. They make you look refined and ladylike."

To his great surprise, her eyes filled with tears. She murmured the word ladylike several times.

"What is it, Okiku? Did I hurt your feelings? Come, come!"

"Ladylike, unladylike. If you want a ladylike woman, why didn't you marry one of those refined Kyoto girls, a princess of a moth-eaten Okuge house with nothing but tradition, heritage and hundreds of other useless things—"

"You misunderstand me. I was teasing you. Don't get angry like that. It spoils your charm. What is the matter?"

"Nothing— But, but Sagami constantly tells me I am unladylike."

"But why? Why does she say so? What's the matter with her?"

"Because I accompany you wherever you go, and I don't follow many other customs of the traditional wife and mother. I didn't shave off my eyebrows when Shinko came, I don't dye my teeth black, and I wear good clothes and use make-up."

"And we are affectionate to each other, huh? Don't take it seriously." He thought awhile. "Just like a mother-in-law, huh?"

"She's worse than that. She used to be kind, but I think she's grown jealous of me now." Okiku wept. "I love you and like to live close to you. If I quarrel with Sagami, one of us has to depart from you, and since she is old and has no place to go, it will be I who will have to leave. I never talk back to her, but it is hard not to answer when she criticizes."

"Do calm yourself, Okiku. I won't let you go. And you couldn't leave Shinko and me, could you?" He tipped up her face.

"That's just it. Lately, when you are away, she keeps Shinko from me, and doesn't let her—"

"What?" Saionji was amazed.

"She doesn't let Shinko call me Mother. That breaks my heart, Prince. All because I'm unladylike, she says. If I were really your *okugata*—" She stopped, alarmed at her own boldness. "And you, you often stay away, and at home you are always reading and you don't seem to appreciate my music any more." All the pent-up accusations of years past poured out. "You follow all the free ideas of the West when it suits you, so I never know where I stand, and Sagami is always criticizing me. I get all the blame."

Saionji stroked her hair which had fallen loose from its pins.

"Sagami makes insinuations about my upbringing and even my people. My family were honorable *hatamoto*. My mother was a lady. She was cultured and devoted."

"Huh, that's right. Some time ago you said that your father was a *hatamoto*, but you didn't say anything more about your relatives. You said they passed away—"

Okiku sobbed. Then she declared that her family had died in defense of the Tokugawa. Her brother joined the *Shogitai* band which was vanquished by General Omura's troops, and her father resisted the government forces at Aizu in the north which was one of the last strongholds of the pro-Shogunites. Fighting until his sword was broken, he was severely wounded and committed *harakiri* before he was made prisoner.

Meanwhile, Okiku's mother, like many other wives and daughters of the loyal Tokugawa *samurai*, helped the defense in building barricades and furnishing food supplies during the siege at Aizu. Immediately before the fall of the stronghold, when she saw her husband's brave end, she instructed the *ashigaru* of the family to take locks of his hair and her own and a pair of the heirloom swords with a message to Okiku, who had just entered the geisha profession. The mother was pierced by her own dagger and died at her husband's side.

"The message stated that I should bury the hair as their remains with due ceremony and take good care of their graves, and keep the swords. I wanted to tell you about it, but I was afraid to hinder your career should people discover you married a daughter of a Tokugawa *hatamoto*—"

"What did you do?"

"I was afraid to have a burial for them because of the strong feeling against us, so I secretly went to the Asakusa Temple where the *Kwannon* is—it's our family temple—and entrusted the relics to the priest."

"Huh, so that's why you often visit that sanctuary."

"Yes, Prince, especially on September 22, the day of my parents' passing."

"We'll see to it that a proper burial takes place, preferably on their anniversary, huh? You people upheld the feudal tradition. There is no more discrimination against the supporters of the old order. Their action was officially forgiven some years ago.—So that explains your frequent outbursts about the Sat-cho leaders.

"Now do you feel better? I only stay away because I must work. As for Sagami, I'll speak to her. She is a good soul, but conservative.

"How would this be?" he asked. "In a few days I will be free. You and I will take a trip to Kyoto. How would you like that? We shall see the scenes of my boyhood days and the grand old capital. We will get acquainted all over again. You can talk about culture, temples, shrines, paintings, and so on. You shall sing for me as you used to."

"To Kyoto?" she said unbelievingly. "All alone with you?"

"Of course. Yes, we'll do it. Come now, wipe your eyes. You are still my star geisha. See, you look like a little girl now."

A few days later the Saionjis, dressed in Western clothes, left for the Shimbashi railway station. Their two jinrikishas were to take them to the Kyoto train.

Sagami and Shinko stood outside the gate and waved good-bye to them.

Sagami murmured: "Ah, this unladylike woman—"

Shinko, alert as always, heard the remark. "Sagami, why don't you like my mother?"

"Why don't I like your—? Oh, yes, Princess, yes, I do, I do like your mother. Come, Princess, let's go into the house."

"Sagami, listen to that whistle, that's from the train, taking Daddy and Mommy to a nice place."

Sagami nodded as she slowly walked to the door, holding Shinko's hand.

The spring sun was already far down in the Western sky when the train bearing Saionji and Okiku pulled out of the station.

Okiku looked at Saionji. They were acting like strangers.

She cleared her throat.

"Prince, how far are we going tonight?"

"We rest in the sleeping-car after a while and arrive in Kyoto tomorrow morning. See, this Tokaido Railway between Tokyo and Kyoto has just been completed. When Emperor Meiji made his first trip between the old and new capitals, it took twenty-one days by palanquin. Now we get there overnight."

"Isn't it wonderful? How fast is the train running, Prince?"

"Huh, sometimes about twenty miles an hour, but most of the time far less than that."

There was a long silence. The little urban houses gave way to pine-woods and rice fields. The train was a friendly steed, putting miles between them and the sharp eyes and tongue of Sagami. Even Shinko seemed remote.

"Okiku." Saionji startled her. "Aren't those pretty, those boats with white sails returning to home ports?"

They became absorbed in the fading sunset over the northeast shores of Sagami Bay.

Idly they listened to a group of army and navy officers at the other end of the car, who were carrying on animated conversations in the dialects of Satsuma and Choshu.

One husky Choshu voice said: "Though he is a civilian, Ito has the audacity which other leaders lack."

The second added: "That's real statesmanship. And Mutsu is a big-hearted fellow. He has already indicated that he wants to have close military co-operation in Korean matters if he should take charge of the Department of Foreign Affairs."

"If Ito becomes Premier again and Mutsu Foreign Minister, as is likely to happen, we can have the chance of our lifetime. Ito's inviting us to his villa may have something to do with this. If he accepts our recommendations, our colleagues in the Army and the Navy may be startled. What do you think, Admiral?"

Saionji unconsciously looked towards them.

"Although I may be optimistic, if Russia stays out of it, we have a chance of winning against the Chinese Navy. Conservative people think it's seven-to-three in China's favor though. Her two new seven thousand ton battleships may be too powerful against our four thousand ton ones. But delay means that the disparity between the two Navies will increase. However, our advantages over them are: the possession of 33 cm. rapid-fire guns on our big men-of-war, and the faster speed of our first-class warships over the Chinese battleships." The booming-voiced sea-fighter pounded the train window. "I must tell you one thing, though, the morale of our men is excellent. Every man is ready to die for the country and His Majesty. Let them come, we'll show them what we can do in spite of our inferior strength!"

"Great!" the first general said. "You Satsuma admirals command the Imperial Navy as you know best and we Choshu soldiers will do our duty on land."

The train slowed down and finally halted. A young man on the platform was shouting the name of the station:

"O-i-so! O-i-so!"

"*O-ben-to! O-ben-to!*" another voice chanted.

"Okiku, here is a boy selling food and fruits. Shall we get some?"

"Yes, Prince."

"Huh," said Saionji some time later, "we are already climbing the Hakone Pass. Do you hear the sounds of the locomotive puffing?"

"Yes, Prince."

"It's about time that our berths are ready. Let's go into the sleeping-car." His smile restored her self-confidence.

"I'm not sleepy, Prince. I'm so excited at thinking of going—actually going to Kyoto with you. When I was a girl, I never dreamed of seeing the ancient Imperial Seat. And to think of riding on a steam train!"

"The country has progressed in some ways since the Restoration in 1868, hasn't it? Although this train is slower than those American and European ones, it is a great improvement."

"Do Kyoto people differ from us Tokyo-born?"

"Some general differences, to be sure, still exist. You see, the Tokyo people are realistic, practical, active, alert and progressive, with all the drawbacks which those virtues entail. The men and women in Kyoto are romantic, impractical, easy-going, dreamy. They observe traditions and are cultured."

"Is it true that they have more faith in superstitions than we have?" Okiku's face flushed. There was always a great delight in hearing Saionji speak in his soft Kyoto dialect.

"That may be true, too, for there are many more temples and shrines in that city than in Tokyo. Some of them are dedicated to superstitions or to imaginary beings."

"How are the Kyoto beauties? You used to admire them and to speak so highly of them." She looked down at her hands.

"I haven't changed my mind on the subject, Okiku. This time you can see with your own eyes and draw your own conclusions. You are such a good judge."

"You are not backing down, are you, Prince?"

"Oh, no, and you are not jealous, are you? Huh, Okiku, they are pretty, but not equal to you, my modern *komachi*, by any means."

Okiku laughed and said: "Every woman has her pride—"

"And some—jealousy, huh?"

"Do the Kyoto girls spend more money on their appearance?" she persisted.

"Generally they do, I believe. They spend more for clothes than food, for instance, in contrast with the Tokyo girls. Furthermore, they are careful when buying so that later they can remodel their kimonos."

"They don't follow the fashions as much as we do, do they?"

"They do. For example, when longer sleeves become stylish or brown the fashion, they had their kimonos dyed that color and made over in the new style at small expense. It's far cheaper than getting a new outfit. However, since that is their habit, when they buy new goods, they take time to select durable stuffs and pay more for them. They are thrifty."

"We are always hurrying, there is no time for us to bother with old kimonos. We make more and spend more, maybe."

"Look, Okiku, we are already passing the Tago-no-ura shores of Suruga Bay. Do you recall the famous poem by Kakinomoto-no-Hitomaro—'Away from Tago-no-ura'? This district is one of the loveliest spots along the Tokaido railway line. From this neighborhood we can see the prettiest view of Fujisan, too."

"Prince, where are we going to stay in Kyoto?"

"Huh, at the suburban retreat of my ancestors in the northeastern part. As I told you, the Saionji home on the palace grounds was removed because of the improvements there. But the Shirakumo-jinsha, our family shrine and landmark, is still there. What would you like to see in Kyoto?"

"Well, I have heard so much about the big shrines and temples, such as the Chion-in, the Nishi-Honganji of the Shinshu sect, the Higashi-yama, the Arashiyama—and—and the Golden Pavilion." She tried to recall other names.

"Is the Golden Pavilion large?" she asked.

"No, it has three stories and is forty-two feet high, forty-two feet wide and thirty-three feet long."

"Not a very big building, is it? Why is it spoken of so much?"

"Huh, it was built in 1399 and experts say it is one of the most perfect specimens of architecture in Nippon, and the garden is exquisite. The building, the pond, the rocks, the shrubs and the whole setting are all in perfect harmony."

"Why is it called the 'Golden' Pavilion?"

"When one of the Ashikaga dictators built it, the roof as well as the inside was painted with lacquer, and covered with gold foil. That's how it got its name. It was the builder's retreat, and he frequently entertained the Mikado and other dignitaries there. But when he died his will stated that it be turned into a temple and new buildings added. During the civil wars they were burned down, but the Golden Pavilion escaped harm.

"And did you know, Okiku, that there was once another group of buildings there before the Pavilion was erected? The property originally belonged to an ancestor of mine. It was later relinquished in favor of the Ashikaga."

"Oh, that's fascinating! How, Prince?"

"This Saionji forefather, a member of the Fujiwara clan, was a very able statesman and lived from 1171 to 1244. To display his wealth and prestige, he built a group of luxurious buildings dedicated to Buddha, used it as his residence, and called it Sai-on-ji. Thereafter, my ancestors used that title. There were already so many Fujiwara families that individual identification by that name was difficult. Some time later a civil war devastated the Saionji temple, but because of the scenic beauty of that region, the Ashikaga chief acquired the property from my forefather and built what we now know as the Golden Pavilion, as I told you before, Okiku."

"Oh, Prince, it is like a legend. I feel as if I were living in the Heian era. Everything in Kyoto has some historical background, hasn't it?" Her eyes danced.

It seemed as if the long-vanished radiance of their courtship were shining on both of them.

"Prince, do the European people you know appreciate the things of Nippon? Like the picturesque buildings and art pieces in Kyoto? Do you appreciate theirs?"

"It is hard for average people to do so, because there is one fundamental difference between the West and East."

"What is that?"

"The Westerners try to conquer Mother Nature; we attempt to adapt ourselves to Nature. Take the example of that magnificent cathedral of Notre Dame in Paris which is complete in itself and asserts the mastery of human effort. But the Golden Pavilion would be incomplete without the pond, the rocks and the shrubs on the site. In fact, it needs that particular setting to give it full meaning."

"Prince, that's beyond me. But how about the *Daibutsu* in Nara we hear so much about? Do they have bronze statues of Buddha in France, Germany or England, fifty-three feet high?"

"Those people are not Buddhists—well, I think it is the largest in the world today. But they are erecting a statue of 'Liberty' in New York to be finished next year. It will be higher than the bronze statue of Buddha in the Todaiji Temple in Nara."

"How did you come to know about it?"

"You see, the whole thing is a gift of the French people to America. When I was in France the money was being raised among the people, and the head of the statue was already exhibited at the Paris Exposition before I left for home."

"Oh, but our *Daibutsu* is older, isn't it?"

"Yes, that was finished in 749—"

"Then it's 1146 years old, is it not, Prince? Do the people in Europe know of the Nipponese?"

"Yes, but only in the circus. They showed some of our countrymen as curiosities or acrobats when I was there first.—Huh, you must be tired and sleepy after our busy day and my long-winded story. Look at that enormous moon just above the horizon of the Pacific Ocean."

"Not sleepy at all. Prince, tell me something more about Kyoto. Oh, Prince, tell me about the *biwa* legend of the Saionji family, will you?"

"I was just thinking of that, too, when I saw the moon. But it's another long tale and you have already heard it from other people."

"From some, but never in full."

"If you insist, since we have nothing to do and we are alone, I will."

"And about your own art of *biwa* music, too."

"You demand more and more, huh? Say, how about those fruits? Wouldn't you like to eat some?"

"Prince, how about that bottle of imported wine that you told me to bring along in the valise?"

"That's what we need. And also that box-lunch I bought earlier in the evening. The dining car offers only poor service and it is closed at this time. We'll have plenty of our own. Wait, I'll get them down for you."

"Prince, here it is, cups, and everything."

As they ate and drank, Saionji told her the family legend.

With a sigh Okiku whispered: "Prince, that's interesting, but it scares me. Do you believe it?"

"No, I don't. But Sagami does. She insisted that I should not marry anybody, but take a mistress. And she believes if I do not offend the goddess of *biwa* music I'll live to be a hundred, but if I anger the deity, my wife and I will die instantly."

"Don't tell me any more. It gives me shivers."

The wine bottle was soon empty. Okiku placed everything neatly aside and sat close to him.

"We are now crossing the bridge over the O-i River, one of the largest streams between the new and old capitals. The moon is high, the Milky Way is clear. There is the North Star. Look at the chain of silvery waves, miles and miles, lazily coming and retreating."

Saionji was light-hearted. Okiku had regained her girlish complexion and also became gay

"Okiku, how about a little song? You don't need an instrument, do you? Come, come, my sweet," he lightly patted Okiku's slender shoulder. She leaned against him

"If you hum the samisen tune, I'll sing some song for you, though I haven't tried for many years. Then you compose a poem on this lovely journey." She looked at him affectionately.

"Do you remember a famous *hokku*, about the Milky Way and rough sea, by Basho, the master of the seventeen-syllabled verses, Okiku?"

"How did it go? *Ara-umi-ya Sado-ni yoko-to Amano-gawa*—was it not, Prince?" said Okiku, her eyes shut as if she were speaking in a dream.

He mumbled its English approximation: " 'The billows come rolling and the Milky Way stretches across to the Sado Islands.' Huh, but neither is the sea below us rough, nor is that land beyond us the Sado. The water is 'pacific' and on the other side is America."

Then she began singing a song of their Nakamura-ro days.

Saionji felt her weight on his arm. His warm eyelids came together; he heard their last stanza blending into the slow droning of the wave.

The pale spring moon shone tenderly through the window on the Saionjis who had fallen asleep, holding each other closely.

The train sped towards its destination.

"*Kurumaya*, take us to Tanaka."

Saionji, in front of the Kyoto railway station, was beckoning to the men.

"Yes, sir." A jinrikishaman who stood a few feet away replied and asked a second to join him.

It was a fragrant spring morning.

Okiku, in Western dress, was near Saionji while the *kurumaya* were loading their light baggage on the vehicles.

"Huh, it is nice to be back in the home town on such a fine day," he said joyously.

"Prince, you look very happy."

"Huh, I feel at home in the heart of the ancient capital. Look at the tops of those mountains surrounding the city on three sides, north, east and west, veiled with the spring haze—exactly as it used to be.

Huh, the sun is beginning to come out, too. Everything seems to welcome us.'

Pointing with his cane, he continued with some emotion: "I came back here on other occasions but never was I so enthusiastic as I am now about Kyoto. Perhaps it's being with you, Okiku."

He turned to their right. "Those high hills are the Higashiyama section, and beyond them is Tanaka."

"Prince, in which direction is that Golden Pavilion you were telling me about?"

"That's to our left on the slope of that mountain in the northwest quarter of the city. See, here it's easy to find a place because in the seventh century the city of Kyoto was planned on a checkerboard system and that fundamental scheme was never altered."

"Where is the late Councillor Kido's resting-place?"

"That's on the Higashiyama hill, a short distance from the famous Kiyomizu Temple. We will pay a tribute later."

"Aren't the people slow here?" Okiku looked around.

"Do you notice it? These jinrikishamen don't come rushing at us like wounded wild boars charging the hunters the way they do in the Shimbashi station in Tokyo. Remember how you used to lament the overthrow of the Tokugawa? During the last few years this city has recovered somewhat, but still it's very dull."

The second man finished loading the baggage.

"Ready, *kurumaya?*"

"Yes, *dan-na.*"

"Follow Karasumaru Street as far as the north end of the palace grounds, then turn to the right. No hurry."

"Yes, sir."

"Okiku, this is one of the best thoroughfares in the city. Before we get to Tanaka we'll cross a bridge over the Kamo River."

"Oh!"

"Do you recall our discussions about it, many years ago? This is like our walk to the Nihombashi one spring morning."

"Yes, yes, Prince, but there was no jinrikisha or train then."

Seifuso, the old Saionji residence in Tanaka, formerly the outskirts and now the suburb of the city, consisted of a group of modest frame buildings. Saionji had arranged with the caretaker to have one house made ready for their temporary occupancy.

They unpacked their baggage, and went out in the garden full of cherryblossoms, with bright yellow globeflowers and red azaleas against the fresh verdure of aged pines and cryptomeria. Shrubs lined a pond where a pair of cranes stood, holding their long bills like giant fishhooks.

The days, spent for the most part in sight-seeing, went by all too quickly. The songs of nightingales accompanied their walks along the hillsides of budding green. At many of the shrine and temple ponds stood weeping willow trees whose slender green branches streamed down towards the water where the early purple iris were opening their sparrow-like petals and yellowish spear-shaped buds of lotus already rose above the ripples.

The schools of large, red and black carp, rushing towards the human shadows for food, were Okiku's favorite sight. It was the season of the year when people still preferred to walk on the sunny side of the streets at the height of a fine day. The charcoal brazier and the *kotatsu*, a charcoal fireplace covered with a quilt, were about to be put away for the season. Yet in the evening the paper screens were still tightly shut.

They began their tours by first visiting the palace grounds where Saionji found his family shrine, Shirakumo-jinsha. They knelt before it and prayed after clapping their hands a few times.

After the prayer, Saionji looked around the palace yard. He was quiet, and Okiku knew that he was greatly moved. "Prince, why are you so silent?"

"Okiku, over twenty-five years ago I left these scenes for Tamba, then Echigo, at the head of the Imperial Expedition."

Okiku nodded.

"There has been a great change for the better. Even the Mikado no longer lives here. You can't comprehend how financially miserable the Court was when I was a boy. There was no money in the Imperial treasury to pay for the repair of the buildings or the grounds which were left to the mercy of the rain, snow and wind as I told you some time ago."

"So you are glad, are you, Prince?"

"I am somewhat confused. On the one hand, I am delighted to see the palace in such perfect order; on the other, I can't help feeling a slight disappointment in the disappearance of the familiar scenes. I regret the removal of my house, but of course I can console myself with the thought that it was necessary for the improvement of His Majesty's estates."

Okiku, who caught the fragrant odor of the cherryblossoms in the breeze, became impish.

"Prince, are you sorry because the broken fences through which you used to ride are replaced by new ones?"

"Huh. We'll follow this path to the Hamaguri Gate."

As they moved on, Saionji repeated: "It is a strange sensation, when I think of the changes, politically, too, which we have come through and that we will probably see many more. But as we say, 'One man is powerless to save a gigantic structure on the brink of its ruin.' I suppose one should not call it ruin, but this site of past glories makes me melancholy."

They were walking side by side. He continued: "Before the Meiji Restoration, although His Majesty was here, this place was left uncared for for lack of money. Then under the new Government, over-enthusiastic for Westernization, the people overran the palace and destroyed the old paintings and murals by great artists. They thought anything of our own was unworthy. They worshipped even trinkets from abroad. Think, the people in the northeast wanted to demolish the monumental Nikko Shrines."

"Wasn't it dreadful?"

"That was fortunately stopped by the late Kido. Anyway, the extreme enthusiasm for the West subsided for a little while, but it swung back to its highest pitch several years ago. Now it is declining again and the trend of the times is towards nationalism."

"How even we children hated the 'Red-Hairs' when the Tokugawa Shogun was active!"

"We were afraid of them. Then we worshipped them, and now we hate them again."

He stopped: "This is the Hamaguri Gate. Around here I first witnessed a really bloody battle between the Tokugawa men and the Choshu *samurai*. The wounded and dead were thrown all about in pools of blood in the heavy dew of a summer morning. And I was the Middle-General. Huh, how excited and proud I was—"

"Oh!"

"A few blocks away from here we'll take a jinrikisha to the tombs of my foster parents, then to those of the Tokudaijis."

"Isn't there a temple for your Tokudaiji ancestors, Prince?"

"Yes. We'll go there, too."

They walked out into the street, and before they had reached the jinrikisha stand Okiku pulled Saionji's coat sleeve and whispered:

"Prince, isn't that an Ohara girl selling flowers in the old-fashioned way?" As she came towards them she called her wares in a sing-song tone.

"Yes. She comes from Ohara on foot four or five miles to the city, carrying the basket on her head. Isn't she a contrast—the way she holds the basket—to the country girl who comes to Tokyo from the suburbs for the same purpose, bearing the flower basket on her back?"

"I am interested in her costume more than anything else. Look, she has a towel over her hair, and her plain kimono sleeves are tied back with a band, and how narrow her sash is. Oh, she's quite attractive, too. The whole thing is very picturesque. I want to buy flowers and bring them to your parents' graves."

Saionji beckoned the girl. Okiku asked for some red azalea and wild iris. The girl stared at her.

"Won't you sell them?"

Smiling, Saionji watched them.

"Okiku, she doesn't understand you." He interpreted for her.

The maiden handed the bouquet to her customer with a pleasant smile while Okiku laughingly commented on her inability to converse with the flower girl, and on the girl's soft accent and naïve politeness.

They walked away in the opposite direction.

Okiku was still talking of the girl's costume. "One peculiarity of her outfit, Prince, is her leggings. Why does she have them tied in front instead of in back?"

"Did you notice that? That was one of the many customs said to have been handed down from time immemorial. In the seventh century, it is said, a member of the court circles had to flee. He did it in the disguise of an Ohara girl. But he was unfamiliar with it and had his leggings back side front. That has been imitated ever since for the last thirteen centuries. That's what they say."

They came to the nearest jinrikisha stand. As they waited for the vehicles Saionji said: "Okiku, after our visits to the ancestral tombs, since the weather seems to be getting warm, we'll go to the Arashiyama hills for cherry-blossoms. And at night we may see the 'night cherry' on the Higashiyama. Some places look prettier later in the season. But some, I imagine, you will want to see many times before we depart."

Time flew while the Saionjis made the rounds and visited every notable part of the ancient city. They met many old friends, acquaintances and well-wishers, who had learned of Saionji's unannounced visit to his home town.

Now the cherry-blossoms were entirely gone, the globeflowers were no more. While the late varieties of azalea, peony, and iris continued to bloom, the lotus in the pond showed a few white flowers with large round leaves and the wisteria with long hanging coralla reached its prime of beauty.

The skylark became common and sang from sunrise to the dark, flying over the fields covered with green and decorated with yellow and purple wild flowers. The songs of the nightingale and the robin were heard less frequently. The boys flying kites began to take refuge in the shade during the midday. Early varieties of the cicada from the pine groves added to the weariness of the hot days with their languorous chirping and at night the frogs from the near-by watering spot raised their unintelligible sounds. The mosquitoes were increasingly annoying. Early in the evening housekeepers had to drive them out from the house by burning incense, and at bedtime the hemp mosquito net had to be spread in the room to keep the tenacious creatures away so that one might get a comfortable night's rest. On dark evenings, the fireflies on the river bank attracted children as well as adults. In the late night and early morning, when all was calm, the distinct, tragic sounds of the cuckoo, one of the favorite sentimental themes in Nipponese poetry for centuries past, were heard by half-awakened ears.

Travelling and the outdoor activities of people in Kyoto increased. The offerings at the temples and shrines multiplied. At every noted visiting-place, salesgirls and the stalls which supplied the traditional gifts grew in number. Men and women changed from heavy to light clothes. Groups of soft-spoken Kyoto beauties strolled along the Kamo River by day and night with fans in their hands.

The historic implications of the monumental buildings, and the sights and social activities in the ancient city, made Okiku understand why Saionji had regretted its modernization.

In the center of the Kyoto gay quarter around the Yojyo bridge, which spans the Kamo River, two types of folk-dances were annually presented in April and in May. Okiku preferred the *miyako* dance that kept more old characteristics than its counterpart, the faster Kamogawa. She was impressed by the historic procession of the *Aoi Matsuri*, modelled after the ancient Imperial march in honor of the Lower Kamo Shrine in May.

On the other hand, it disappointed her to find that Kyoto people no longer followed the traditional way of enjoying the evening cool in the Kamo River. Up to a few years ago, they had placed specially constructed benches in the shallow, running water. Their bare feet in the cold stream, they conversed and drank on hot summer nights. But the construction of the new canal from Biwa Lake extending along the river had put an end to that unique custom.

At first she had made fun of the narrow little Kamogawa, comparing it with the Sumidagawa in Tokyo, but its clear, transparent water, with its eternal rhythmic motion and chanting, drew her irresistibly as time went on. Many a warm, sticky evening she took a walk along the stream with Saionji.

Once, after dusk, when she was walking along its bank, Okiku saw the new moon in the clear sky on the edge of dark Higashayama. The moon became brighter and brighter. Her eyes were drawn to the stream. The gleaming moonlight was reflected on the water which appeared as a silver screen of thousands of waving pieces assembled by the faint music of nature. The mountain peaks and the teahouses on the bank were inverted in the mirroring water. She gazed at it. She did not know whether the water was moving upstream or down. Her sense of direction was gone. She shut her eyes and opened them to find the silent Higashiyama still standing before her.

Saionji was contentedly fanning himself while Okiku packed their few belongings.

On an impulse she looked outside. Clouds were gathering in the distance. In the garden the flowers stood motionless.

Suddenly a red camellia dropped to the ground, broken at the neck. Involuntarily her eyes closed to shut out the sight of the evil omen. After a while she turned to Saionji.

Still fanning, he told her his plans: "We'll return to Tokyo by way of Nara and Osaka where we may visit my brother, Sumitomo. Huh, do you think you have seen enough of Kyoto?"

"Yes, Prince." She talked rapidly to hide her melancholy. "I saw many things that I had heard of and yearned to see. I enjoyed it all very much. But what shocked me were the sights in the Teramachi, the temple streets, where we saw the sacred Buddhist and temple images and articles marketed like knickknacks in every store, block after block. I thought the Asakusa Square in Tokyo was bad enough." She shook her head.

"That is surely unique, isn't it?"

"And I saw the masterpieces by the Kano family and Ogata Korin and many other great artists, and got acquainted with the Kamo River and various parts of the city. I bought so many presents for Sagami and Shinko and others."

A tremulous light illuminated her face. The mood of the past weeks was already fast slipping away. Then the pebbles scattered under the wheels of the approaching jinrikisha.

"The seashore is the only place to be during the summer, isn't it, Saionji-san?"

"Yes, true, Genro Ito. What is the name of your villa?"

"I named it *So-ro-kaku*, from an historic Chinese name. I wish you would get a house in Oiso. It is only two or three hours' ride on the new railroad. Yamagata has one in the next town, but he'll move in here, too.

"Well, I haven't had much time for leisurely chats since you returned from Germany. I don't want to talk about business, but I sent for you to tell you a few things before I forgot them."

Ito, in his summer clothes, had received his visitor at his Oiso home, a little over forty miles south of Tokyo. His fan now and then touched the thin beard.

Taking out his own folding fan, Saionji said: "No matter where and when we meet, we talk of nothing but business, Genro."

"Yes, the business of the nation. That's our favorite subject, but you are not losing your interest in the fair sex, are you? You used to be my best comrade, but I am afraid you are becoming too much of a family man."

"Do you blame me for that? Ha, ha."

"Well, I want you to be Vice President in the House of Peers. Then later I want you to sit in the Privy Council. Those offices may be tiresome for you, but they will give you prestige by virtue of which I can invite you to my Cabinet as I have planned for so long. Say, first with a minor portfolio of the Minister of Education which will provide your proper training.

"My Cabinet has lasted fourteen months, and none of the other four, since 1885, lasted more than twenty months. But I have a good reason for believing that mine this time will last longer than any of them,"

He grasped his beard with his left hand.

"Do you have some ingenious schemes?"

"Not schemes, but I know one thing is sure to come, that is an armed conflict between China and Nippon over Korea. And that conflict will cement my power. Follow me:

"You remember almost ten years ago when you came back from Austria I predicted to you the unavoidable clash on the Korean question? Although Russia is now inactive on the peninsula, China is becoming increasingly aggressive. This Chinese statesman, Li Hung-chang, is able and crafty. He has an eye on that territory. After conquering that country he might suddenly bring his vast land and sea strength from there to our shores, as we are separated only by a narrow strait."

"Do you mean like the Mongolian invasions in the thirteenth century?"

"Yes, yes. Li is ambitious and proud of China's military strength. Moreover, he has heard that our Cabinet and the Diet have no sympathy with each other, that the Lower House freely criticizes the budget programs, and that the Premier often dissolves the Diet. He concluded that Nippon is gradually disintegrating, so that no matter what may be done to Korea, Nippon can't raise any material objections. In this line of thinking he encourages his political protégé, Yuan Shih-kai, now the Chinese Minister to Korea, to block every possible move towards our progress in better relations with the peninsula. See, the young Yuan was only twenty-five years old back in 1884 when he precipitated a revolution there. We must watch these two men very closely. Recent intelligence from our men in the territory shows the Chinese are active in military preparation."

"Do you have a better prospect of winning a war with China now than at the time in 1885 when the Chinese sailors under Admiral Ting Ju-chang devastated Nagasaki?"

Ito's head dropped slightly.

"Well, much better, but it's not at all sure, the military men say. The chief trouble, of course, is our navy. While China has eighty-two warships and twenty-five torpedo boats with a total tonnage of eighty-five thousand tons, we have twenty-eight warcrafts and twenty-four torpedo boats with fifty-nine thousand tons. And the Chinese battleships are new and powerful. The comparison of the land forces, too, is discouraging. We have only one hundred and twenty thousand men against the Chinese standing army of approximately three hundred and fifty thousand men."

"Huh."

"And the financing of the coming struggle is the greatest problem. We don't know how much money we need or how to raise it."

"But it's coming anyway?"

"I am sure of that. Our problem is whether we shall lay our neck under the enemy sword in fear and trembling or whether we shall take up arms and fight against the slow encroachment from the continent in defense of our country and our Imperial Family."

Characteristically, Ito bit his lower lip and planted his fan securely on one knee. He continued: "In our group, if anyone is qualified to handle this first real international struggle of new Nippon, I am the one. I certainly don't want Yamagata or Matsukata to manage it."

Ito's boasting of late had grown more frequent, particularly in the presence of Saionji, who took it as good-naturedly as he did the Genro's frankness. At the same time, Saionji recognized that Ito and Yamagata were growing increasingly jealous of political honors and prestige, although they buried their hatchets when they were confronted by common political enemies. Each of them was drawing up his respective Sat-cho followers and supporters.

"So you want to conduct the life and death combat by yourself?"

"Certainly. Both Yamagata and Matsukata are merely self-confident. Of course, Yamagata is an able general and Matsukata a remarkable financier, but when they come to the practices of constitutional government they can not come up to my level, because, as you know, I was the one entrusted by the Emperor to edit the Imperial Constitution, and I have instituted all other important modern political organizations. I showed the others how to operate them."

Throwing his shoulders back, Ito looked straight into Saionji's eyes and said: "While I understand everything thoroughly, what do they know? They can't handle the Diet, for instance. When the Representatives opposed the government bills, they dissolved the Diet as if they were throwing worn-out wooden clogs away. They still think that physical force is stronger than reasoning and fail to recognize the growing political consciousness and training of the people. By no means are they the men for this forthcoming undertaking. No!

"Now if I carry the Sino-Nipponese conflict decisively in the country's favor, my political life will be really crowned with triumph, because I shall solve two fundamental problems in one stroke.

The Chinese menace in Korea and the eventual threat to our country will be definitely minimized, and in doing so I shall have perfected the integrity of our people for the first time. We have crushed many internal uprisings since the Restoration under the new Government. We have demonstrated our power, it is true. But the entire nation was never fully united in one 'ball,' as the late Kido used to say. However, if we can advantageously mobilize our people against an enemy nation, every Nipponese, whether he is against us or for us, will be confronted with the common foe, and will certainly do his best. In order to unite the German Federation and to build his political prestige, Chancellor Bismarck applied the same tactics—picking quarrels with other countries—"

"You surely admire the Iron Man, don't you? But it's rather risky, isn't it, in our case?"

"Certainly it is. This China, this 'Sleeping Lion,' is an enigmatic power in the Orient, though she lost against the Europeans in the 1840's."

"And if we lose?"

"Then we'll continue to be the underdog in the Far East for another generation or more. We shall have to make the best explanation we can to the people. But there is another reason for my decision. War will create an artificial remedy for the depression. Since the last few years, while the prices of our daily needs went up, wages, agricultural products, and other things have either come down or stood still. The people are blaming us for the present condition. If we raise money in some way for war purposes and put it into circulation, prosperity will return once more. Don't you see, war is inevitable?"

"Okiku, how do you like our new suburban house in Omori? Though simple, don't you think it will serve our purpose? We'll use this place as my city office-residence, and the Omori home as our main living-quarters where you, Shinko and Sagami and the others will spend most of the time."

"Prince, the new house is quiet except for the festivities at those neighboring Buddhist temples of the *Nichiren* sect. Their followers beat the drums so much."

Saionji, still the Director of the Bureau of Decorations, was waiting for Ito's next move. Meanwhile he was at his town house with his family. Weariness had again cast its shadow on Okiku's face, but her beauty had mellowed rather than faded with the years. In her voice there was still a hint of the serenity of their days in Kyoto.

"Prince, why is it you have changed your residence so many times?" Okiku jokingly asked him.

"I meditated on the same question the other day, but I couldn't find any concrete reason for it. It may be due to the growth of my activities."

"It doesn't seem to increase your material fortune. You've already changed four or five times since you came home from France fourteen years ago, haven't you?"

"Maybe more, but I can not figure it out."

"You like to live in different sections."

"I may be unstable mentally."

"No. I think, Prince, you haven't found surroundings to satisfy your taste."

"That may be the case. I am fond of natural simplicity. I love to go to the outskirts of the city. I did it in Paris, too. Some people think it is monotonous to see the Musashino, but I enjoy it. Too much artificiality doesn't suit me.

"By the way, some time ago, when I went to Ito's Oiso retreat, I liked the town very well. You know the beautiful seashore around there."

"Are you already planning to move to Oiso?"

Saionji beamed. "Huh, I just bought the Omori house. I think that will be enough for a while."

"Well, your brother, Sumitomo, may give you enough money."

"In Europe, notable politicians usually come from wealthy families, but in Nippon all the new leaders come from the penniless homes. By the way, my brother may bring the Sumitomo House ahead some day. It's strange to see my own relative a successful, big-business executive. But many people tell me that he will be a great man in industry. They may be flattering me though."

"Your brother, Tokudaiji, is the Lord Keeper of the Privy Seal and Meiji Emperor's most trusted dignitary, and your younger brother the Sumitomo head. That's enough for one family. Prince, what do you expect to plant in the garden of the Omori house?"

"Nothing much, Okiku. Orchids again, and also some iris, which you like. I'll do it myself. Though there is little space I like to keep it as natural as possible."

"Your naturalism." Okiku laughed.

Saionji rested his fingers that had been busily carving a piece of wood with a sharply pointed knife.

"Huh, somehow, I like to see things undisturbed. Around the new house there are still many relics of the old Musashi Valley. And another good thing is that from there on quiet nights we can hear the roar of waves in Tokyo Bay."

"What are you doing, Prince? Whenever you have time you bring that piece of wood and that knife and play with them."

"Huh, this?" He stopped and held up the wood between two fingers. "When I was a boy at Kyoto I used to see courtiers doing a lot of engraving or carving on hardwood or ivory or metal. I am trying a simple outline."

"You don't have an idle moment, do you, Prince? You either practice calligraphy or read books and magazines, or take care of antiques, and now that—"

"Are you lonesome, huh?" He stopped and smiled at her.

"Well—"

"Well, what?"

"Well, would you care for tea or something now, Prince?"

"Ha, ha. Yes, thanks. Some young fellows may come over tonight."

"Tonight?"

"Or some other time. You know, Takekoshi, Sakai, Makino."

"Like you some years ago, they are fashionably dressed, are they not? And some of them are literary—"

"And brilliant, too. You ought to know Sakai who was originally Nakae's protégé. I've known him since the days of the defunct *Oriental Liberal Newspaper*. Takekoshi, you met him too, is Foreign Minister Mutsu's favorite follower. Makino is quiet and looks easy-going, but he has common sense. He is the second son of the great Satsuma leader, Okubo Toshimitsu. He was adopted by his aunt's family, the Makinos."

"Is he the one who went abroad when he was a little boy to study with his brother?"

"That's right. He first went to England, but changed to America and studied in a high school at Philadelphia, then he came home and finished his schooling. On my way home from France I met him at our legation in London where he was a clerk. We have known each other ever since. He has been Governor of Fukui Prefecture, and he'll go to Ibaragi Prefecture. He is in the city now—"

"Oh, there they come, Prince." She arose to leave, casting a long backward look at Saionji.

The rainy season was already far behind. The tradesmen had made their routine preparations for the big annual sales during the Lantern Festival season, the traditional Eastern Christmas. The farmers saw their rice plants grow beyond the need of daily care. They were able to rest. Their only worry was the forthcoming typhoon period; once it should be safely past, the rice harvest in the fall would reward them for their hard labor since the early spring.

But uneasiness pervaded both town and country. At the railway stations, at the key seaports and in the cities where military barracks were located, things were moving faster every day.

Nevertheless, the Lantern Festival was celebrated in the customary manner. The gaiety was greater, as usual, in the rural sections. There the young men and women, with children and elders, nightly assembled either in the public squares or temple yards or before private houses in which some member had passed away into the hands of Buddha within the previous twelve months. They danced to their own slow, monotonous music and songs, and frequently presented amateur pantomimic plays. This tribute originally to the dead had become a vehicle for their greatest merrymaking of the year. It was a celebration that lasted until daybreak three or four nights in succession.

In the gatherings it was rumored that the retired men and officers in the army and the navy had been officially notified to be on call.

In the late afternoon of July 25, the thrilling sounds of the bells of newspaper boys mingled with their cries. All over the country the news flashed: 'The Imperial Nipponese Navy smashes the Chinese Fleet near Feng-tao in Korean waters!'

The victory tidings finally had broken the long strain and thrown the people into a joyous uproar. A martial mood prevailed.

Another extra immediately followed: 'The Oshima Mixed Infantry Brigade marches on after defeating the Chinese Army at Asan, Korea!'

Sons and brothers of the farmers and merchants were dressed alike in khaki uniforms, with knapsacks strapped to their backs, bayonets on their hips, and the rifles on their shoulders. Under the command of the grim-faced, long-sabred, local battalion officers, they marched behind the Imperial Colors towards the debarkation point for the war front. On their way, thousands of their relatives, friends and villagers stood as they passed, waved flags and shouted *"Banzai! Banzai!"* the cheer that was first heard during the military reviews following the inauguration ceremonies of the Imperial Constitution in 1889, and which now had become the expression of popular acclaim.

Those who left for the front and those who remained, high and low, were equally determined to do their utmost to defeat their enemy and erase the rankling memory of the unpunished Chinese outrage at Nagasaki nine years before.

No human sacrifice was too great for the Nipponese to uphold the national honor. Even the officials and politicians forgot their political differences and began to work in perfect harmony for the execution of the military campaign.

On August 1, 1894, His Majesty declared war against China, the 'Celestial Empire,' which for the past sixteen centuries had been Nippon's 'Mother Country' intellectually and spiritually, but of late her tyrant politically.

Korea was the scene as well as the goal of the hostilities. Although on land and afloat the Imperial forces had won the initial victories, the final outcome of Nippon's first international struggle was uncertain. The Empress contributed to the voluntary war funds out of the Royal allowance. Emperor Meiji was at that time in the prime of his life, being in his forty-second year. As Commander-in-Chief of the Imperial Army and Navy he appeared at the military headquarters every day in his simple khaki uniform, receiving Cabinet Ministers and conferring with generals and admirals about the oversea conflict.

Premier Ito's ambition for the country had been realized. The Nipponese were for the first time an integrated force.

"Saionji-san, I want you to go to Korea to investigate the attitude of King Li and other influential people regarding the present warfare between China and Nippon."

The interview took place in Premier Ito's Nagatacho office. He was careworn and nervous.

"How soon shall I leave?"

"Right away."

"How are the present conditions on the war front, Premier Ito?"

"So far, satisfactory, but we mustn't be too optimistic, by any means. However, fortunately our army dominates the area around Seoul, the Korean capital. Now, to review the situation briefly for you—"

Ito laid the papers in his hand on the table, picked up a cigar and silently pushed the cigar box towards Saionji.

"Last December when the Chinese dispatched troops to Korea in violation of the Tientsin Treaty of 1885, Foreign Minister Mutsu, in order to uphold our treaty rights, ordered our soldiers there too. Then the native uprisings took place there in May. That added more complications. When our Minister to Peking, Komura Jutaro, informed us that another large Chinese contingent was crossing the Yalu River, the natural border line between Manchuria and Korea, and was marching into the peninsula, we sent Otori Keisuke as our Minister to Korea with a mixed infantry brigade commanded by Major General Oshima Yoshimasa." Premier Ito's bearded face was full of determination. "Then on July 25, off the island of Feng-tao in Korean waters, our warships damaged the Chinese squadron."

"And sank a transport too."

"Yes, Saionji-san, Captain Togo Heihachiro of the *Naniwa* sank the transport *Kowshing* carrying Chinese soldiers. That ship was chartered by the Chinese Government from a British concern. We have not yet received full information, but the British Minister has lodged a strong protest with the Foreign Office. We trust that Captain Togo had sufficient grounds for taking this drastic action."

His voice was steady.

"Huh, we have the Korean capital under our control, anyway."

"It's just the beginning. We declared war only three weeks ago. Two things which disturb me are the possibility of Russian aid on the enemy side, and our finances for the war. But our military men, encouraged by their opening success, expect to bring the war to a speedy conclusion."

Ito dropped his cigar ashes on the floor as Saionji left the office; the Premier dug into the pile of papers on his desk.

The advance guards of the Nipponese Army had already reached the Korean side of the Yalu River after sweeping through the country north of Seoul for four months. The Imperial Navy, by incapacitating the Chinese North Sea Squadron commanded by Admiral Ting Ju-chang, on September 17, 1894, took complete command of the Yellow Sea.

"It is amazing to see these smashing victories on land and sea, Premier Ito. I just arrived from Tokyo in response to your telegram."

"It is, Saionji-san." The wartime Premier spoke absentmindedly.

They were in the temporary office building, which sheltered the government officials in Hiroshima City, almost at the southwestern tip of the largest Nipponese island. The Imperial Headquarters had been advanced there in September in order to supervise more efficiently the war with China.

"Now, as I told you when you returned from the Korean mission that Education Minister Inouye Kowashi, because of severe illness, could not remain in the Cabinet any longer. I recommended the acceptance of his resignation to His Majesty. Since then a regular minister has been lacking. I want you to give up your Privy Councillorship and to take his portfolio."

"Huh, I have some ideas I wish to advance—"

Ito interrupted him with his usual friendly but overbearing manner. "We have no time to argue in these critical days. We must face the seventh session of the Diet which has been ordered to convene here in Hiroshima City from October 18-22. Will you assume the duties tomorrow, October 3?"

"Yes, Premier Ito. Accept my thanks."

"Is there anyone you'd like to have as your personal councillor for the Education Department? The Minister can appoint a man of his own choice—"

"Huh, I'll ask Takekoshi—"

"He seems to be capable. Foreign Minister Mutsu admires him. He is stylish like yourself, ha, ha."

"Huh."

"That's all for today."

"It was truly inspiring to witness the last session of the Diet. No dissenting voice was heard when the bills for unprecedented war funds were introduced. But the fighting sectors still give me concern." Premier Ito was addressing his Cabinet.

"One hundred and fifty million yen is no small amount of money," Finance Minister Matsukata Masayoshi remarked. "So far, the annual national outlay has not amounted to more than eighty-five million yen. Despite that fact the opposition was strongly against the budget. But when it came to a head the representatives were unanimous in voting the war funds which were nearly twice as large as the ordinary annual expenditure.

"And we are sure that we can raise the amount." Matsukata concluded his report.

Premier Ito then requested Admiral Saigo, the Minister of the Navy, who had temporarily supervised the War Department in addition to his own, to report on the developments of the land campaign.

"At present our expeditionary forces are very active in the different fronts and, with the aid of the Imperial Navy, will soon storm Weihaiwei before they advance towards the Chinese capital. Their most notable victory since last fall was that of the Second Expeditionary Army at Port Arthur. Our men captured the fortress in one day's battle, although the Chinese concentration was reported to be ten thousand infantrymen, amply supplied with arms and ammunition and powerful artillery pieces. The enemy's weakness lay in lack of training and will to fight—they were mostly newly recruited mercenaries."

Admiral Saigo then went on to describe at length the naval activities, concluding: "The capture of Weihaiwei, from which base the enemy navy has been operating, is already in sight. If we should take that Chinese stronghold we can dominate the sea and thus enable our land forces to march to Peking without serious obstacles."

"What developed in the sinking of the British *Kowshing*, Minister Saigo?"

"Premier, the information we got from the men responsible for it has been handed to the Department of Foreign Affairs—"

Foreign Minister Mutsu, who had just come into the meeting, took up the question. "Although a settlement has not been reached, the proper British authorities are friendly. We expect an amicable agreement soon."

"Foreign Minister, what more have you to say?"

"Premier Ito, I shall summarize it briefly. At present most nations are friendly to Nippon, and some are anxious to act as intermediaries for peace with China. About three months after the outbreak of the war, the American Minister approached me with a proposal of such negotiations. I consented on certain conditions, but that fell through. Before that, our Minister at the Court of St. James's reported that the British Government had sounded out Germany and Russia as to whether they would join in mediation, but the latter two were indifferent and the British dropped the matter.

"About the same time a Frenchman, a self-styled representative of the Chinese Government, was here. But I paid no serious attention to him. Then came those two Chinese officials with whom we refused to negotiate because they did not have proper authorization from their Government."

The Foreign Minister looked first at the Premier and then at his colleagues, and added: "That's how we stand today."

"Well, sooner or later we must talk peace with the Chinese. What conditions will we demand?" asked Ito.

No one spoke.

The Premier turned to Mutsu. "Foreign Minister, what is your opinion?"

"Although the public demand varies, I have the following six points which I would like to submit for your suggestions and approval: (1) The recognition of Korean Independence by China; (2) the territorial concessions of Southern Manchuria, including Liaotung Peninsula, Formosa, and the Pescadores, where our forces have dominated; (3) three hundred million Chinese silver dollars indemnity; (4) the renewal of the Sino-Nipponese Commercial Treaty based on the same conditions which Peking grants the Western Powers; (5) the demand for more treaty ports, and (6) the temporary occupation of the invaded territories by our troops until China fulfils her obligations."

"That's good, that practically covers our conditions. Just what are the other public demands, Foreign Minister?"

"Many newspapers oppose mediation. They want to see an actual Chinese surrender and direct negotiation. Some political factions urge us to be prepared to take control of the four northern Provinces, if China disintegrates as a result of our victory over her."

The Foreign Minister sank back in his chair, apparently exhausted from his ceaseless activities.

"If there are no suggestions as to the Foreign Minister's points, which will be offered to the eventual peace conference, we shall ask Minister Mutsu to submit them to His Majesty for his approval." Premier Ito glanced at his colleagues.

"Premier," began the Finance Minister, former Premier Matsukata, "who is going to represent our Government at the peace conference?"

"Well—" Ito hesitated.

"You see, I believe it is not advisable for you to sit with the Chinese delegation—" Matsukata continued, but at this point he was interrupted by the Foreign Minister.

"I do not see any reason why he should not."

"Well—"

"Divide the honors, bluntly speaking, that is your idea, is it not, Matsukata?" General Yamagata, who, owing to his sudden illness had just returned from the front where he was the Commander-in-Chief of the expeditionary forces and took the War Portfolio, jumped into the breach.

Ito preserved a stony silence.

"I can take your place in the conference since you have so much to do. That's all I have in mind," Matsukata persisted.

"Because each Minister does his part so well, and departmental co-operation is perfect, I have very little to do, particularly at this time. Therefore, I will be with Foreign Minister Mutsu to meet the Chinese."

"If Minister Li comes—" Mutsu began.

But Ito interrupted saying, "I know him, I met him at Tientsin in 1885."

"That would be helpful," Education Minister Saionji murmured.

They breathed more easily.

"Telegram, sir!" a member of the Navy Staff came to his superior.

All turned their eyes on the officer, whose right hand rose in salute with mechanical precision.

"Read!" said Admiral Saigo, who was usually very quiet, in a thundering voice.

" 'Weihaiwei taken.' " The officer saluted again and left.

"On to Peking or immediate Chinese surrender! His Majesty—*Banzai!*" shouted War Minister Yamagata. All joined him in another *Banzai!*

Everywhere the 'Sleeping Lion' of the Orient suffered defeat after defeat at the hand of the 'unknown' country. Her most celebrated statesman, Li Hung-chang, himself came to Bakan and signed the treaty with Nippon's Premier, Ito, and Foreign Minister, Mutsu, on April 17, 1895, after eight months' bloodshed since August of the previous year. China accepted the major demands made by victorious Nippon.

Lantern parades and celebrations were held throughout the country, now unified by a war against great odds and by an unexpected and speedy triumph.

Most of the officials immediately returned to Tokyo from the Hiroshima Imperial Headquarters.

Only Premier Ito, General Yamagata, Admiral Saigo and Marquis Saionji and a few of the staff remained.

"Telegram from the Tokyo office, sir!"

Nonchalantly, Ito opened it. As he read, his face paled.

"Hey, you!" he shouted to his secretary. "See if the War and Navy Ministers are in their offices."

He scribbled a message.

"They are in, sir."

"Send this message to Foreign Minister Mutsu at Maiko."

Ito rushed to General Yamagata's office. "Yamagata, it's terrible, terrible."

The War Minister, the Chief of the General Staff and their Navy colleagues were looking over a large map.

"What is it, Ito?"

"Oh, you Saigo, you here too," Ito said dully.

"What's the matter?" Saigo got up from his chair.

"It's terrible. Russia demands that we return Liaotung Peninsula, one of our major war-prizes, to China."

"Russia? Why Russia? What we won by blood and flesh?" Yamagata was stupefied.

"Ignore it. We shall defend our rights to the last man," the military men said in chorus as they rose to their feet. General Yamagata went on: "China ceded it to us by the Peace Treaty signed a week ago; it's ours!"

He turned to Admiral Saigo. "We shall immediately instruct our contingent to march to the Chinese capital before Russia lifts her finger."

"Wait—" Ito raised his hand. "Yamagata, not only Russia, but—"

"But who else?"

"France and Germany."

"Germany, too?"

"Yes, Germany also joined the protest."

"Germany!" A whispering came from every mouth.

The enraged Yamagata once more spoke up: "Though Germany was our benefactor in many ways, she must not interfere. As for Russia, we can whip her, too. Our spirits are high." He jumped on a chair. "On to Peking! On to Russia!" His eyes flashed, his right arm stiffened high in the air.

The Navy Minister was quietly tracing the chart. Raising his eyes from it, he murmured: "H'm-m!" The Admiral made no other comment, but his aide volunteered: "The spirit of the fleet is at its highest, but combined opposition would be too much, sir. Our ships are still in southern Chinese waters after the Formosan and Pescadores campaigns."

"Several communiqués, sir." A Navy staff-officer burst in with the usual salute.

"Read them!" Ito's voice was hollow.

"These are from the strategic Korean ports and also Port Arthur, sir. All Russian and French warships in the respective Korean and Manchurian harbors have cancelled the shore-leave of their officers and men, have taken on fuel and provisions and stand ready for further instructions."

"So!"

The officer continued: "At Port Arthur, the Russian Oriental Squadron has been concentrating ever since our occupation and the warships are fully prepared for emergencies."

Admiral Saigo said at last: "They do mean business."

"Ito, what does the Foreign Office have to say about this?" Yamagata asked.

"I sent a message to Foreign Minister Mutsu at Maiko Resort. Since his long over-work aggravated his illness, I advised him to rest after the conclusion of the peace negotiations. Although I sent a message, there hasn't been time enough to get his reactions."

"Those 'Red-Hairs' fear for themselves since our unexpected victory. Their friendship doesn't amount to anything," one of the staff said.

"There is no hope of defeating the Russian fleet," grumbled the Admiral, staring unseeingly at the naval chart.

"Gentlemen, we shall have to give our answer immediately. I will undoubtedly hear from our Foreign Minister soon." Ito took a deep breath. "We can take one of three courses. We can reject their demand outright. We can invite other Western Powers to sit in on an international conference to discuss the matter. Or we can yield to their demand and return that major prize of our victory."

"Never!" several muttered.

"But, Gentlemen, as Admiral Saigo just said, we are unable to cope with the combined opposition—I simply cannot believe that Germany took part in it," Ito added irrelevantly.

Yamagata ventured: "Since America, England, and Italy are friendly to us, we might be able to minimize the demand if we call an international conference."

There were no comments for some time.

At last Saionji spoke up:

"Diplomatic history shows that interference such as we have now experienced originates in envy of a rising nation. Therefore I cannot see that a world conference would be of any avail. Hostility towards us must be growing in spite of amicable gestures. Because of our limited strength, I think the wiser policy is to yield for the present."

To everyone's surprise, Ito agreed.

"The press, the politicians and patriotic organizations will criticise our decision. No one knows better than I what it means to surrender at this time. But as Saionji said, in view of the weakness of our defense forces—" he choked on the words—"we shall be obliged to recommend to His Majesty the return of the Liaotung Peninsula.

"But, Gentlemen," he raised his voice resolutely, "this is not the end of the affair. I promise you that with your co-operation, within the next ten years we shall have behind us the loyal determination of every Nipponese to be avenged for this interference. In ten years this young nation will have come of age. There will be a reckoning. And that reckoning will be only the beginning."

Mutsu, in his quest for health, had moved from Maiko Resort to the Atami Hot Springs. He was taking a sunbath on a veranda overlooking the peaceful bay below, when a visitor was announced.

"It's Saionji, Minister Mutsu, Saionji." The Marquis approached him from behind. "How are you these days?"

"I am much better, thanks, much better. It is kind of you to come."

"You certainly look much better." Saionji took a cushion to the veranda, and faced the ailing statesman.

"Yes, Marquis Saionji. You see, fundamentally, my trouble is with the lungs. They say the air in this place is saturated with the moisture of the mineral vapors from the hot springs. It seems to help." A little color came into his cheeks.

"Huh, that's what I've heard. So it really does the trick. By the way," he added, watching the effect of his words, "Premier Ito confided to me that because of your part in the Sino-Nipponese War he will recommend your elevation to the rank of count."

"Oh, me, a count?" A new light animated Mutsu's face. "Away from Tokyo I am ignorant of affairs, even in my Department. Tell me," he asked breathlessly, "what does Ito recommend for Matsukata and Yamagata?"

"Huh, that question is a ticklish one. I won't take sides, but the situation seems to be like this: Ito, who is, no doubt, entitled to the highest honor, showed no hesitation in doing justice to Ito by recommending himself for the highest decoration, I mean for the Grand Cordon of the Chrysanthemum. For Matsukata and Yamagata

he asks the next grade, and the three of them will be elevated to
marquis."

"I see, Ito takes the major credit. Well, I suppose he is really the
better man. But that trifling personal matter will finally break up the
Cabinet, I fear. Do you remember, Marquis Saionji, once when we
were at a cabinet meeting just before the Sino-Nipponese Peace Conference, Matsukata volunteered to replace Ito as the chief delegate?
I knew Matsukata's motives." He paused thoughtfully. "Well, what
other news do you bring? How did the Diet react to the military expansion programs?"

"The opposition made a good showing, but in general, the bills received strong support. That means that the seven divisions of the
standing army will be increased to thirteen, and the navy from one
hundred and twenty thousand to two hundred thousand tons. It may
cost more than we think, but of course the two hundred million silver
dollar indemnity from China will cover part of the expense."

Mutsu drew a long breath between his bearded lips.

"So we are to have a strong army and navy, eh? I believe you, too,
do not favor ruthless military expansion. But when I think of the humiliating dénouement of the Liaotung affair, it is necessary. During the
two weeks since the protest was first lodged on April 24 and our
proclamation of returning Liaotung Peninsula on May 10, I fought
every inch to save the major war prize and our face."

"I know how deeply you felt the Three-Power intervention. And
Premier Ito to this day cannot reconcile himself to the fact that the
Kaiser joined them."

"Yes, that further wrecked my nerves and health. I have sometimes
felt that my life was a failure." Cold sweat broke out on Mutsu's forehead. "As Ito expected, the military and the patriots demanded armed
resistance against those strong European nations. They derided my
inability to cope with the situation through diplomatic channels. They
shouted that the Sino-Nipponese War was won by armed forces and
lost by civilians. But they knew as well as I that defiance would have
meant a struggle between a new-born baby and an infuriated giant."
He closed his eyes.

Saionji laid his hand on Mutsu's knee. "You must not call yourself
a failure, Minister. On the contrary, the public is already beginning
to appreciate your genius in keeping our attention concentrated on
China in order to consolidate our gains as much as possible. A lesser
man would have been confused by the disturbances abroad and at

home. And I remember how you solved a problem which had been menacing the new Government since 1868, a problem that had caused the resignation of many statesmen and cabinets. I refer to your success in revising the treaties with the Western Powers before the last war. No longer can the foreigners exploit Nippon under the so-called 'Consular Court System.' Thanks to you we are almost on a par with the Westerners. And also thanks to you we have extraterritorial rights in China under the new treaty.

"Think what progress we have made! Do you remember how in 1885 we could not punish the Chinese sailors for their outrages at Nagasaki and had to deliver them to their own consulate? And now we have our former overlord under our heels."

Saionji's comments gradually brought relaxation to Mutsu's face.

"Thank you for your kind words, Marquis. They have, although perhaps undeserved, lightened my depression. I must admit that in spite of the burdens of my office, there have been some high lights, such as our meeting with Li Hung-chang when Ito and I talked peace terms."

Saionji saw that Mutsu was anxious to tell the story. He nodded encouragingly.

"Li was gifted with a most handsome appearance. He was born to be a statesman and diplomat. Marquis Saionji, I can see him before me vividly. He stood over six feet, was well-built, with a long oval face, high forehead, closely-knitted eyebrows, small but brilliant eyes, a long pointed aristocratic nose, and wore a well-proportioned, white beard which added to his dignity."

Mutsu gently stroked his own beard as he went on: "This Chinese was not only a man of prepossessing exterior, but also mentally equipped for the international diplomatic controversy. He was a veteran in many fields, alert, well-informed, experienced and witty. He was already over seventy, but had a clear silvery voice and an elegant manner."

"The physical contrast between him and Ito must have been extreme, Minister Mutsu."

"Yes. Our Premier's five-feet-two and his thin beard—well—Li paid Ito the greatest tribute by saying he could trust even his country to so able a statesman, and so on. They knew each other, they had met at Tientsin. After plenty of flattery, the Chinese statesman began to persuade the Premier to alter our peace conditions. I was worried. But although Ito had received the compliments with due regard, his answer was clear-cut—a flat refusal."

Mutsu breathed deeply once more. "At the time of the Tientsin negotiations, China was the master of the Orient, Nippon the underdog; in 1895, the position was reversed. At the last peace conference we had the dagger at the 'Wounded Lion's' throat. No matter how clever he might be, Li was defenceless. After much ado he accepted our terms. I often think I saw a picture of actual transition in the Oriental diplomatic arena during that negotiation." Mutsu smiled with contentment.

"But I am boring you. What other news have you?"

"Huh—" Saionji hesitated, "only something that might amuse you. Ito, in his recommendations for awards, included two members of the Iwasaki families and two of the Mitsui financial house as recipients of baronies. That was in recognition of their services to the country during the last war."

"Is that so? That's something new. In Europe they confer titles on moneyed people, don't they? But what effect will that practice have in Nippon, Marquis?"

"Eventually money-worship, I imagine."

"It's true the Mitsubishi House, from the days of the Formosan Expedition in 1875, has co-operated closely with the Government. So did the Mitsui House which among the big corporations was one of the early converts to the new Regime's side in the Restoration era. They have built their fortunes by helping the authorities ever since."

"You knew the founder of the Mitsubishi House personally, didn't you, Minister Mutsu?"

Mutsu's eyes shone. He became animated.

"Marquis Saionji, I did, very well. Iwasaki's life was a fascinating story. Though some people criticize his methods of attaining success, he was a genius as an organizer. He was a Tosa *samurai*, entrusted with his lord's trade in the feudal days. When the feudal system was wiped out back in the 1870's, he had the sizable fortune that had belonged to his former lord. He put it into shipping under the trade-mark of Mitsubishi, '*three water-chestnuts*.' Then came the famous Formosan Expedition in 1875. At that time you were in France—"

"Huh, I was."

"Iwasaki's business and political rivals made serious accusation. But he cleverly evaded them. Perhaps you have heard how. He convinced the official in charge of transportation that shipping was the most vital factor in connection with Nippon's first overseas expedition, and that he should be empowered to handle all the transportation activities. The Government had no ships. He made the authorities buy some from England and America with public funds. He asked that those steamers be put into his charge during the war, and after the war, that the fourteen steamships be given to him gratis. He argued that the Government would find it too expensive to keep them.

"Then Iwasaki got the promise of a ship subsidy of over a quarter of a million yen annually. I always admired his victory over the competing foreign transportation companies in Nipponese waters. The Mitsubishi ships with the emblem of *three water-chestnuts* finally drove a British concern and the Canadian-Pacific from our coastal shipping."

Saionji nodded, and Mutsu went on: "His phenomenal rise as a commercial power invited domestic rivalry from the Mitsui group. But the undaunted Iwasaki once more showed his mastery just before his death in 1885 by simply out-manoeuvring the opposition in creating the present Nippon Yusen Kaisha. Under it, he amalgamated the Mitsui shipping and put his business successor and younger brother, Iwasaki Yanosuke, in control. And now that house owns various industrial and commercial enterprises besides."

"Huh."

"Premier Ito used to oppose the Mitsubishi, but of late they have become very friendly. As a matter of fact, Ito brought the late Iwasaki's son-in-law, Kato Komei, into the Foreign Office. Kato is now our Ambassador to England. Backed by the Mitsubishi, he will some day be a powerful political figure in Nippon."

It was an old story to Saionji, but to humor his sick friend he listened patiently.

"Ito has taken many people directly related to the Mitsubishi into the high posts, hasn't he?"

"Yes, he has, Marquis Saionji, notably Goto Shojiro, the Minister of Communications, who is the father-in-law of Iwasaki Yanosuke. The presidents of the Bank of Nippon and the Nippon Railway Company were also Mitsubishi men, not to speak of pro-Mitsubishi politicians in commanding positions.

"How about your brother Sumitomo Kichizayemon? He is not a prospective recipient of honors, is he?"

"No. He is not powerful and not old enough to be mentioned—"

"Though your brother is young he is the leading business man in

Osaka, I am informed." He added: "Well, isn't it interesting though, Marquis—whether we like it or not, money begins to talk?"

"Yes, Foreign Minister. The public affairs involve more and more economic problems and the Government and concentrated wealth are becoming inseparable partners. The politicians are steadily losing to the growing power of gold, and they are beginning to feel pressure from the wealthy. The best indication of this is Ito's recommending the financial magnates for honors."

They were silent for a while and watched a small boat passing. Saionji said at last: "I played a trick on Premier Ito recently."

"What was it, Marquis Saionji?"

"Huh, Ito wanted to revise every paper issued from the Department of Foreign Affairs. I was rather annoyed—"

"So was I." Mutsu leaned back against the pillar.

"I told the subordinates to make drafts in English."

"Ah, you are clever. I'd never have thought of that."

"The Premier knows the language, but he does not quite trust himself to revise the communiqués in English. That trick worked wonders. He does not bother me any more."

Saionji looked at his watch.

"I see you are anxious to go. I have kept you too long. You have no other news for me?" Mutsu asked.

"No, everything is fairly quiet at present. The pending problem in the Foreign Office is the dispatching of our special envoy to Russia to the Czar's coronation and to settle the proposed Russo-Nipponese treaty over Korea. Yamagata, who proposed it, is hoping to be the delegate. But before the matter requires serious attention, you'll return to office—"

Mutsu began slowly: "I want to keep you just a moment longer. It is not fair to my colleagues and especially to you, that I have kept my title and yet stayed away from Tokyo so long. You have been doing double duty in the Education Department and the Foreign Office. Furthermore, my sixth sense tells me that I will not return to active life again."

"Oh, don't you worry about us, and don't let your sixth sense bother you—I couldn't have done much with the educational questions, anyway, in the war years. The nationalists, as you know, object to my outlook—"

"Marquis Saionji, I appreciate your friendship and unselfishness. I have seen no other public man of courtier origin so well-versed in and so singularly devoted to the affairs of the nation. I expect you some day to become the dominant figure in the Government. At any rate, I have decided to resign from the Office and I have recommended you to the Premier as my successor. I know how anxious you are to carry out your long-cherished cosmopolitan principles in the field of education, but I believe the Foreign Office is more important now and needs you. You have taken charge of it during my absence. You are the man for the job. I am sure Premier Ito agrees with me."

The visitor murmured an ineffectual protest. He saw how emaciated Mutsu was. His arms and legs resembled yellowish bamboo sticks and his long moustache and full beard made his features harsh. Saionji desisted and instead murmured gently: "How do you spend your time these days?"

"Oh, I occasionally look over the papers you send to me. But it isn't necessary, because your supervision is more than enough. Some time ago I began to write my memoirs, particularly of my Foreign Ministership. But it won't be published now, perhaps thirty or forty years hence. And then I'm looking forward to a trip to Hawaii for my health. I stopped there on my way home from Washington, and found it a lovely spot. The climate is ideal, and it's quiet. I shall take my phonograph with me."

"Huh, you are still fond of it?"

"Yes, but it's getting old and the records are wearing out and no importing-house carries them. So I cling to my favorites, the American national anthem and the Southern melodies."

Hoarsely, he hummed 'Old Black Joe.'

Saionji left him reluctantly. It was their last meeting.

Mutsu died in the late summer of 1897 while Saionji himself was recuperating from an acute illness in Southern France.

As Mutsu predicted, the second Ito Cabinet, which spanned the Sino-Nipponese War period from August 1892 to September 1896, came to an end because of the personal differences between the Premier and other Sat-cho leaders. During its life, Marquis Saionji first sat as Education Minister and then as Foreign Minister.

Early in the following year, Saionji, for the fifth time, left for his 'second native country' to recuperate from his fatigue and to acquaint himself with the contemporary European situation.

While in France he had an attack of appendicitis, but recovered without an operation. He met Ito, who came to Europe with the Imperial Prince, Arisugawa, on his congratulatory mission to the sixtieth-anniversary celebration of Queen Victoria's reign. There were other reunions with friends whom he had known in early days. He frequently reminisced about his strange meeting with Komyoji over twenty-five years before at the Café Américain in Paris. On one occasion he wrote a poem to the memory of his cherished companion.

Towards the end of the same year, Ito and Saionji returned home.

Saionji was once more to head the Ministry of Education, under the now venerable Choshu statesman, in Ito's third Cabinet. Formed in January 1898, it was very short-lived, lasting only five months. Saionji found that an operation for appendicitis was now necessary and resigned from office a month before Premier Ito hung up his toga.

From then until October 1900, he held no official title, but Ito frequently consulted him.

Since both men had time on their hands, they often met at their old meeting-place, the teahouse. Ito was again making plans for the future. There was an air of secrecy about him. Saionji waited patiently.

One night in the teahouse Ito spoke: "Saionji-san, that trip of mine to England with Imperial Prince Arisugawa was not in vain."

"Huh."

"I met many influential British statesmen from whom I had important suggestions. That's what I want to discuss with you." He refilled both cups with warm sake after he had ordered the entertainers to retire.

"What impressed you most, Genro Ito?"

"Now wait. You must listen to me without interrupting. I never let anyone interrupt. Ha, ha, Saionji-san. We must drink some more before we talk about our business. You are getting independent."

"Do you think so?"

"You are very sarcastic, too. Anyway, I have in mind to organize my own political party. See, in England they have the Liberal and the Conservative parties, respectively headed by William Gladstone and Lord Salisbury. As party leaders, these men stay at the helm while they have public support."

Slowly raising his right hand, he whispered: "Now, don't let this leak out, because I don't want Yamagata or Matsukata and their followers to know before the organization is perfected."

Saionji saw determination and purpose in Ito's eyes.

"Huh. So you want me to be your lieutenant, do you?"

"Precisely. Not only you, but also your young followers are to come into line. I have spotted several trustworthy men, most of whom are your acquaintances, too, like Matsuda."

"I have known him since I was in France as a student."

"That's right. And Hara Kei who is alert and full of fighting spirit. You know him also. To get substantial strength we must have a considerable number of the Representatives signed up. We must work quietly. We shall enlist our members from the existing parties like Itagaki's and Okuma's to make up over one hundred and we might better have one hundred and fifty."

With a grin, Saionji asked: "Why your sudden conversion to the party system? You wrote and spoke against and suppressed it in the past."

"Well, frankly, political prestige is not enough to keep the Premiership, and our clansmen are getting old and feeble and will soon die out. And on the other hand, look at the younger men elected to the Imperial Diet, for instance, Ozaki Yukio and Inukai Ki. The quality of their statesmanship is still unknown, but they have proved their ability to remain in the Lower House, since they enjoy the confidence of their electorates. No matter how many times we drive them out by dissolving the Diet when it opposes our measures, they come back again with more fire and strength. In fact, they have not failed in general elections since the first Session in 1890.

"Now, if I, like those British statesmen, have my own party consisting of stable Representatives, I can regain and perpetuate my political power. And there is still another important point in this venture, namely the continuation of my national programs. At present there are many vital issues—for example, the readjustment of land taxes, the adequate protection of our budding industries, a fixed foreign policy towards our continental neighbors, Korea, China and Russia, and the further expansion of our military programs. Any one of them is too big to be solved in a few years. I may not be able to settle them in my time, but if I have a party to support these programs, that party will carry on after I am gone."

"So, Genro Ito, you have changed your views on your own Sat-cho clansmen, political parties and public opinion, too. You are afraid that your clan-domination will disappear with you people pretty soon. You no longer believe that the voice of the people is something that can be ignored if you don't see the daily newspaper. Every time the papers made too much noise, you used to throw the editors and publishers into prison or hush them by chasing them out of Tokyo. But that doesn't work any more, huh?"

Ito's already flushed face became radiant with sake now. "You rebellious Okuge-sama. The child is father to the man, that's what they say. Do you still bear a grudge against me because I interfered with your editorship of the *Oriental Liberal Newspaper?*"

"Huh, no, I'd forgotten all about it, but I judge you are conscience-stricken since you still remember the incident."

"Anyway, I like you and I can trust you, although sometimes you make me impatient because you lack an aggressive spirit—that vital thrusting forward in rain or fire. No matter what we do, we are fighting for His Majesty's nation. That is our one and supreme motive and end. If we lose sight of this cardinal maxim, politics will degenerate and politicians will become spineless. I do admire the present leading party men for their fearlessness, though they oppose us."

"Your repeated intimidation has not been enough to scare them?"

"Look at Itagaki and Okuma. Itagaki barely escaped death when he was stabbed by the attacker's dagger and Okuma had his leg blown off, but they came back and fought against us harder than ever."

Ito shook his head and continued speaking about his plans. He suddenly shouted: "Listen!"

Saionji must have been napping, but Ito was in good humor. "As soon as the organization of the party is completed, I'll lead the Cabinet once more, but you will not be a member this time. I'll put you in a better post than that, so that at an opportune moment you will slip into my shoes to carry on my policies. In other words, I want you to get a chance to learn the lessons of real leadership. Of Premiership and party presidency."

Saionji looked blankly at Ito. In the next room a geisha sang softly.

Governess Sagami had been yawning frequently and now she was drowsy, her eyelashes fighting hard to keep apart, her needle often pricking the finger of her left hand, and her thin-haired gray head nodded from time to time.

Okiku also showed signs of weariness. First she sat properly, with her legs folded back under her body, and held her book with both hands. Her elbows rested on the edge of the brazier.

As the cold night wore on she leaned sideways, one foot slipping out of her kimono skirts. She frequently puffed at her long bamboo pipe.

At first she was cautious, so as not to disturb Sagami, but later almost carelessly, she banged the metal part of the pipe against the ash-tray.

She read steadily, often looking up at the large clock. She, too, was yawning.

Every time Okiku hit the pipe, Sagami started up and brought her mending and needle back into the proper position. Her eyes regarded disapprovingly Okiku's relaxed pose. But the glance was momentary. Despite her rigid self-control, the lateness of successive nights was too much for the older woman.

The book dropped from Okiku's hands onto the matted floor. She picked up her tobacco sack and pipe again and watched the governess' constant nodding. She dug into the brazier to find a tiny speck of fire like a fire-fly to light her tobacco. She succeeded, inhaled the smoke deeply and lazily blew it out. As she tapped the ash-tray with the pipe to remove the ashes, she said, grinning broadly: "Sagami—"

There was no answer. As Okiku struck the pipe harder for the second time, she repeated: "Sagami!"

"Oh, yes! Master!" Sagami awoke with a start.

The mending and needle dropped to her lap. She sat up, utterly confused. She looked around, but the master was not there. Instead she saw Okiku smiling at her.

"Sagami, won't you go to bed? I'll wait a little longer, though he may not come home tonight, either. I'll retire if he doesn't come back by three o'clock."

To conceal her embarrassment—for she disliked to be caught in what she termed an 'unrefined' position—Sagami looked sharply at Okiku, who still held her undignified pose.

"What did you say? You are going to bed before he comes back?"

"Yes, don't you think that's better? We can't stand this every night. He didn't return last night or the night before, though we waited until sunrise. He doesn't mind."

"Say, to whom do you think you are talking?"

"Well, I beg your pardon, Sagami, if I hurt your feelings in any way. But why do you speak so harshly tonight? Did I do something objectionable?"

For years Okiku had successfully averted encounters with Saionji's faithful governess; tonight an ominous tide bore her inevitably on.

"Not tonight or last night." The vertical lines between Sagami's eyebrows deepened.

"Well, I didn't think I was offending you."

"H'm," Sagami looked Okiku over from head to foot and continued: "I have wanted to tell you a few things for some time. I said when I first met you that you would not be Saionji-no-okugata. Did you know what that meant? I know you did. Since you are not *okugata*, you are not my superior here."

Okiku's eyes grew large with surprise. The other woman went on: "And therefore you have no right to tell me what to do in this Saionji household, and even concerning the training of Princess Shinko." Her lips quivered and her hollow eyes were fixed.

Okiku was startled. "But, Sagami, I never tell you what to do. And Shinko is my child." She sat up. "I don't care for social dignity or anything like that, but if you call Shinko Princess, and recognize me as your master's mate, why can't you respect me a little?"

"That's one thing I wanted to explain to you. In Saionji's house, the master has never received a regular wife. No matter what family the woman came from, she could only be the master's mistress—"

"But when you persuaded me to accept his proposal you yourself told me there would be no difference whether I were his *okugata* or not. And you pointed out the fact that those big statesmen like Genro Ito, and scores of others, married women of my profession—"

"Let me finish what I have to say. I don't care what others do. You may be his 'wife' in private, but in public the master is supposed to have no wife, therefore you are not my superior here. In spite of that you call me, 'Sagami, Sagami,' like my master. And you speak of Princess Shinko as if she were your child. But she is not." She shook her head.

"What is she then?" Okiku asked with a sardonic smile.

"She merely borrowed your body as a temporary shelter before she saw the light. You gave her birth, but you are not her mother in the true sense of the word. You have no authority over her. That's why *I* take special care of the 'Princess.' "

"But you can't deny that I'm her mother and I have just as much right and responsibility to Shinko as the Prince does." Her voice trembled in her determination.

Sagami became firmer than before. "Stop that nonsense! That's based on the hypocritical idea of the West, called the equality of the sexes. Didn't you ever read the *On-na Daigaku*, about the conduct of women? According to those noble Confucian codes of conduct there is no such thing as equality for women. The weaker sex can't exist without men."

Okiku clasped her hands in her lap and her eyes opened wide. "But you don't mean that Nipponese in this enlightened era will conduct themselves according to the rules set many, many centuries ago by the Chinese. That's ridiculously old-fashioned. In every way the country accepts the ways of the West.—Why not the codes for women's conduct, too? Some young women educated in America have opened schools for girls under government protection and some foreign missionaries also are educating young Nipponese girls. Such a great educator as Fukuzawa Yukichi completely proves the Confucian ideas of womanhood to be antiquated. This tells—"

Okiku picked up the book she had been reading during the evening. "This book tells us why the old ideas are useless now and explains why new conceptions must take their place. Furthermore, you said that woman can't exist without man. But that is not always true. I was an entertainer and lived my life comfortably by my own toil, never relying on any man."

"A glib tongue like yours is one of the most objectionable features of woman. And anyway, I am the governess to my master, trusted by his foster parents. There was the closest mutual affection and faith between us—as between mother and son before you came into the house."

Okiku became angry. "Oh, was there? Did I steal his affections from you? That's his fault, isn't it? Not mine—"

She was contemptuous; Sagami was almost purple.

"Don't you dare imply that I'm jealous of you. That isn't so, that isn't so. That's another thing. A woman must not show jealousy. You are cheap-bred. You think that you are a virtuous woman, yet you speak of going to bed before he comes home. In your ill-mannered family that might have been the practice, but not in this noble household."

The older woman gathered up her mending and arose.

Okiku had endured everything so far, but the governess's reference to her family broke the dike. "Sagami, will you keep my family out of your vile remarks? My family was spotless. Their financial troubles and my becoming a professional entertainer were only forced by circumstances. Until then my family was a flourishing *hatamoto*. I shall defend its name at any cost. In my veins runs the blood of a true Kwanto *samurai*. Don't make any mistake about that!"

Sagami's chin was high in the air, but she was somewhat taken aback. Okiku, still sitting on the mat, glared at the governess and continued. "I didn't start this—you—you began. But let me remind you, we can't live on your traditions which formerly meant absolute poverty and complete self-denial."

"Just because you don't conform to the traditions of high society," Sagami retorted.

"Why, what do I do that is not becoming?" Okiku kept at her enemy.

"Your 'Red-Hair' clothes make my head ache. And you go out with the master, walking side by side in the street. The respectful, disciplined and refined lady never does that, she always follows him."

"But what can I do? It's his way. He wants me to walk by his side. What am I to obey, the conventions of high society or my husband?"

"He is not your *husband*, you are a chambermaid."

Okiku reached for her pipe. She spoke slowly but distinctly: "All right, it doesn't matter. Since I love him so much, I don't care what you say or what you do, if it is for his and Shinko's good. I do everything to please them. But if you don't like something he does, I wish you would speak to him instead of blaming me for it."

Sagami stared back. Then as she approached the screen, she shook her gray head vehemently: "Unimaginable in high circles! Your smoking is another one of your evil habits."

V

PARTY PRESIDENT AND PRIME
MINISTER

CHAPTER V

PARTY PRESIDENT AND PRIME MINISTER

"Prince, what are you doing?" Okiku asked hesitantly as she sat beside Saionji at their Omori home.

"Huh, a little writing for the new magazine started by Takekoshi and some others."

"For *Nippon of the World* that you named for them?" Her eyes were fixed unseeingly on her fan.

"Yes, Okiku, that's right. They are coming to get the manuscript today."

Saionji rested his brush on the desk and turned to her. "Isn't it hot, Okiku? See, my *yukata* is soaked with perspiration. We may have a thunder shower later."

Okiku began to fan Saionji again.

"We are lucky, Prince, that we are not in the city where the low, frame houses stick together like the teeth of a comb. On a day like this, people can hardly breathe there."

Both looked out into the garden.

"Huh." Saionji picked up his own *uchiwa*. "You love this place in the summer but not in the winter, don't you? But I love it all the year round."

"I have always liked it, Prince."

He looked at her sharply. The recent note of deference to his opinion did not suit her. Where had the other Okiku gone, the 'Spitfire' of the Nakamura-ro days?

"Look towards the northwest. As far as our eyes can reach we can see the vast Musashino. I hope nobody builds houses in front of us." Saionji got up and walked towards the edge of the veranda, Okiku following.

"Huh, there comes a delivery-man from the Mitsukoshi store."

"Oh, Prince, what did you order?"

"Just a trifle."

The man brought a fairly bulky package and went away.

"Prince, shall I open it?"

"Huh. Somebody is coming, those young friends."

"My, they have bicycles!"

"Marquis Saionji," Takekoshi, the leader of the visiting group, announced, "today we have brought with us a new friend, Kunigita Doppo. He is young, but he was a star war correspondent on board a warship during the Sino-Nipponese War and now is considered a new light in journalistic and literary circles. In fact, he is an outstanding novelist—"

"Huh, you mentioned him to me the other day when I was in the billiard parlor of Koyokan Hall."

"Yes, Marquis."

"Kunigita-kun, glad you came—"

Sakai, another visitor, broke in. "He is a great realist."

Kunigita's face was pale, he had a moustache, black hair, eyebrows slanting upward, sparkling eyes, a pointed chin and slender shoulders. Unlike Takekoshi, who was in a neat linen suit, Kunigita and Sakai wore summer kimonos. All had their fans.

The newcomer bowed politely.

Okiku, who had taken the package inside, returned with a tray of wineglasses and bottles, and greeted them: "Welcome, all of you."

The visitors beamed, but whether at their charming hostess or because their favorite drink was within reach was a matter of speculation.

Saionji's maid-servant brought in two other trays: one with plates of sliced raw fish and vegetables with vinegar and soy sauce, and the other with more glasses and bottles of beer.

"This is very informal though. What would you prefer, sir, wine or beer?" Okiku asked Takekoshi, now one of Saionji's most intimate followers.

"Well—" Takekoshi put out his hand.

"Take your choice, friends," Saionji said.

Takekoshi continued: "Before we accept your offer, we would like to speak to the Marquis regarding the object of our visit."

"Takekoshi-san, drink first. You need not worry." The host smiled.

Okiku filled Takekoshi's glass. Following his example, everyone accepted beer.

"Here, we drink to the Marquis!" Takekoshi proposed the toast.

Out of doors, not a single green leaf of the now almost fully-grown rice plants beyond Saionji's yard was moving. Hundreds of small flies danced in the air.

Each emptied a few glasses. The hot late-afternoon sun, the extreme humidity and the drink caused them to sweat. But despite the oppressive weather they became light-hearted and discussed every imaginable subject: domestic politics, social problems, dramas, educational reforms, the contemporary trend of literature, the first labor movement, the opening of the modern private banks by the Mitsui and the Yasuda Houses, the territorial acquisitions in China by the Powers, the rumor of the secret treaty between Russia and China against Nippon, Hawaii's refusal to permit Nipponese immigration, and women's fashions.

In the meantime, Saionji handed a bulky manuscript to Takekoshi.

"Thank you, Marquis. The public will be eager to read the account of your life. I shall see to it that the story appears in installments in our magazine as soon as possible. It will be entitled *The Miscellaneous Writings of—*"

He looked at the host who said: "*To-an.*"

He laid it down and whispered to Kunigita, the war correspondent: "Read this some time."

"Yes, Takekoshi-san."

After another drink, Kunigita opened the Saionji manuscript and began to look through it.

Sakai saw him. "You don't need to read it now. There must be plenty of breath-taking and fascinating facts in the life of our chief."

The reader ignored the interruption. He frequently bit his moustache.

Sakai repeated his statement. Kunigita raised his eyebrows, but Takekoshi intervened. "Well," he said, wiping his round chin, "in the political field Marquis Saionji, frankly speaking, is still a secondary character when we think of the Genros, but within a short while you'll see him head the Government."

"Those courtiers had very little to offer and were too tender-hearted towards the brusque clansmen—" Sakai interrupted, but Takekoshi once more put his handkerchief to his face and went on: "Marquis Saionji remained in the stormy sea of politics despite the fact that he could have chosen steady and undisturbed court duty if he so desired. But he continued to be active and has already headed the Education Department twice and also the Foreign Office. Furthermore, his Choshu mentor, Genro Ito, is anxious to bequeath his political fortune to him."

The ordinarily reserved Takekoshi went on and on, concluding that they must publicize the Marquis as much as possible: "Because Marquis Saionji himself, quite contrary to the practice of the political leaders, avoids all limelight."

Sakai, patiently waiting, said: "You are correct in that, Takekoshi.

I came into contact with the Marquis at the time he and my teacher, Nakae, and others organized that short-lived *Oriental Liberal News-paper*. He never boasted about himself. My teacher used to say that Marquis Saionji was too serene and unselfish to be a politician. What I want him to emphasize when he becomes a dominating factor in the country is the social side of national affairs. See, in 1872 there were only thirty-three million Nipponese. In the last twenty-five years the population jumped to forty-three million, yet nothing has been done to better their lot. The average person is left at the mercy of the upper economic class—"

They stared at him uncomprehendingly.

Takekoshi ventured: "Sakai is ahead of our times. In our country the problem of labor and capital is not serious yet. We have too few factories, and the farmers are accustomed to their hard life."

Sweat streamed from Sakai's forehead. He kept on talking, his shoulders lifted and his kimono sleeves tucked up: "True, but if these economic and social disparities are neglected they will some day shake the governmental structure of the country. To deal with these new problems adequately, our leaders must know something about the new political philosophy, Socialism—"

"Already the talk of Socialism is sending shivers down the backs of our public men, Genro Ito, for instance," Takekoshi interrupted, "is such an able man, but he is frightened—"

"Nonsense." Sakai came back quickly. "Since we have accepted Western industrialism, the application of the principles of the Second Internationale will be the only solution. It will not disturb the economic and political order of the nation if properly applied. Whether you like it or not, Takekoshi, it will come with tremendous force. Our new labor movement is the best example. The oppressed class is waking up. In the Western countries, where the industrial stage has advanced, the labor movement is also forging ahead. In Paris, May Day was first observed in 1890, while I was there."

The animated Sakai continued to discuss Socialism, finishing with his experiences at the Conference of the Second Internationale, which was held in 1891 in Brussels. He looked at Saionji who had also been there. Since Sakai's return from Belgium, he did not let anyone forget that he had represented the Nipponese Socialists abroad.

Kunigata finished reading from Saionji's autobiography.

Takekoshi turned to him and asked: "Well, at any rate, there are many startling facts heretofore unrevealed in the Marquis' life, are there not, Kunigita?"

Kunigita raised his pale face and said: "Not that I know of."

"What?" the inquirer exclaimed as the others stared at Kunigita.

Saionji, who had been listening to their discussion, lifted his eyes towards the darkening clouds in the southwestern sky.

There was a brief silence.

"There must be," Takekoshi persisted.

"Nothing more than we know about; in fact, less," he replied.

"Huh." The company was taken aback.

With sparkling eyes, after peering at Saionji, Kunigita resumed: "This is very interesting, nevertheless." The listeners were puzzled. He went on: "Because the author does not dwell on his part in the various political changes of the past."

"Do you mean to say that the man who was the Commander-General of the Tamba Expedition, then the head of the army in the Echigo Sector, and later appointed Governor before his twenties, has nothing interesting to say?" Takekoshi turned to Saionji.

The host was calm. "Huh, that was true, but I was only a figurehead. I only did what leaders like Saigo, Kido, Okubo and Iwakura told me to do, particularly in the actual military warfare in which General Omura gave me the most advice. He and Saigo had mapped out the entire campaign. Their lieutenants, Kuroda and Yamagata, who later became premiers—and are now Genros—were assigned to me as my chiefs of staff in the north."

Smiling, he went on: "At that time, those first four men I have mentioned overshadowed everybody, they were the brains and forces of the new Government."

"So those Satsuma and Choshu men, Kuroda, Matsukata, Ito and Yamagata didn't amount to much, is that it?" Kunigita asked with glee.

Saionji merely smiled.

Kunigita clapped his hands. "Here is one man in our political circle able to tell the truth about himself."

"That's an interesting interpretation." Takekoshi seemed to be disappointed in the manuscript.

"His personal advancement, I take it, he ascribes to nature's course. Natural, very natural, it is. I admire this type of philosophy. After all, what can we human beings do against the forces of nature? Our life is a bubble on earth, we don't solve anything, do we? There are no ideals, there are only daily necessities."

The young novelist was talking to himself, but they all listened. His host, too, was attentive. Okiku fanned flies from the dishes and contentedly looked at the few crude watercolors pinned to the partition.

"Is that your literary view?" Saionji's inquiry brought forth another long discussion of contemporary Nipponese literature by the young man. He summarized the tendencies since the beginning of the Meiji Restoration.

"Roughly up to the 1880's, our novels imitated those of great men like Saikaku and Bakin who flourished in the Tokugawa period."

"But the influence of translations of European books began to appear," Takekoshi commented.

"Undoubtedly, Takekoshi-san, first in our versions of political novels of the French Revolution and the Nihilists' writings of Russia, then came the influence of the pure novels, like Hugo's and Turgenieff's.

"Some of our masterpieces, like the *Imado Suicide* which describes our social evils, reflect European trends."

"Don't you think our current nationalism will affect literature?" Takekoshi asked.

"It may, but it takes a long time. As a matter of fact, political changes have had no effect on our literature for nearly twenty years. The same will be true in the future, too. Literature is difficult to mold, but once it congeals, it retains its given form for some time."

Takekoshi had been studying the childish drawings. "Did the Princess do those?" he inquired of Okiku when the comments on Kunigita's literary views were over.

"Oh, yes, Takekoshi-san."

"Huh, Shinko brought them home from school." Saionji beamed when he overheard the question. He walked over to the partition and took down two of them. "You see, she drew one for me and the other for Okiku. She knows I am fond of orchids and Okiku likes iris. They are not bad for a grammar school student, are they?"

The proud father handed the pictures to Takekoshi. All looked at them. To everybody's amazement, the reticent Saionji went on and on with his admiration of the color combination and perspective of the drawings.

Most amazed was Okiku. "Prince!" she exclaimed.

"What?"

"You mustn't—"

"Why? Not bad, are they?"

Now Saionji took them from the guest's hands. "See, they look better at a little distance." He held them at arm's length.

"Is she at school now?" Takekoshi asked.

"Yes." answered Okiku, who was also visibly pleased with the unreserved praise.

"She is very clever and lovable besides," Takekoshi added.

Saionji smiled happily.

"Prince, shall I put them back?" she asked.

"Huh."

Saionji was still absorbed in his child's drawings.

Sakai was impatient. "Marquis, what has been going on in the development of party organization?" He was anxious to put an end to the discussion of literature and to the father's boasting.

"Huh, Takekoshi-san knows more about that than anybody else." Saionji grinned and put the drawings back on the screen.

"Let's drop politics." Takekoshi wanted to avoid the subject.

"You needn't pretend, it's common talk that Marquis Saionji and others will organize a political party under Genro Ito, and Premier Yamagata will resign his post in protest."

Takekoshi admitted that he knew something about the new party prospects.

"Ito is sincere about it. When his Choshu colleagues protested, he announced that if they object to his activities because he is a Genro and holds many decorations, he is willing to surrender all his honors and become a private person so that he may lead the Party."

There was no further discussion of the problem.

The host said: "I want you all to come to the surprise party I am giving for Genro Ito. He is sixty-one years old, and it is time to celebrate his second great anniversary in accordance with our tradition. Since we don't observe birthdays every year like the Westerners, I am planning to have a unique affair."

They all accepted Saionji's invitation.

Takekoshi, who had frequently looked up at the open sky, interrupted.

"Marquis, we must bid you good-bye. It looks more and more as if we'll have a big thunderstorm. Look at the menacing clouds piling in the southwest, they've already swallowed the sun."

Sakai broke in again: "The rentals for our bicycles are mounting every minute. You live far away from the Ginza, Marquis, ha, ha, ha."

"We must hurry." Kunigita was already standing.

"Huh, come again," said Saionji. "Come again, and tell me more about literature," he added, turning to Kunigita.

"It's my greatest honor and pleasure to become acquainted with you and your lady, Marquis!" The young novelist bowed twice.

The troop of bicycle riders had hardly rolled out of sight when thunder shattered the death-like quietness.

The Saionjis, who were standing on the veranda to see the visitors off, looked at each other. Okiku grasped Saionji's arm impulsively. "Oh, Prince, that stopped my heart-beat!"

Calmly Saionji remarked: "Are you afraid? A big thundershower will wash away this heat and humidity."

"There is something ominous about it. Something like that will happen to you and me," she murmured. "Something quite sudden and yet long awaited." She clung to his arm.

He did not answer.

There came another flash of lightning with louder thunder.

"Oh, the rain. Such big drops, like bullets exploding on the ground. They shoot up the dirt. And look at those grasshoppers jump." Okiku withdrew her hand and talked rapidly.

"Huh." He still looked skywards.

"Oh, Prince, look at them," she said, pointing to the housewives in the neighboring backyards, busily taking in their washings from the bamboo poles.

They watched the farmers in bamboo hats and blue working-kimonos running home from the rice fields.

Now came the streak of purplish lightning, and the noise of the increased rainfall and terrific claps of thunder were deafening.

"Miyo, did you shut the *amado?*" Okiku shouted to the maid.

"Yes, ma'am, I did."

The maid had closed the sliding wooden doors all around the house, except at the front where the Saionjis were. Immediately after the first thunder, she sat down to pray in a dark corner. She shut her eyes and covered her ears with her hands.

"Prince, shall I close the *amado* here, too? The splash of the rain will wet the veranda."

"Huh, but leave some open, Okiku. It's fascinating to watch a thundershower."

Okiku came back to his side. They stood in silence for a while. Now that the rain had come full force, her forebodings faded.

"Huh, look at this irrigation ditch," he said, pointing to the small canal separating his house lot from the paddy field. "In a few minutes it will overflow."

"Prince, look at the farmers with their bamboo hats and straw rain-coats going back into the rice field again. What are they going to do with those small spades on their shoulders?"

"Huh, they want to regulate the irrigation," Saionji answered.

"Well, the farmers certainly have to work very hard, don't they, Prince? We've seen them since we came here, working every day, and their returns are very small, they say."

They closed the remaining *amado* and entered the living-room.

"Miyo, what are you burning there?"

"Ma'am, this dry bamboo leaf. Its smoke will drive the god of thunder away from the house."

Okiku and Saionji laughed aloud, but Miyo was serious. At every new clap of thunder she put more bamboo leaves into the charcoal brazier.

"Miyo, do it if you like, but will you open the *amado* so that the smoke may go out?" Saionji said, and a moment later, looking outside, "Miyo, that was the last one, see? The sky is getting clear, and the rain lighter. The yellowish sunbeam is already striking that roof top."

He turned to Okiku. "Huh, our young visitors were full of energy, were they not?"

"Yes, Prince."

"By the way, Okiku, where is the package that was delivered this afternoon?"

"Here it is, Prince. Shall I open it?"

"Yes, let's see."

"What are these? One *yukata* and several pieces of material for women, all for *yukata*."

"The one already made is for you. But I want you also to pick the best material in those bolts."

Okiku unfolded the *yukata* and put it on. "Oh, Prince! It's lovely." She fingered the light blue iris pattern. "My favorite flower," she murmured with a tremulous smile.

"Huh, I'm glad you like it. It's very becoming."

Okiku walked to the mirror.

"But, Prince, how can you buy these things?"

"Huh? Money."

"Master"—the governess came in and bowed to him—"I'll go to the school for the Princess."

It was Sagami's custom to take Shinko to her school in the morning and bring her back in the afternoon.

"Sagami, will you take Miyo along?" Okiku asked. "The road may not be good after the shower."

Sagami's gray head went up. "The ground is dry and I am still capable of—" She glared at Okiku.

"Huh, Sagami, you are right—" Saionji intervened. The governess beamed with joy.

"Thank you, my Master!" She bowed.

"See, Sagami, it's not a question of your condition. But Miyo is not doing anything at this time in the afternoon. I think you'd better take her along as your companion."

Sagami muttered to herself and left the room.

When the governess and maid were out of the house the Saionjis spoke of the materials.

"It is wonderful to be able to get these new patterns, cheerful—"

"And cheap, too."

"Why is it, Prince?"

"Well, the Mitsukoshi store, the original drygoods division of the Mitsui House, tried a new system right after the Sino-Nipponese War and now other big merchants do the same. The proprietor wanted to sell clothing to a larger number of people than before."

"Oh."

"But the public couldn't afford to buy. Besides, they wouldn't have been interested, even if they had money, because for generations there had been practically no change in material and pattern."

"I know that very well, Prince. I can still wear some of the expensive clothes I used for many years. Then we adopted the European clothes from head to foot overnight and discarded them quickly, too. Do you remember, Prince, how I tried to get accustomed to the clothes you bought for me in Paris? We don't see any more society ladies in European costumes."

"Huh, they may revive as our intercourse with the West increases with speed of travel. And, of course, our general economic and living conditions must be improved also."

"Prince, but men seem to keep European clothes."

"Huh, I think that's because the government offices beginning with the Imperial Court and business places, too, are being Westernized in every respect, while our homes are not. While working at a table with a chair, it's far more convenient to wear European clothes than our large-sleeved kimono. But at home we still relax on the mat as our great-grandfathers did. But after the Sino-Nipponese War times improved and more people had money. So the Mitsukoshi store hired artists to work out designs to suit people's tastes.

"Then they made hundreds of pieces of one kind—for instance, this 'wave and plover' pattern—so that the cost of the design and other expenses are little for each piece. They advertise it by having all the star geishas wear it. Besides, the store will sell you any length now, a few yards or the whole *tan* twenty-seven feet long. In that way they can produce cheaply and sell cheaply." Saionji looked at Okiku in the new *yukata*. "You see," he went on, "before, material of good quality was made to order by the weavers, who had only subdued patterns, and the common people wove at home."

"Anyway, it's a revolutionary step for women after more than thirty years of the Meiji Government," Okiku said, folding the new *yukata* on the mat. "But, Prince, how about the new codes of conduct for women?" she added.

"Huh, Okiku, that takes much longer. Most of our people are conservative. They think such a change touches a vital core of society. If a woman gets the notion of freedom and independence, the conservatives believe that it will strike a death-blow to family life. Should that happen, of course not only the women but also the sons and brothers would assert their freedom and independence. And they contend that the individualistic conception of society is harmful to a country like ours."

"Prince, but the opposite has been true for so long, the family was a unit, for better or for worse."

"Huh, everything was based on that unit. If anyone in a family committed a disgraceful act, his immediate relatives, even uncles, aunts, and cousins were ostracized, if not equally punished, and by the good acts of an individual the family circle likewise benefited."

"But, Prince, would it be so harmful to society if housewives were given a little more freedom of action and speech? They are still 'things' in the eyes of their husbands. The men tyrannize over them, though they sacrifice all they have. The wives belong to the men as the clogs do to our feet. Will—what was it?—'individualism' ever come to Nippon to stay?"

"Huh, whether we like it or not, we will be forced to it if we follow the Western way, particularly their industrial system."

"Well, Prince, when I said the housewives needed a few more rights,

I meant that if the man demands moral virtue of his wife, why doesn't he—?" She hesitated.

Saionji looked at Okiku with some surprise.

She continued: "Why doesn't he behave accordingly? By that I mean particularly his habit of keeping mistresses. It may not be as bad as having affairs with married women."

"Huh."

"You see, Prince, I admit that women too are at fault. Those young geisha in particular. They don't know anything about their professional lines, samisen, dancing and singing. They act like prostitutes these days. Almost every one of them looks for an opportunity to be a mistress."

"What has that got to do with man's moral virtue, Okiku?"

"Well, women must wake up, too. When I was in the geisha profession, I didn't allow anybody to touch me. Many others were just as virtuous as I. I was an entertainer and nothing else." Her lips closed firmly.

"Until you got your man you stood up very well, didn't you?" Saionji smiled.

"Ho, ho, you tease me, Prince. I did because I loved you. I could give up even my life for your sake."

"To get me?"

"No, you know, Prince, to make you happy at all times."

"That's a bit fantastic, isn't it, Okiku?"

"No, Prince. I still love you. I can prove it to you by deeds. That's why I don't bother you about your geisha house visits."

"That's not—"

"I know all about them, Prince!" Okiku's eyes blurred.

"To be sociable with my politician friends—"

"I don't blame you for accepting their invitations," she interrupted, "and even going farther than that—"

"Okiku, what are you driving at! I can't follow you." Nevertheless, he did not meet her eyes.

"Oh, Prince, I know too well. As they say, 'as a serpent knows a snake's way' or one devil knows another. I know the geisha's way by which I came and—"

"Don't you know me?"

Okiku kept on: "I know you and love you. That's why, no matter how many sleepless nights I have to wait at home for you in vain, I haven't said a word about your all night absences."

"You don't understand me—"

"I do, Prince, and believe in you. Didn't I keep up my belief from the days of your self-imposed retirement thirty-odd years ago at the Nakamura-ro where General Omura and Councillor Kido, the pillars of the new Government, treated you as a pet? Then you were a penniless, smooth-faced and soft-spoken young man. Nobody knew what you would be. But your unselfishness impressed my young mind. Soon I discovered your sincerity. These two qualities hypnotized me because they were so rare in the teahouse. I knew that the first time I bowed before my patrons as a full-fledged geisha."

"Huh, I'm a bit confused by your argument, but you are always sincere, too."

"Prince, I say this to you now without any hard feelings on my part. When you get tired of me I'll depart, not because I hate you or your new acquaintance, but because I love you. As I said, to make you happy is my greatest ambition. If you can have a better dream with a young round-faced geisha, I'll find my way out."

She wiped her eyes. "Prince, please, promise me two things: Let me help Shinko as much as I can, and also let me be your best—" she sobbed softly—"your best friend as long as I live."

"Okiku, what's the matter? Why this sudden outburst?" Saionji glanced at his watch and looked outside.

"Nothing, nothing, Prince. I wanted to tell you that I still love you. But—but I, I can't stand seeing anybody come between us. I don't want to be like the housewives who pretend not to know when their spouse's affection is stolen."

"Calm yourself, Okiku!" he said sympathetically.

"I am sorry for these tears, Prince, but when I think my parting day is nearing I want to see two things settled—"

"What are they?" He concealed his embarrassment.

"One is to see Shinko settle down—and the other is to see you become His Majesty's Chief Executive, *Soridaijin*. I dedicated my life for Shinko's sake to the Asakusa *Kwannon*, Goddess of Mercy, and for your sake to the Tsurugaoka Hachiman Shrine at Kamakura."

The rain had carried the heat and clouds away. The sky over the Musashi Valley was like crystal. A small rainbow stretched its sash from the corner of the Saionji house to the end of the rice field. The flowers that Saionji had planted in his little garden had freshened in the rain.

From the distance came the cheerful voices of Shinko and her school-mates.

Shinko's laughter brought a smile to the Saionjis' faces.

Okiku composed herself and returned to the bolts of cloth. She asked cheerfully: "Why do you want me to select the best materials, Prince?"

"Huh, I want to have my family crest, called the *Mitsu-tomoe*, three conventionalized waves in the shape of circling comets, dyed into it and have two dozen *yukata* made of the same pattern for the geisha girls—I have never used the crest before."

"What?" She dropped the piece and stared at him.

Grinning, he said: "Don't get excited, it's for Ito's sixty-first anniversary celebration. I'm going to take the geishas to Oiso to cheer him up."

"Can I come too?"

"Huh—yes, why not?"

Okiku selected a light blue 'wave and plover' pattern.

"How about a little walk in the new *yukata*?"

"Yes, Prince."

"Father! Mother! I'm—" Shinko dashed in. "Oh, are you going out?" Looking up at them, she pleaded: "May I come?"

The tension of the afternoon vanished. The sky, far on the horizon, was now veiled with thin pink clouds.

A party of pretty young geishas, uniformly dressed in white *yukata* of the light blue 'wave and plover' pattern with the *Mitsu-tomoe* coat-of-arms, and wearing their hair in *shimada* style, boarded the train at Shimbashi. They were escorted by Marquis Saionji and Okiku and their young friends, all in their summer kimonos. The party brought musical instruments and food with them.

On the train Okiku got acquainted with the geishas and acted as if she were their older sister. While she helped to rearrange their di-shevelled hair and make-up, her eyes often flashed over them. She smiled when she saw a round-faced geisha flirting with Saionji.

The young novelist, Kunigita, teased the girl. "Otama, don't be too babyish!"

Okiku caught the name. She studied her all the way to Oiso.

"Genro Ito! Genro Ito! Are you home?" Saionji shouted.

There was no answer.

"Genro Ito?"

"Who is it?" Ito called. "Saionji-san? What—? What is this? My! All these beautiful girls!"

Ito, characteristically stroking his beard, asked: "What is this, Saionji-san, this sudden invasion?"

"Huh." Saionji looked at the geishas. "What do you say?"

"Genro—" Otama began. Then all her comrades burst into a loud chorus: "Genro, a happy birthday to you, and many more happy ones."

"I never thought of celebrating my birthday this way! Thanks to you all."

He grasped Saionji's hand. "Oh, thank you!"

Tears of joy blinded him as he looked into Saionji's face.

Then he greeted Okiku and the others.

The members of his household came to receive the unexpected guests. The villa was dedicated to merrymaking. All the paper screens were removed to convert the many rooms into one.

"Genro Ito, we've brought everything, food in *orizume* and sake. We did not want to bother your servants too much. The only thing your cook need do is heat sake."

Everything was arranged. Ito and his wife, surrounded by the Saionjis, Takekoshi, Sakai and Kunigita, faced the two rows of geisha and the Oiso beach.

First the entertainers played the samisen together and sang lyric *Takasago*, the hope for a long and happy life.

Warm sake was served in small cups. The party became livelier and noisier every minute. Now half the geishas danced to the samisens, tabors and drums; the others danced a fast and light *cappore* and then some Kyoto dances.

Everyone present exchanged *sakazuki* with the Genro. Ito became expansive.

During the intervals of the music and song he conversed with Saionji and Okiku. He suddenly asked her: "Will you sing for us?"

"Well, Genro, I have been out of practice so long and I am getting old—"

"No, no, don't be too modest. I know your ability. Just one, and I won't ask you any more. Don't you remember after Saionji-san came back from France and met you with me? That night your performance was simply superb. I still recall some of it. That was the night he snatched you away from me." He laughed and shook his head. Saionji beamed.

When Saionji encouraged her, Okiku consented and said:

"Otama, will you accompany me on the samisen? I'll sing one song for this happy occasion."

All clapped their hands, but some of the younger geisha looked doubtful, for her reputation had been made when they were yet unborn.

As she concluded, there was great applause, for she was still superior to the entertainers there.

Okiku responded with an encore.

It was late afternoon when a small boat decorated with flags and lanterns appeared in the bay near the Oiso fishing village.

"I engaged it for our return trip. We are taking you with us for a leisurely sail."

"Saionji-san, you tempt me. I was not feeling elated for reasons which you know very well."

"That's what I suspected, so we came over to cheer you up."

Before they left, Kunigita, the novelist, leading the geishas, sang a navy song. "*Kemuri-mo tatazu kumo-mo-naku—*" all joined them, clapping their hands.

"Ah, this really invigorates me. The war days that those words recall were the most exciting in years."

"Don't you worry, you'll have more of them, Genro."

The party walked down to the pier and boarded the boat.

When they rounded the tip of Miura Peninsula in Tokyo Bay, the summer sun was sinking behind the mountain range in the west. Twinkling lights on both sides of the ship became gradually brighter. There was no wind, no wave; the water was smooth.

Towards the Ryogoku, fireworks illuminated the sky.

Ito was drinking with Saionji.

A few feet away, Okiku's eyes were idling on Otama, through the increasing darkness.

"I came to Tokyo to take care of some business matters and to attend the House of Peers. You know I was just elected from Osaka as one of the largest tax payers of the Prefecture."

Saionji's visitor was his younger brother, Sumitomo Kichizayemon of Osaka, whom he still called Takamaro. He was slightly over thirty years old and handsome; his black hair was parted on one side. The features were prominent, with a high forehead, brilliant eyes, aristocratic nose and firm lips. Unlike Saionji, he wore eyeglasses and a moustache.

"Huh, I'm certainly glad to see you, Takamaro. You are looking fine. How was your European trip? Did you learn much?"

"Yes, brother. From the hints I got during the tour, I've devised a few ambitious plans. It may take some time for them to materialize, but I'll establish my own banking system, invest more in mining and smelting and pay more attention to other heavy industries."

"Huh, so your visit was worth while?"

"Yes. Some day I'd like to rank in those fields with the Mitsui and the Mitsubishi."

"Huh, you are very ambitious."

Sumitomo looked around.

At last he said, "Brother, I have been thinking for some time—"

"What is it, Takamaro?"

"This location and the size of your house may not be ideal for you—"

"Ha, ha, I knew it. I was sure you'd say that. But it is large enough for me and I love this lonely place. Oh, by the way, many thanks to you for the money gift you sent me when I was recovering from my last illness."

Sumitomo bowed.

"As I was going to say, I have recently invested in quite a few houses in Tokyo. Some of them are in good condition. One, in the Surugadai Heights, may be suitable for you. It's close to the palace and government offices."

"Huh."

"I can have it remodelled to suit your needs. Besides the main living-quarters, there are a few additional buildings for servants, guards and caretakers."

"That's much too large. How could I meet the running expenses?"

Sumitomo smiled genially. "If you don't mind, I'll pay all the expenses."

"That sounds too good to be true."

"Will you live there, brother?"

"Huh, I like to move around, all right."

Both laughed.

Sumitomo had more suggestions.

"You see, brother, all of your political friends almost without exception have splendid houses in Tokyo and villas at the summer resorts, too."

"I don't see how they have enough money to do that, but they have, haven't they?"

"I intended to buy you a house at your favorite summer resort, also. I had the Kyoto buildings at Tanaka, which you had turned over to me, put in good condition, preserving the original features as much as possible. Didn't you stay there one summer with Okiku? If you want to go there again, it's ready at any time."

"You must be making a lot of money these days, Takamaro."

"Fortunately, during the Chinese War, I accepted some government orders for small arms and coal. That put me on the right track. When the war was over, I found that the Sumitomo fortune had more than doubled the amount left me by my foster father. I was glad to have added something to the family fortune."

"I can imagine your feelings. Our father was proud of Brother Tokudaiji, and of you, but he was worried about me."

"He would be proud of you, if he had lived this long and had seen your political advancement. It is now the general opinion that you'll be Genro Ito's successor."

"Huh, Ito and I get along better than Ito and General Katsura, perhaps. The general and I served together twice in Ito's cabinets. Katsura is an able man. But Ito thinks he is too crafty. In addition, he is allied closely with Field Marshal Yamagata with whom Ito isn't on good terms these days. They are all from Choshu, but politically they are divided."

"Speaking of politics, I heard you and Genro Ito have launched a campaign to organize a new party. I'd like to help you if I can."

"Takamaro," Saionji said gently but with decision, "I advise you now never to meddle with politics, directly or indirectly, like those big financial magnates. But I appreciate your kind intentions."

"Why not?"

"First of all, you are destined to be a businessman. With the capital you have you will be reasonably successful. Secondly, if you become closely allied with politics, win or lose you will invite public resentment, although at times you may make huge profits out of political manipulations. I don't think that is profit, that is graft."

"H'm, that sounds logical, brother Saionji."

"I don't mean to preach to you, but that's how I feel about it. And another reason is my relationship to you. If you and I advance further in our respective fields, the people will speculate as to what extent we help each other behind the scenes. As long as I am in politics, I want you to stay out. However, I understand and deeply appreciate your anxiety to promote my political fortune with your material assistance."

Sumitomo nodded.

"Huh, how is your wife?"

Sumitomo smiled broadly. "Thanks, Brother, she is well. She is eager to have you visit us oftener, but we know you can't get away. May I take Shinko along when I leave the city? Her spring vacation has begun, hasn't it?"

"Yes. She will be delighted."

At Genro Ito's villa in Oiso, now known as Nippon's 'second political center,' a secret conference was going on.

Present were more than ten men, mostly elderly, all in kimonos. They sat on the matted floor. Ito, the host and leader of the group, occupied a large tiger skin spread on the mat. Smiling, he alternately stroked the tiger's whiskers and his own as he directed the meeting. Saionji was next to him.

Ito looked over the draft of articles and by-laws of the new political party and murmured to himself: "The 'Seiyukai,' the Association of Political Friends, that's fine—"

When he finished he asked: "Well, what are our membership prospects?"

"The Diet members who have signified their intention of joining us number over one hundred and forty—" someone began, but another broke in, saying: "In a few months we'll induce some others to make it one hundred and fifty or more."

"That's splendid," Ito nodded, and went on: "So that my public announcement and the formalities will be in order in the late summer."

He exhaled the cigar smoke leisurely towards the ceiling. "H'm, half of the three hundred Diet members under my control with definite constructive policies for the country! Good! When I begin to drive this time, there will be no one who can block my way—neither Matsukata, nor Yamagata, nor any combination with their henchmen."

Unconsciously, he grasped the neck of the tiger skin and said: "It will be like charging into unarmed mobs on a giant tiger. I'll smash every opposition to pieces."

"Genro Ito," Saionji said, "what stand should our Party take if the mob uprisings in north China are prolonged?"

"Oh—" The Genro brought his bearded chin down, his eyes flashed over the group. "That's a serious problem. We must watch it closely.

But at this stage, our government has meagre information." His eyebrows knitted. "See, the Western diplomats at Tokyo have been put in charge of this affair by their home governments because their representatives left the Chinese capital. These diplomats have often met since the outbreak of the trouble, but they cannot agree as to who shall command the allied troops in China to protect their countrymen from the mobs, the Boxers, who are ultra-reactionary foreigner-haters. The Boxers are estimated to number only thirty thousand, but now it's reported that the Chinese Regular Army is taking a joint stand with them against the outsiders and pro-reform Chinese leaders. They murdered many, including our consular official, and destroyed much property."

Ito chewed the butt of his cigar while he talked. "These foreign representatives in Tokyo are jealous. That's what kept the allied troops from taking decisive action at the scene of the disorder. You know our men newly dispatched are headed by Lieutenant General Yamaguchi Motoomi. In accordance with diplomatic custom, he should be in supreme command of the united forces there, because he is the highest ranking officer. But they didn't want to see the Nipponese head them. If they agree to let our general lead the attack, the Boxers will be defeated in no time and the foreign residents rescued without further loss of life and property.

"Recently, however, they agreed to our plan because of the imminent danger to their own people, since the Western countries can't send their men as quickly and easily as we can. Lieutenant General Yamaguchi was put in command, but they have grown to formidable strength. It may take some time to pacify them. They are active mostly in and around Peking."

"What is the real cause of this uprising?" Ito was asked.

"A few years ago, when I visited China, I foresaw some trouble. There was widespread discontent in the two opposing camps of politicians. The progressives were headed by Emperor Kwang Shu and supported by Kang Yu-wei. The conservatives were under the Empress Dowager, assisted by Prince Tuan Chun, whose little son has been on the throne since Emperor Kwang Shu was forced to abdicate."

"Somewhat resembling our situation before the Meiji Restoration," Saionji observed.

"Of course. The progressives under Kang attempted to reform the antiquated political system after Western models. They were overthrown by Prince Tuan's clique. In our case, we, the progressives, won, but in China they lost. The present anti-foreign uprisings are the result of disagreements between the leaders."

"Anti-foreignism doesn't get anywhere. We tried it but dropped it—against the Big Powers," Saionji commented.

"Anyway, it's hard to deal with the Western nations. We learn by our experience with them. One day they seem upright and friendly, the next day they turn into blood-suckers. During my last trip to China I saw Westerners seizing the best and most strategic sections of the country for themselves.

"After the war, Russia, Germany, and France forced us to return Liaotung Peninsula to China in the name of peace in the Orient. But Russia took over Port Arthur and Dairen. Germany got Kiaochow Bay, France took her share in South China. Even England, who had been friendly to us during that war, occupied Weiheiwei as soon as our troops marched out of there. They are worse than fire-thieves. And to think that we used to rely on Germany!"

"Sir"—Genro Ito's servant came into the meeting-room—"the Minister of War, General Katsura, wishes to see you. May I show him in?"

"Well—"

"Genro Ito, since he is here, how about inviting him in and listening to his reports of the Chinese situation?"

"Ask him to enter."

General Katsura Taro, who was one of the youngest Choshu men to take part in the Restoration wars, had studied in Germany in the 1870's. His many military reforms were inspired by Prussian examples. In the Sino-Nipponese War he commanded the Third Division. Following that he was made Governor-General of Formosa. When he headed the War Department under the second Ito Cabinet he proved his ability as a politician.

When Ito resigned the Premiership, he remained in the following Cabinet under Count Okuma. The latter resigned shortly in favor of another Choshu leader, Field Marshal Yamagata, who had been Premier once before. Yamagata retained General Katsura in the War Office.

Of late, the public regarded Katsura as the natural successor to Yamagata.

General Katsura was well-built, erect, with broad shoulders, enormous head, grayish hair closely cropped, high broad forehead, eagle-like eyes, round chin and moustache. He was in uniform with medals on his chest and a sabre at his hip.

He showed no sign of surprise when he found Ito's followers sitting in conference with their chief. Ito, still resting comfortably on the tiger skin, greeted him: "Ah, Katsura, glad you came in. Sit down. We have been discussing China and want some information badly."

The general raised his right hand in military salute, directing his eyes first to his provincial senior and former chief, then to the others before he brought his hand down.

He removed his hat and sabre and the servant carefully carried them away. He seated himself on a cushion and crossed his legs on the mat.

"Nice to see you gentlemen all assembled together. Am I not interrupting an important meeting? I just stopped in on my way home from the office—I live a short distance from here—to chat with the Genro."

The air of formality was lifted.

"Katsura, do you have any important news regarding the Boxer Rebellion?"

The general hesitated.

"All trustworthy men here."

His eyes travelled around the faces and back to Ito. "Well, three new developments: One is a series of new outbreaks in Manchuria. The second is a request that we relinquish the allied supreme command. The last is that our battalion deliver the Chinese capital into the hands of the allies."

"That's good news!"

"Yes, that's really gratifying, Genro, because our officers and soldiers proved to be dependable, although they were assigned to the hardest quarter. Their bravery won praise from the foreigners."

"So our military machine got its first international recognition there, eh?" The Genro and the others were pleased to hear it.

"We had anticipated this outcome, however," General Katsura resumed. "In Manchuria the Chinese mobs destroyed the Russian railway tracks and rolling stocks. But they were smothered by the Russian military guards. What I do not understand is the rapid increase of the Czar's army in the region—and still more puzzling is the second point I mentioned."

"H'm."

"That came about in a strange way. It came from Germany at the request of the Czar. The Kaiser cabled to our government that the Czar wanted to have a German Field Marshal, Count von Waldersee, appointed to the supreme command of the allied army in China, so the German Emperor asked our consent. Foreign Minister Aoki, who is pro-German, as you know, quickly obliged him with it."

"What?" Ito groaned. "What did the Kaiser have to do with our decision? Can't we make up our own minds? Why doesn't the Czar communicate directly with us? Nippon is not a German or Russian protectorate."

Ito savagely bit off the tip of his cigar. Saionji, smoking calmly, said: "That's a real Kaiser-like approach, is it not?"

The War Minister nodded gratefully. "Yes, Marquis Saionji."

"H'm, the Kaiser and the Czar seem anxious to co-operate. Germany sends her Field Marshal to take the supreme command while Russia increases her troops in North China and South Manchuria. I can see trouble ahead for us in that region." Ito murmured to himself.

There was a slight cough beyond the veranda of the meeting room. A voice from the outside asked: "Is Ito home? It's Yamagata. May I come in?"

Premier Field Marshal Yamagata opened the paper screen before the host responded. He wore his snow-white hair very short. From a distance, his well-shaven, elongated face with white trimmed moustache gave him the appearance of a retired college professor. This 'Father of the Nipponese Army,' was a veteran of many battles of cannon and wits.

At the time of the Restoration he was a commander of the government troops and was assigned to Commander-General Saionji in one of his campaigns. By virtue of Yamagata's ability and by the good grace of his provincial seniors, he assumed, after their passing, the clan leadership of the military as Ito led that of the civilian elements. However, despite his local backing, his fame was overshadowed until 1877. In that year the greatest soldier-statesman in new Nippon, Saigo Takamori of Satsuma, fell on his own sword at the end of the unsuccessful rebellion.

Yamagata was the man to bring the modern Imperial Army to its later size and power. In the meantime, building on his military reputation, he shouldered the administrative burden of the Government. After Ito instituted the cabinet system, he had his opportunity, being one of the few Sat-cho men to become Premier and Genro.

He had to his credit the great victory over the better equipped and numerically superior Chinese forces in 1894-5.

That brought fame to Yamagata and his officers, among whom was Katsura, and to the Emperor's army. This achievement for His

Majesty and the nation was equalled in civil life only by Ito's monumental work of editing the Imperial Constitution.

The political house of the Sat-cho became divided between the soldier and the statesman. The differences between the leading Genros were glossed over every time they faced common enemies, domestic or foreign. But as soon as stormy days yielded to peace, the cleavage widened.

While Yamagata continued to dislike the political parties, Ito now took them as the inevitable outgrowth of the application of the Imperial Constitution. Despite his attitude, Yamagata as Premier had to bargain with party men. Ito followed the same tactics. However, when Ito was deserted by the 'hired soldiers' in the Diet because they were dissatisfied with or had too quickly consumed the 'bait' given out by the Cabinet, he was disgusted. When Ito decided in desperation to build his own party, the Constitution had been in force almost ten years.

His new attempt was constantly opposed by the machinations of Yamagata, but Ito persisted.

Thus, in the summer of 1900, Genro Ito and his followers were ready to bring the Seiyukai, or the Association of Political Friends, into the open.

Yamagata was anxious to learn of its progress, and so now he himself stalked into the enemy camp. When he faced Ito and his visitors, the Field Marshal greeted them formally.

"Oh, Yamagata!" Ito's eyes gleamed with mischief. He sat up on the tiger skin and extended his hand in a gesture of welcome.

The newcomer took his place near Ito. A momentary silence was broken by the host when he said amiably:

"Well, we have just heard from Katsura that the Chinese situation is growing rather complicated. What are you going to do about it?"

"Oh, yes, that's true. Ah"—he shook his head—"why talk so much? I hate that jabbering about nobody knows what—like 'sparrows' wedding ceremonies.' They don't accomplish anything." He spoke right out, referring to the diplomatic conferences over the Boxer uprisings and political gatherings.

"Your typical idealogy which disregards public opinion and settles things with one stroke of a sharp sword—success or failure." Ito grinned.

The irritated Field Marshal retorted: "I act according to my best judgment. My judgment is usually as good as anybody's, if not better."

He seemed to realize that his statement was a bit too strong. "Ha, ha, Ito, it's my frank expression. But don't you agree with me? I do my best. Their opinion doesn't amount to anything. At best they make a lot of noise, these newspapers and party politicians." He struck the ash tray with his cigar. Pointing to the ashes, he added: "Just like that, they don't amount to anything."

Ito kept his eyes steadily on the Field Marshal. The others feared that the exchange of sharp words would break into heated argument.

Yamagata resumed: "I have done enough this time. I put rules into effect with an Imperial Ordinance that will prevent job-hunting politicians from upsetting the administrative personnel in the Government. Henceforth, only the ministers and their immediate subordinates will come and go when there is a change of Premiers. The minor officials will stay and be promoted according to seniority and merit."

"That was a wise move." Ito half-heartedly approved. He was gazing into space behind the smoke of his cigar. A faint smile passed under his thin moustache.

The Field Marshal, suddenly removing his own cigar from his mouth, asked Ito point-blank: "Ito, when will your party be ready for action?"

"H'm!" With a scowl Ito swung his body towards Yamagata. The group was shocked and breathless.

"When will your political party be ready for action?" Yamagata pressed for a reply.

Ito tried to smoke to hide his embarrassment but the fire was out. "Tsk, tsk!"

His struggle with the cigar was amusing to the onlookers.

Then Genro Ito too smiled. The tension eased.

At last Ito said: "I don't know!"

The spirited questioner and all the others burst into loud laughter

A tiny frame structure, nine feet square, was located among the aged plum trees on Genro Ito's Oiso estate.

It was an early summer morning. A man approached the entrance. He stopped at the half-open door and peeped into the dimness.

Someone there sat before a small table with a vase of flowers. He was staring at portraits on the walls. The figure was motionless.

"Genro Ito, why are you meditating here at this hour? I looked for you all over your place and no one was about. I thought you might be taking a walk."

"Oh, Saionji-san! You appear all of a sudden. It is an unusual time for you to come from Tokyo." Ito remained in the chair.

"Huh, some time ago I rented a small cottage near the station and am taking a rest there. I like this Oiso. As you say, it's cool in the summer and warm in the winter, no snow or frost. These days fishermen hustle out to fish in the late afternoon and return at sunrise with their cheerful boatmen's songs."

"So you like the place, eh?" He still sat there.

"But I don't want to see too many summer-resort seekers from Tokyo."

"Ha, ha, you are selfish this time. You, too, are one of them."

"But I mean it."

"See, this Oiso is the only beach on Sagami Bay convenient to the capital. Here we have shallow water and a sand beach without rough waves, so it's good for swimming. At the other fishing ports around here the water is too deep. We also have all accommodations," Ito said mechanically.

Ito's eyes remained on the portraits. He talked to them. Saionji was still outside.

"Genro Ito, what is this?"

Ito suddenly came to himself. "Oh, didn't you know I had this built some time ago?" He rose from the chair. "I didn't tell you, eh?"

He was animated.

"Come, come right in," he said, taking Saionji by the arm.

"Look at these three big Chinese characters, which are still fresh with black ink. Can you identify the writer of *Shi-Ken-Do* or 'Four Sages' Arbor'?"

Saionji faced the calligraphy-frame. Ito pointed. "This is by His Imperial Highness, the Crown Prince Akino-miya Toshihito."

"Huh, and the portraits are of Sanjyo, Iwakura, Kido and Okubo."

"Now, Saionji-san, you see what it is." Ito's face changed from joy to reverence.

"This is my small part, as we say a 'hair of nine bulls,' to repay my debt to these four great senior statesmen. I call them the 'Four Sages' who taught me and helped me personally in my early career."

"Huh, I thought you were phlegmatic about such things as moral debt—"

"Ah, that is not true, you know it well. Where would I be without them? My very humble origin—we need not go into that. I grant that in some cases I pushed forwards regardless of the means, only to secure my end. In so doing I often turned my back on my benefactors. This was especially true with regard to Kido who originally discovered me and put me on the right track."

Ito's eyes watered. His nasal voice went on: "Don't think I am superstitious, but I still ask their souls for guidance whenever I am confused as to my future course. With the Four Sages I deliberate on complicated problems before I make up my mind. I meditate on what Sanjyo or Iwakura might suggest with their unselfishness and reverence towards the Emperor, or what Kido would do with his ideals and foresightedness, or how Okubo would solve things with his imagination and skill."

The Genro's sincerity brought vividly before Saionji the figures of these late statesmen. To him they were also close. Although he was too young to be politically intimate with them as Ito was, he had as a boy attended Court with Sanjyo, who was related to him by family ties, and with Iwakura. Both were many years senior to him, however. From the hundreds of courtiers, these two nobles had taken the leadership together with the Satsuma and Choshu men.

Saionji gazed long at Kido's portrait.

After a while Ito began:

"You know, Saionji-san, I was meditating here this morning about the present conditions. Now we have organized the Seiyukai Party despite Yamagata. He, in protest, will dump all problems into my hands and probably he'll retire from active politics.

"What does the Westerner say, 'history repeats itself'? It may or may not, I don't know, but here I am in a position similar to that which my original benefactor, Kido, faced from the beginning of the Meiji rule. He wanted to incorporate the principles of parliamentary government in our political system. Okubo and others opposed him—I was on Okubo's side—so Kido was dissatisfied, but he tried hard.

"Now, as we look back on his entire career, he appears to have been sincere. Almost every progressive move the Government made was primarily from Kido's brain. In some instances Okubo took the idea over and put it into practice."

Ito became eloquent: "Okubo argued against the 'deliberating assembly' which existed for a while after the first year of the new regime. He didn't like Kido's effort to frame 'the Imperial Oath of Five Articles,' his idea of adopting a constitution in 1873, or the 'governors' assembly.' But Kido insisted that the people must be given a chance to try, otherwise they would never learn. And he emphasized that a despotic or dictatorial government would not last long because national affairs would reach a complexity and magnitude that no single man could handle. He said that we had to enlist able people from a wide range. He used to say that one of the most effective and ideal ways to do that was by parliamentary procedure. His idea was crude, but he had the essence when we didn't understand."

Usually boring, Ito's long political speech interested Saionji this morning.

"Now over twenty years after Kido's death I am trying to enter real constitutional politics, as head of the Seiyukai Party. But Yamagata opposes me." Ito smiled sardonically. Indicating that they should leave the Four Sages' Arbor, he asked: "Did you come here soon after the formal announcement of the Seiyukai Party's organization?"

"Yes."

"Does anyone know about your summer cottage here?"

"Huh." Saionji looked at Ito and broke into a broad smile.

"Your brother, Tokudaiji?"

"No, guess once more."

"Well, your favorite new geisha?"

"Genro Ito, you missed again."

Saionji wiped his smooth face with his handkerchief, and fixed his eyes on Ito's. "His Imperial Highness, the Crown Prince."

"Oh!"

His cigar fell from his mouth, but was caught in mid-air.

"You don't mean to say that the Crown Prince visits your humble summer house, do you? A visit by His Highness is a great honor."

"No, he didn't."

"Oh!" Ito was puzzled. "I thought you said he did."

"No, I said he found out where I was. When he was at the Hayama Summer Palace, his messenger came to say that he was in the vicinity with Prince Arisugawa and wanted to call on me—"

"You don't say that you declined such a great honor, did you?"

"I did."

"You—" Ito stared at Saionji's changeless face.

"Well, let's not talk about it. It's beyond me. I can't think any Nipponese subject would act like that, refusing a lifetime privilege," Ito grumbled.

Saionji was amused. "Huh, but you don't know the real circumstances, the size of my temporary quarters and its condition. There are only three rooms of modest size, the largest being the eight-mat one, and no decoration or anything. It is as bare as it can be."

"Well, why do you squeeze into a place like that?"

"That's enough for me. But that was nothing; the really dramatic phase of the proposed visit was rather comical."

"Oh?"

"You know my young friend Takekoshi, former councillor to the Education Department? He was with me at the time the Imperial messenger arrived. He fled to a maid's room to get out of the way."

Ito laughed out loud: "That stylish Takekoshi in the maid's chamber! It must have been an interesting sight."

They passed through the garden towards the main house. The leaves of the plants still held dewdrops on their tips. They sparkled like diamonds under the morning sun.

"Genro Ito, what has developed? How does Marshal Yamagata stand now? Is he going to resign the Premiership in protest of your party presidency?"

"I was coming to that, that's one of the reasons why I was meditating in the Four Sages' Arbor. Let's sit down on this bench in the shade. From here we can see Sagami Bay at our feet—on fine days you can even see O-shima Island and the volcano. See, the water off this shore is dark blue, almost black. They say it's because of the warm ocean current and also because it has the deepest sea-bottom of the entire Pacific."

"Don't they say that has something to do with our repeated earthquakes?"

"That may be so." They sat down.

"Well, returning to the present political situation— But before we go into that I must tell you one thing, that the President of the Privy Council, Kuroda, is critically ill. He may not recover this time. Should anything happen to him, we want you to succeed him. If I nominate you, the other Genros, Yamagata, Matsukata, Inouye, and Oyama would not disapprove."

"Isn't it too bad Kuroda should be so ill? When he was with me in the Echigo sector in the 1868 civil war time, he was a hardy *samurai*."

Saionji was deeply moved, but Ito continued:

"See, your being President of the Privy Council will make the Emperor happy. His Majesty seems to think a great deal of you, and is most pleased to see you steadily coming up on the steps of the political pyramid. It won't be long before you reach the top.

"Well, I am sure Yamagata will resign soon. What he said the other day at my home when he burst in on our supposedly secret meeting, do you remember, was true. I carefully analysed his statements made in excitement and came to that conclusion."

"So, Genro Ito, backed by the Seiyukai Party, you will try once more."

"Not backed by, but as President of the new Party." Ito stroked his beard. "But"—he dropped his voice—"here is the other angle. Inouye suggested to me that I should put you in front this time, and with my powerful party I could guide you from the side line. Having me, the most influential and His Majesty's favorite Genro as your adviser, you can't fail."

It didn't leave any impression on Saionji. He made an incoherent remark about Ito's villa. "Your place is certainly in a lovely location."

"What, oh, my house? Do you like it?" Ito was just as incoherent; probably he was absorbed in political questions.

Suddenly Saionji said: "Say, Genro Ito, I came to you this morning to borrow a few pictures for my summer cottage."

"Certainly, but did I keep you this long?"

They smiled at each other.

"But, Saionji-san, why don't you buy a small estate here? The one next to mine, for instance, could be obtained very reasonably. If you don't have money, there'll be some way to get it."

"My empty purse can't get anything. When I save enough out of my salary, I'll purchase that house. I am not clever at all at money making—"

"Nonsense, if you want to, you can make a deal with your brother, Sumitomo, for example. But—they say the young Sumitomo is brilliant but unapproachable in that respect."

"Genro Ito, I am proud of my younger brother, glad he is unapproachable. If he follows my advice he will be satisfied with ordinary profits and keep his hands clean of deals."

"I don't mean to insist that you do like the others."

"But I am going to accept his proposal."

"Oh, you are, without a deal, eh?" Ito said with mild cynicism. "What's the proposal, Saionji-san?"

"Among many properties he has purchased in Tokyo, he says one in the Surugadai district will suit me. That house is being put in order for me."

"Well, well, well," the Genro waved his hand, "that settles your

housing problem, but I know you have another difficulty, Saionji-san."
Ito was grinning from ear to ear. "I'll bet you'll break your neck in
settling the other affair—"

Saionji smiled and said: "What do you mean? Otama?—My relationship with that young geisha?"

"That's right. How are you going to clasp her to your bosom? A
few millionaires are after her and you have Okiku. If she comes to you,
what?" Ito made a gesture.

"I am not quite sure, frankly speaking, how to beat off her wealthy
suitors. As for the rest, it's simple because Sagami and Okiku have
agreed that I must have a son of my own."

Ito stared. Then he whispered into Saionji's ear: "Don't you think
it's rather late?"

Both laughed.

"Huh, Genro, I guess we'll change that subject—"

"No, no, Saionji-san, that's a most harmless topic. It won't make
anybody mad or tax one's brain."

"Huh, it's almost noon."

"Just wait, Saionji-san, don't leave. Let's go to the Gunkaku-ro and
have a drink or two with lunch. I'll let my servant bring the pictures
to your place."

"*Josho*," Ito shouted at the woman operator as they entered the
Gunkaku-ro.

"Oh, Genro Ito, many, many thanks for your favor—"

"Get something light, Marquis Saionji is with me." They walked
upstairs.

Hardly had they sat down when a maid came up to Ito to announce
a visitor.

The guest presently appearing was another Choshu Genro, Inouye
Kaoru.

"Oh, Inouye, you just came over at an opportune moment. Join us."

Saionji through the windows was watching the lovely scene below
where a long row of pine trees, the town road and the white sand
beach ended on the promontory.

"Oiso is certainly restful, is it not, Marquis Saionji?" Inouye began.
"Look, there are hundreds of people, some swimming, others strolling
along the surf or taking a sun-bath. The tide is low and the water is
clean and calm, a few ripples roll up and break lazily."

Trays were brought in, each with a covered lacquer soup-bowl and a few plates, one of which had Ito's favorite dish, sliced raw fish and vegetables.

The informal party was well under way when the arrival of Premier Field Marshal Yamagata was announced. By this time they were fairly drunk. To Saionji it seemed that the small white sails which were passing not far from the shore jumped forward, backward and sideways.

"Oh, Yamagata, I haven't seen you for some time. Have a few cups."

"Ito," the Field Marshal began formally, "I am ready to give my answer to your party activities. Do you remember when I came to your place and asked you when your group would be ready? Since you completed your party organization it was my turn to act. Here is my answer," he pulled out an afternoon copy of a Tokyo newspaper and opened it before them.

The full page headline read: "Premier Yamagata Resigns."

"I have no hard feelings against anybody, you know. But remember, Ito—"

"What?" asked Ito, holding his head steady for a moment.

"You think your way is best for His Majesty and the country, as I do mine," said the Field Marshal.

Ito presented his cup to him. Before Yamagata dried his he repeated: "But, Ito, remember politics is a game of *shogi*. You and I as the players need not always move the leading figures up front to win. And it's about time for me to retire. I'm sixty-two years old—"

"Hey, don't be so formal. You are three years and Ito is five years younger than myself. After all, we are friends of long standing," Inouye suggested.

"With that reminder I return this cup and I'll join you full-heartedly."

Extending his arm to Ito, Yamagata repeated, "A game of chess! Well, here's to your next move. Ah, I am relieved, I feel that my back is literally free from burdens. Ito, give me another one. Inouye, Saionji-san, come, come, don't ignore me. Send your *sakazuki* over to exchange with mine."

One after another the Field Marshal dried the sake cups and returned them to the original holders.

The party continued until late in the evening.

Saionji suddenly awoke.

"Prince, are you all right? Won't you take a little water?"

"Oh, Okiku, thanks." He was not sure whether he was at his Omori home or at the Oiso cottage, but after he had taken the glass of cold water Okiku offered him, he came to himself.

Near the veranda of his cottage, he had his head on Okiku's lap. She fanned his perspiring face.

"Hu-u-uh!"

He yawned, stretched and fell back again.

"Prince, do you know what you did?"

"Huh, I met Ito, Inouye and Yamagata, too, at the Gunkaku-ro—"

He looked up at Okiku.

From the side the pale moonlight fell on her face. Her profile was still a perfect specimen of traditional beauty.

"Huh, I must have had plenty of sake—" He realized he was at Oiso because of the intermittent sounds and salty odors from the beach.

"You must have—and it was too potent for you, because you had not had much after the operation."

"Besides, Okiku, I went over to Ito soon after my breakfast and he took me over and we drank without eating much—"

"Then what did you do?" She laughed gently.

"Huh, I came back, I suppose, but how I don't know."

"You didn't come back home alone, did you?" she grinned and added: "I was with you."

"Huh!" He rose. "Were you?"

"Yes, just as I came past the Gunkaku-ro, I heard Genro Ito's usual hearty laughs. I went in there to see if you were with him. He was still standing on the top of the staircase, teasing the maids. When he saw me he rushed down to me and told me you had left the house alone, insisting that you could come home. He told me to follow you right away.

"You left from the south exit as I came in from the opposite corner. I just missed you there. I rushed out to the street and saw you trotting only a short distance away."

"So you followed me?"

"Yes, all the way you murmured to yourself, you sat down on the rock by the road-side, watched the ocean, and you told me how pretty a maiden I was—"

"Huh, I never knew that, but how did you happen to come over?"

"Well, you would laugh at me if I told you—"

Saionji took another glass of water.

"You know I went to visit the Tsurugaoka Hachiman Shrine at Kamakura?"

"I know you do that often."

"Prince, I visited the Shrine for the hundredth time today. My promise that I had made to pray there that many times at certain intervals, should the god relieve your illness, has expired."

"When did you start that?"

"When you were in France last time and got appendicitis—I was so worried about you, yet I couldn't do anything for you so I invoked the god, as other people do under similar circumstances."

"Huh, so that's it."

"Usually I go straight home, but today, when I offered my last prayer, something told me to see you, so I came."

Okiku smiled and went on: "What did those Genros tell you there, Prince?"

"Huh, as usual, hundreds of different things. They talked and talked of their past achievements—"

"You didn't hear very much in your napping, maybe?"

"I remember one or two things. Huh, yes, they told me they'll recommend me to be the President of the Privy Council to succeed Kuroda. And Ito and Inouye suggested that we should adopt a young man to be Shinko's future husband."

"Oh, did they?" Okiku was agitated. Sliding to his side, she asked: "Who is he?"

"The eighth son of the Mori family of Choshu, their former lord. His name is Hachiro, and he's six years older than Shinko. Since we have no son, Ito and Inouye think it's wise for us to adopt him now, and when Shinko finishes her education at the women's college we'll let them marry."

"Then Shinko would be eighteen," Okiku mused.

She shrugged her slender shoulders. "Well, but do you think they'll get along all right? You know, you and I knew each other long before we—"

"True, Okiku, but it's a difficult thing, is it not? We can't very well tell our daughter to look for her own man since other people are once more conservative in that regard and make matrimonial affairs strictly a family, not a personal, matter. And in addition, these days we hear so much about college and university students being degraded. Especially those smart ones, they say, exploit innocent daughters of rich and well-known families."

"That way, Prince, we can avoid any possibility of Shinko's becoming involved with an unworthy man—"

"Yes, Okiku, they told me the young man is an upright fellow and—"

"And the country's leading Genros are Shinko's *nakaudo*, Prince. That adds great dignity to her wedding."

"And that brings me closer to the Choshu people. The families of the former Choshu lord and mine were related in the past. I have been in intimate contact with Lord Mori since the time of the Restoration. See, Okiku, it was this boy's grandfather who first began to elevate the vassals on their personal merits. That practice was followed by the boy's father. Among those who benefited by this were General Omura and Councillor Kido, through whom Genro Ito was originally raised from footman to the rank of *samurai*—"

"Hachiro may have that progressive quality, too, Prince."

"I believe so. All these things made me consider the proposal seriously."

"Prince, Sagami will be delighted to hear that. She always says that 'Princess' must marry a man of high social standing and heritage."

"Huh, to satisfy Sagami and you, too, the Mori family is one of the few former feudal lords to whom the title of Prince was granted. But these questions are secondary. Under no circumstances will I cloud Shinko's future happiness by any hasty action."

His paternal love and affection for his daughter rang through his gentle voice; Okiku nodded in confirmation.

Then, beaming at her, he said: "After all, the decision depends on Shinko. So I am thinking of inviting him soon and introducing him to her to see how they like each other."

Okiku shut her eyes and meditated for a while. "Oh, this very morning, Prince, I prayed to the Goddess of Mercy for her happy marriage—"

"Don't overburden *Kwannon*. You seem to bring everything to her these days," said Saionji in jovial tones.

She became silent again. The moonlight threw its ray on the grounds beyond the shadow of the eaves. Its light was strong enough for Saionji dimly to see Okiku.

"Okiku, you look like the Goddess of Mercy herself."

It was a fine afternoon in the later spring. The air was dry after the strong wind.

Premier Ito sat on the couch, coatless, near the window in his office on the second floor of a small Western building. His blue serge trousers had lost their creases and his knees protruded like the eyes of an excited crab.

The cigar was burning away on the ash tray, his untouched lunch dishes shared a large rectangular table with official documents, books in native, Chinese and Western script, stationery, official and private letters, several old swords presented to him by his friends, and cigar boxes.

On that same table the Premier usually read, wrote, ate and drank. He used the modestly furnished living-room on the opposite side of the house only for visitors from foreign countries or from the Imperial House.

His bearded face was dark, yellowish-pale, and his cheekbones stood out because of loss of weight. His eyes were sunken. There was no sign of his fighting spirit.

He had been looking expectantly through the window at the ground below. Feebly he picked out a short sword about a foot long from the center table. It was one of the *Masamune* swords.

In his lean shaky hands Ito held it horizontally before his eyes, the blade upward, and slowly unsheathed it. His eyes were fixed on the sparkling steel, reflecting the afternoon sun. It was so brilliant that a stream of mist seemed to spout from its tip.

First he was breathless in admiration of its workmanship, then his thoughts travelled back.

It was the symbol of power, loyalty and the *bushido* of the *samurai*.

Many a great statesman in the past rose and fell with the sword; many a nation, large and small, was created and destroyed by the sword.

Ito murmured: "And many defeated warriors took their own lives with it instead of remaining to suffer humiliation."

He meditated.

Now the *Masamune* dagger was vertically in his hand before him. His eyes slowly fastened on the sharp cutting edge of the blade.

He saw his own weather-worn figure reflected in the sparkling steel.

Another face, smooth and well groomed, appeared beyond his own.

"Oh, Saionji-san!" said Ito as he quickly sheathed it and turned to the caller standing at the entrance of the room. "Glad you came." With a smile he invited Saionji to come in.

"Huh, Genro Ito, you look sick. Don't get up. Did you call a physician?"

"Well, I'm not ill exactly, but they have been telling me to take a complete rest. It is no time for me to stop. I'm a man. I can't show my back to my enemies. I'd rather die fighting than make a shameful retreat. So long as my physical strength and stamina lasted I stood my ground, but—"

"Huh, you will collapse if you persist. You look like a ghost from an abandoned grave. You'd better lie down." He assisted him. "Shall I call the doctor?"

Genro Ito, lying on his side, raised his hand. "Don't bother.—You are the only one who can save me from misfortune and the utter destruction of my public career."

Saionji sat down. Ito sank slowly onto his back. A long silence followed.

Then he murmured monotonously: "After I succeeded Yamagata as the Premier for the fourth time with the Seiyukai Party under my command, Yamagata delivered the first blow. He had resigned the office partially as a protest to my new activities. Through his superior influence in the House of Peers, which also resented my progressive moves, Yamagata blocked every important legislation I introduced and had passed by the Seiyukai majority in the Lower House. To get the Lords' approval on important measures I had to secure special Imperial rescripts addressed to them. Yamagata humiliated me to the last degree—I lost face.

"Do you remember, Saionji-san?" Ito glanced weakly at Saionji and went on: "Do you remember, when we were at the Gunkaku-ro one afternoon last year, Yamagata came in and said that politics was a game of chess and the next move was mine?"

"Yes, I do, Genro."

"I did move by succeeding him as the Premier, then he did all this to me. I feel as if I had been punched squarely on the chin. This setback has already wrecked my nerves. Then the Seiyukai itself began to crumble."

Ito breathed deeply and kept on: "I had to dismiss Hoshi Toru from the Ministry of Communications because he had been accused of accepting bribes. He was one of the most forceful men. I tried to cover him. That caused the shattering of the already weakened party unity. See, Saionji-san, you have been the President of the Privy Council all this time and are not acquainted with the members, but there are all types of men in the Party."

"Huh."

"In the meantime, Finance Minister Watanabe Kunitake acted very queerly. Without my consent and of course independently of his colleagues, he commenced to readjust the fiscal programs for the next year after they had been passed by the Diet. That invited a shower of criticism from all over and disclosed the disunity of my Cabinet. You see, that was the last blow. I have been trying to reshape my Administration and—"

"Huh, Genro, only your will power made it possible for you to remain on duty."

"And here I am physically broken down—even my chronic ailment which did not bother me for a long time has reappeared, my bleeding piles."

Ito fell back again, his hands clenched and teeth set.

"I hate to admit my defeat publicly—"

"Is there anything I can do for you?"

"I must ask your co-operation. Saionji-san, until I regain my health I want you to be the Acting Premier, that is, to keep the post open for me. I want to try to come back."

"But, Genro, that's a bit too great a task for me."

"No, don't argue with me. I shall ask His Majesty for a special decree empowering you to assume temporary leadership of my Cabinet without altering your official status as the Privy Council President. That's my only consolation. I'm placing you a step farther into the political limelight."

The Saionjis were at their Omori home waiting for Shinko's return from her school one Saturday afternoon.

At Saionji's request, Shinko had been sent to the English-French Girls' High School instead of the Peeress' Academy after she finished her public school education.

Whenever the Princess was expected, Saionji's aged governess insisted that she should welcome her home. Sagami, accompanied by the maid, had gone to the Omori railway station early.

"Well, Prince, how do you happen to have so much money lately? I asked you once, and when you began to tell me, something interrupted us."

Saionji was meditating.

"Prince," she began to repeat the question.

"Yes, Okiku. Huh, money? I paid our small debts and also arranged to buy the estate next to Ito's at Oiso, but there is still some left."

"Oh?"

"I want to sell this house when the Oiso deed is executed. Did I tell you that brother Sumitomo wrote me the Surugadai house will soon be ready for us?"

"Well, as to spending the money, I have many suggestions—a kimono set for yourself, for instance. You haven't bought any clothes for a long time. But how do you happen to—?"

"Huh? Yes, yes. Sumitomo sent me a large sum as a special present for my recovery from my last illness. For quite a while I considered returning it, but I have rejected his kind offer every time. I don't want to hurt his feelings. See, he seems to be so anxious to help me financially."

"He probably finds much joy in doing so, Prince."

"That's right. So at last I decided to accept it."

"But you don't care to spend any for yourself."

"Huh."

"Prince," said Okiku with a broad smile. "I have a wonderful idea."

"What is it?"

"How about our sending Sagami and Miyo to Kyoto on a vacation?"

"Huh, I was thinking of it too, but I didn't know how you would feel about it. But, Okiku, one difficulty is Sagami's stubbornness. She will not go."

"Yes, I know, Prince."

"Because she knows I don't have any other income than my salary which she considers is barely enough to keep us going respectably. She never went back to Kyoto after she came to Tokyo over thirty years ago. Do you think you can convince her some way?"

"Well—you see, Prince, Sagami nowadays often talks of the old capital. I was sorry that we could not give her a trip, but as you say, she would not listen, anyway, unless we had some reason for her going."

She patted Saionji's hand softly and said: "Prince, this would work."

"What, Okiku?"

"See, now Shinko's vacation is beginning. Let Sagami take her along. Every time Shinko went to Kyoto Sagami commented mournfully that she ought to see the ancient capital with someone who could really show her things."

"You mean to make her Shinko's special guide?"

"And Miyo, Shinko's servant."

"Huh, that's a great scheme, Okiku. Sagami would swell up like a peacock."

Then looking at Okiku, he added, "But you'll be disappointed, won't you, if Shinko goes away during her vacation?"

"Well, Prince, you will too, I know; but after all, we can't have everything we want. We must give in sometimes." She looked down. "I used to think I must have everything I wanted and I didn't like Sagami at all, but—"

"You changed your mind, huh?"

"I found that in many instances Sagami was right. I thought the traditional ideas of the housewife's sacrifice for the sake of her family, husband and children were outdated, but there is something to it, too— Some satisfaction in doing so."

The sounds of slowly moving jinrikisha wheels approached.

"Ah, Prince, she is coming—"

The Saionjis came to look at their beloved Shinko's returning home.

At a short distance from the house, on the narrow gravel road, they saw their daughter in the carriage, and Miyo and Sagami on foot coming home.

Shinko seemed to be anxious to have her rikishaman run as fast as he could, but the governess was travelling along beside it. At the railway station Shinko had suggested that Sagami should ride and she walk. The governess was greatly pleased with her kind suggestion but said:

"Oh, no, Princess, I would never think of it, not even of riding in another carriage beside you. I'm merely your servant and very proud of that fact. Riding in your carriage, no, no, Princess." With a smile on her wrinkled face she straightened her 'bow-shaped' body. "Ah, you are the cream of human goodness to consider this humble wretch in such a kind way."

Shinko then said to her: "Shall I have my suitcase and packages put on the carriage and walk with you? It's a short distance."

Sagami shook her head. "No, no, Princess. You'll not." Taking her by the hand to the jinrikisha she murmured: "You must preserve your dignity. A lady should not touch polluted soil even with her foot."

Shinko saw no need of further argument with the old servant and obeyed.

Sagami once more stretched her hip to look up at her Princess in the *kuruma* and whispered: "You are like a white lily just budding into the world, so graceful, noble and pure—"

They started to move and Sagami began talking to herself: "My Princess, my Princess! She asks *me* to ride. Ah, a noble lady."

Sagami's walk was slow. She looked like an old woman in a Nipponese *No* drama. Her head, thinly covered with gray hair, fell forward. The hip was bent again. Her originally lean physique had lost flesh. She put out her left foot, then her right foot, then her left as if they were keeping time with an antiquated pendulum.

"See, Okiku, Sagami has stopped again on the corner to look up at Shinko."

"No wonder it takes time to come home."

"But how proud Sagami looks."

Okiku waved her hand at her daughter.

Shinko waved back. The summer breeze played gently on Shinko's long black hair, combed back and held together with a pin and a large red ribbon at the back of her neck.

"She has grown so much, hasn't she, Prince? She is wearing the new *yukata* I sent her a few weeks ago, her dark brown *hakama*, and brown shoes—"

"Yes, Okiku, and she's growing very pretty."

Okiku beamed at Saionji.

"Many people tell me she's your double," he added.

Presently they entered the yard.

"Father! Mother!" Shinko shouted to them, waving her hands excitedly.

As soon as the *kurumaya* dropped the carriage handle onto the ground she jumped off like a deer and rushed to her parents. Taking their hands in hers, she looked joyfully into the smiling faces. Okiku stroked her long black hair.

To her father Shinko said: *"Comment allez-vous, mon père?"*

Saionji seized her hand and kissed it and said affectionately: "Pay special attention to that language, some day I'll take you to Europe."

"Saionji-san, here, I have made a shield for your new house, 'Rin-so.' You are literally my next door neighbor now."

"Thanks, Genro Ito. I'll hang it over the gate myself." Saionji took the thick cedar board with its two Chinese characters in black ink.

"I imagine you people are busy. I'd better not bother you any longer," said Ito, who was looking much better. "Well, Saionji-san, what do you plan for your new household? Are you going to employ new servants here?"

"Oh, no, Genro Ito, I'll take my staff back and forth with me. I can't afford to keep help here and in Tokyo too."

"What did you do with your Omori house?"

"I sold it."

"Oh, I see," Ito said, proudly looking up at his own estate, "but you can transfer the Surugadai buildings?"

"They aren't mine. They belong to my brother, Sumitomo. I hated to accept them, you know, Genro, for I am accustomed to live within my own meagre income."

"It's certainly convenient to have a home in Tokyo, especially with no financial obligations. Well, I'll sit down here on the veranda for a minute."

"Huh, I will not be chased out on account of the back rent, at least."

"Didn't you say Sumitomo had proposed to pay for the upkeep?"

"Yes, that's the agreement. But I'll pay as much as I can."

"Isn't it strange, Saionji-san? Look at the hundreds of politicians waiting to jump on the businessmen like a horde of hungry foxes near the chicken yard—sometimes the order's reversed—for bribes large or small. Here you have your own brother with whom you could make profitable deals; but you contentedly sit back, read books and magazines, do a little engraving or arrange bunches of orchids. You are really a rare specimen among the greedy human beings in this materialistic world."

Saionji was watering the transplanted orchids. "Huh, you don't seem to have accumulated much despite your political reputation and the length of your service."

"Well, I spend as much as I get."

Saionji finished the watering and came to Ito's side.

Suddenly the Genro burst out laughing. "Ha, ha, I thought you were slow, but the way you dismissed Finance Minister Watanabe changed my mind. When it comes to public questions you sometimes exhibit remarkable determination."

Genro Ito was referring to an incident which had taken place some time before when Saionji took the posts of Acting Premier and then *Premier ad interim* to relieve Ito. Saionji still held the latter position.

"That was the only way to deal with him since Watanabe refused to co-operate and declined to resign. As soon as I became the *Premier ad interim* I advised His Majesty to discharge the Minister and I took the post."

207 PARTY PRESIDENT AND PRIME MINISTER

"I can't recall any occasion when a Minister refused to resign with his chief and had to be dismissed by the Emperor. Now, according to the Imperial Constitution, the Minister is independently appointed by and is responsible to the Crown, but for political expediency when the Premier resigns, all the Cabinet Members follow his example." Then he asked: "Saionji-san, you didn't hear anything about Katsura's attempt to organize the next Cabinet, did you? Since you won't assume the burden of a regular executive, I believe we'll have to let the General do it."

"No, Genro, I haven't heard anything about it.—By the way, you seem to have your old spirit back."

"Yes, I feel fine. I spent some time at a resort away from official duties. When I asked you to relieve me, I felt miserable, but one consolation was that I could put you in your temporary post. I hoped that you would get some experience—I suppose you'd like to remain as the Privy Council President, eh?"

"Yes, when the Premier is ready to be sworn in, I'll be released from the provisional Premiership and keep the Privy Council seat. What is your plan now?"

"Well, for further mental rejuvenation, I am planning to leave for Europe soon. From now on we need to keep in constant touch with the leaders of other countries and to see Nippon more objectively once in a while. When we are too close to Fuji-san, we can't get the whole view.

"I'll stop at Yale University in the United States and receive my degree of Doctor of Laws. When I come home I can tell you a lot of things about Western countries— Oh, there comes Inouye. He must have some information for us."

"They've decided on Katsura," the jubilant visitor entering Saionji's gate shouted. "Katsura'll accept on condition that you promise to help him, Ito."

"What?" Ito's voice was cold.

Inouye comprehended quickly. "You see, Saionji-san refused, my own attempt was a failure, Yamagata is definite about his retirement and there is no Satsuma man willing to jump into this gap to succeed you. Since you resigned on May 10, almost four weeks have passed under Saionji's provisional Premiership. It's a disgrace to Sat-cho statesmanship. If we let the matter run on any longer, His Majesty and the people will lose faith in us and everything will end in disaster. Then we will never recover our supremacy in politics. The people, who have been completely inarticulate and who could be effectively and easily gagged up to now, make a lot of noise through the opposition parties these days. We've got to be careful about that angle, too, if we are to continue dominating the nation's affairs. And it had to be a Sat-cho man."

Frequently Inouye showed remarkable eloquence and persuasive ability.

"That's true. Then what have you decided, Inouye?"

"Well, the plan has advanced this far: First of all, Katsura, accompanied by Yamagata, will visit you here tonight and personally pay you his respects and beg for your approval and future assistance. Then tomorrow, Monday, the ceremonies of His Majesty's appointment will take place."

Although it was said in perfectly good faith and sincerity, Inouye's presumptuous attitude made the listeners grin.

Ito said teasingly: "If I don't back him up, then what?"

Inouye took the remark seriously. "Say, are you still at odds with Yamagata and Katsura?"

Saionji laughed. "He is teasing you."

"So you don't oppose him, eh? That's good. Show your big-heartedness this time. Let General Katsura try his hand."

Inouye's pleading gestures suddenly came to a stop when Ito put a question. "Inouye, you and I have been the best friends for over forty years, since the days we went to England as young students. I know your motives and intentions are honorable, but we can't take everything for granted. Because of your good nature you sometimes assume too much. Did you exact any promise from Katsura that he will not trap me if I help him? If you didn't, and Katsura kicks the dirt in my eyes with his hind paws, what should I do?"

Inouye's hands dropped to his sides as he heard Ito's low-voiced but emphatic words.

"Did you think of that?"

Then Inouye nodded to himself. "Oh, Ito, I'll go back to Tokyo and confer with him and be back tonight to see you." Turning to Saionji, he said: "Marquis Saionji, I'll come again to see your house."

He had already passed through the gate.

Ito and Saionji laughed heartily, with Ito commenting: "Oh, Saionji-san, he is a good-natured fellow, Inouye is."

"Prince, this new house seems so vast. In comparison with our Oiso home and with every house we have lived in thus far, the place is enormous. The little buildings on each side of the gate have rooms, too."

"Don't you worry about our extra space; it will be filled in no time if our young friends find out that we have moved into this Surugadai house. Did you see the view from the corner? We can see the city far south, east and west, even Fujisan on a fine autumn day."

"Prince, your brother, Sumitomo, is very considerate, isn't he?"

"Yes, Okiku. I told him not to do any extensive renovating. But he had every fixture made to suit my taste and for your and the servants' convenience."

"Did you see, Prince, we have city water and gas in the kitchen and electric lights in every room. Now we have ample space for each one of us."

"Oh, that reminds me that a room in the building parallel to the gate must be kept vacant. Tomorrow the Metropolitan Police will assign me a detective as a house guard."

"What, Prince, a detective'll come to live here?"

"Yes."

"Why?"

"Huh, I, as the President of Privy Council, according to police regulations, am entitled to have that protection, but I declined every time I was asked, because I didn't think I needed a guard and we didn't have room for one. Now we have enough room to keep a guard and we need one, perhaps. They say many hoodlums roam through the city these days. In my absence you, Shinko, Sagami and the other servants wouldn't know what to do if they broke in."

"Oh—"

"Some people are coming into the yard."

"Oh, Prince, so soon. We are always interrupted."

"Marquis Saionji," a voice called at the door.

"Okiku, that's Takekoshi."

As Okiku opened the porch door, Takekoshi, Sakai, and Motono marched in. "Good evening!"

"Good evening, Takekoshi-san. Huh, you have others with you. How do you do, friends?"

"We came to congratulate you on your new home," Takekoshi said. His companions were busily inspecting the rooms.

Sakai commented: "Well, I just paid my respects to the Marquis at his Oiso home a few weeks ago and now he appears here. If I had to keep track of you, Marquis, I would be dizzy."

"But if you walk off with the Marquis' clogs every time you come, you'll not be popular with the Saionjis," Motono teased him.

All sat down.

"Well, if I ever get a *pair* of the Marquis' footwear, it will be all right," Sakai went on merrily. "But last time I left the 'Rin-so,' I had one of the Marquis' and the other was my own. I noticed it after I got on the train."

"So you captured the prize safely, eh?"

"No," Sakai was shouting, "the funny part was, though the size was the same, the Marquis' had a grayish string and mine a brownish one. I was embarrassed! I didn't know it until I discovered my fellow passengers staring at my feet. I wished I could hide them like a tortoise hides its head."

"Maybe your head, too, huh?" the host was greatly amused.

"Marquis," Takekoshi said, changing the subject, "both Motono and Sakai are due to leave for Europe soon."

"Huh, for what country?"

"As an unofficial staff member of the delegation to the Paris Exposition. Marquis, until I sail for Europe I'll be here every day and take a rest. This place is roomy, quiet and clean."

"Don't be too sure about that," Takekoshi interrupted.

"Well, first come, first served; I may even stay here tonight."

"Motono-san, are you leaving for France, too?"

"Yes, Marquis," said the diplomat cheerfully.

"I'd like to go with you. I love France."

"See, Marquis, Motono got his promotion; the announcement will be made tomorrow in the official gazette. He'll represent Nippon at Paris," Takekoshi said.

"Congratulations to both of you."

"Marquis, when I come back from France I want you to help me get a steady job. I have jumped around enough. I don't want to die in a strange country. I'd like to have my remains buried with my ancestors' like other Nipponese."

"What's the matter, Sakai? What's got into you? You sound sentimental." Takekoshi looked at him.

"I don't know why I feel that way."

"Well, Marquis, before we get into a heated political discussion, I want to finish my second mission tonight."

"What, Takekoshi-san?"

"You know Kunigita, the novelist? He is looking for shelter. He is the proverbial impoverished writer."

Saionji nodded sympathetically and said: "Takekoshi-san, do as you see fit. If he wants to have a quiet room, there is one next to the place I keep for my house-detective. He can stay here as long as he wants to and he can dine with my family."

"He is somewhat temperamental. He drinks a lot—"

"Huh, all literary men are emotional and fond of drinking," Saionji said.

"But he goes to extremes."

"Huh, how soon does he want to come?"

"Any minute. In fact, I shouldn't wonder if he might even appear tonight. I tried to dissuade him but—" He shrugged his shoulders.

Sakai was still talking: "Marquis, tell us some of the inside dealings in connection with the formation of the Katsura Cabinet. How long will the Sat-cho clique dominate our politics? Their strength is a direct reflection on the Nipponese political parties that are just as corrupt as the clannish bureaucrats."

"Maybe the lesser of two evils, eh?" Motono remarked.

Sakai kept on: "I hate to see the Sat-cho monopolize the Premiership but I dislike the corrupt party-politicians, too. The public began to express its resentment against them by direct action. Look at the tragic end of Hoshi, the ex-Communication Minister. He was a clever politician. His rapid advancement startled the people."

"He was a barrister trained in England, and learned the political technique of Tammany Hall, of the Honorable Croker of New York City, when he was our Minister to the United States from 1896 to 1898," Takekoshi said quietly.

"I don't know how he got his methods, but he deserved the punishment. I admit the assassin Iba Sotaro must have been a crank, but the public was with the murderer. He was stabbed to death right in the Tokyo municipal council's office—"

"Okiku, how about a bottle of wine?"

"That's fine, we always welcome that." Sakai approved.

"Well, Prince, I just ordered *osoba* for the guests," Okiku announced.

"Huh." Saionji assented pleasantly and remarked: "Okiku is becoming old-fashioned little by little."

The ever lively Sakai brightened. "Marquis, old-fashioned or new-fashioned, I'd like to have both wine and buckwheat noodles."

"Say, do you think our traditional social manner too reserved?" Motono inquired slyly.

"I certainly do. We Nipponese tend to be too formal and restrained, thereby displeasing our hosts—"

"I know, I know, Sakai." Motono waved his hand.

Takekoshi's mouth twitched. "Sakai, you drive dullness away, all right. What will we do when you go?"

Motono turned to the smiling host. "Marquis, have you noticed the public excitement over Russo-Nipponese relations?"

"Huh, a little, but since I've been away from Tokyo, I am personally not familiar with the agitation, Motono-san."

The pouring of the wine interrupted the conversations, then Motono resumed: "I witnessed the opening meeting of the *Kokuryukai*, the Black Dragon Society, some time ago. The public is still vague about that group's power to mold general opinion, but the nationalist faction, if unchecked, will push the sentiment against Russia to the breaking point in no time. And now some professors and journalists are taking their side."

"Huh." Saionji was attentive.

"Although the present advance of Russia into Manchuria followed the Sino-Nipponese War when she intervened in the peace settlement, I imagine nobody at that time foresaw that this last Boxer Rebellion in Peking would give the Czar such an opportunity," Takekoshi said calmly.

"That's right, Takekoshi. That Chinese trouble in 1900 seemed to have given a sudden twist to Oriental affairs, particularly between us and Russia. Considering the past record of Russia in the Far East, the basic argument of the Black Dragon Society has some sense. Russia at present is eager to take every opportunity to dispatch more soldiers into Manchuria. Their number is already far too large for the mere protection of her possessions there."

"Do you think though that the Black Dragon Society will stir up trouble?" Sakai broke in.

"Yes, I believe it will. The nucleus is composed of nationalists from Fukuoka Prefecture, the members of a society called 'Genyo-sha,' now led by Mitsuru Toyama. You see, being from their neighboring prefecture, I know their temper and determination to fight, and their singular concern over the country's attitude towards the continent—"

"Why are they so sensitive about China, Manchuria and Korea?" Sakai wanted to know.

"Well, I think they are primarily anxious to protect themselves against any possible invasions from the continent which is a short distance away from them across the Tsushima Straits."

"So they are afraid, eh?"

Motono grinned at Sakai. "Don't you think that's natural, Sakai? The history of the terrible Mongolian invasions in the thirteenth century was written in their ancestors' blood, while your forefathers merely heard the story."

"May I interrupt? The *osoba* is here," Okiku said.

"We can talk while we eat," was Sakai's comment.

"Huh, it is a Tokyo custom to distribute *soba* among the neighbors when you move into a new neighborhood," said the host as he received his bowl of buckwheat noodles from Okiku.

Putting his chopsticks down, Takekoshi added: "It had its origin as a tribute or admission to the new neighborhood, I believe, for the term *soba* corresponds in sound to that of 'neighbor' and 'beside.' "

Sakai was already asking for another bowl. "Motono, do you think this Toyama you mentioned has influence enough to sway our Government?"

"I am not so sure at this stage but it is quite possible one of these days you'll find that Toyama's 'unseen' hands manipulate the nation's Premier."

Saionji, laying down his chopsticks and bowl on the tray, commented in a soft voice: "Huh, as to Toyama—I heard an interesting story about him from Ito. When Ito was busy with the formation of the Seiyukai Party, he wanted Toyama to join it, too, and invited him to dinner to discuss the matter. As soon as he began to talk about it Toyama shut his mouth tightly, like an irritated clam, never to say yes or no all evening. He apparently enjoyed the dinner, however."

"He's a funny fellow!"

"Yes, Sakai," the host agreed. "After that, Ito had his intimate followers go after this man. Several of Ito's lieutenants, one after another, invited Toyama to dinner. He came and enjoyed the treat, but not one of them was able to get even 'yes' or 'no' out of him."

"Right or wrong, he must have tremendous will power. I, as an ardent Socialist, oppose any war or violence." Sakai was now inspired by many glasses of wine. "But since every legal means has so far failed because of the Sat-cho bureaucrats and corrupt politicians, I wish that the Toyama faction would kill off those leading exploiters."

"I don't see any good in that under organized government," Takekoshi disagreed.

"That's it," Sakai said, tucking up his kimono sleeves at the shoulders. "For whom is the Government organized under the Imperial Constitution, anyway? Did the Sat-cho bureaucrats get the sole charter to monopolize the Premiership under that document? Can you tell me?"

He turned to Saionji.

"Marquis, my beloved chief, when you become Premier, I have one piece of advice to offer and it's a mighty good one, too. That is, to throw your influence towards the readjustment of economic and social problems."

"Ah, your Socialism, eh?" Takekoshi grinned.

The Socialist's voice was now booming: "I am proud of your liberal outlook. Your intimate friend and my teacher, Nakae, who died too soon, was also an ardent believer in the French School of Socialism." His voice dropped. "He passed away poor and disappointed. I was grief-stricken when I heard the news."

He looked straight into the host's eyes, which also expressed Saionji's sorrow for the passing of the bespectacled scholar with whom he had become acquainted during his Parisian days.

Takekoshi said: "Oh, Motono, you spoke of Russia's warlike preparation in the Far East awhile ago—"

"Yes, and the Czar is throwing his full energy behind the project of double-tracking the trans-Siberian railroad from European Russia to Manchuria."

"Will Nippon ally herself with any power against Russia, do you think? You are a diplomat, you must know something about the matter."

"Well, isn't that problem hotly discussed among the Genros, Marquis Saionji?" Motono shifted the question to him.

"Huh, I can't say because I'm not one of them."

Something dropped at the door. A harsh voice came:

"Is Marquis Saionji home? I am here to stay. All my property, a few manuscripts and a kimono, is in this wrapper."

Then the intruder shrieked: "You shut up! You, *kurumaya*, you won't get anything. How can I pay you? I haven't a cent. If you don't go, you'll get my fists, instead."

The Saionjis and their visitors looked at each other in silence. There came other incoherent babblings:

"I'm not drunk, am I? I am Kunigita, a poor author, looking for a shelter from 'eave to eave,' ha, ha, ha! Marquis, will you pay the jinrikishaman his fare?"

All smiled broadly.

It was at Genro Ito's Oiso villa. The host and Saionji were in an extended conference.

The Genro sat on his favorite tiger-skin rug, smoking a cigar.

"It's no use, Saionji-san, it's not advisable for me nor for the Seiyukai Party to prolong my leadership. I was anxious to rebuild my political prestige before I left the active field of politics, but it is of no avail now. I'll be satisfied with being a Genro.

"For the second time I am caught by the Katsura-Yamagata trap. They requested an Imperial rescript of His Majesty to relegate me to your present post, the Presidency of the Privy Council, so that Katsura could continue his Premiership. If I go into the Privy Chamber as its head, as such I will be automatically disqualified from leading any political activities or party."

"But, Genro Ito, you cannot leave the Seiyukai Party leaderless."

"That's why I am recommending you to take the presidency of the Party. You and I exchange positions."

"I'll vacate my chair at any time if His Majesty wishes me to, but I don't want to assume the Seiyukai leadership. You and I cannot decide arbitrarily like that. It's the most important concern of the organized party. Besides, since I have been the President of the Privy Council during these years, I don't even know the members."

"But if the members of the executive committee accept you, which I have no doubt they will, will you take it?"

"Huh—"

"Furthermore, Saionji-san, I may be called to do a bit of work, a real job. For that reason, too, I have determined to follow the Imperial command. I see that we are heading for an international conflict shortly. With Russia."

"That has been talked about much, but that mustn't paralyze everything, though I sympathize with your present predicament."

Genro Ito recalled his relationship with Field Marshal Yamagata and Premier Katsura. "Yamagata caused the downfall of my last Cabinet, and Katsura succeeded me. I let that pass. Then they discredited me completely by their careful propaganda during my last Western trip. It was this way:

"I left the country in September 1901. Receiving the Degree of Doctor of Laws from Yale University in America on my way to Europe, I went to France. On my departure, Premier Katsura had asked me to call on the Russian leaders to create friendly feelings between Nippon and Russia.

"I was primarily in favor of settling the Korean question, that is, the supremacy over that country, by an agreement with Russia. With that in mind and also at Katsura's request, I proceeded from Paris to Moscow. After I had begun negotiating with the Czar's Foreign Minister Lamsdorf on the matter, Katsura cabled me to go to London where our Minister Hayashi was about to complete the Nipponese-British alliance. I was to help Hayashi to carry it through. I went to London right away and the Anglo-Nipponese alliance was concluded."

He puffed at his cigar again and continued. "I need not emphasize that I was interested in that British angle, too. You know it very well. Then what happened?"

Ito raised his knees and circled them with his arms.

"Before I returned home the people were led to believe that I had opposed the alliance, so the credit for our epoch-making success in tying ourselves with the most powerful nation under the sun was all given to Katsura.

"After I came back from the European trip I directed the Seiyukai to oppose the measures introduced by Katsura's Ministers. The Premier dissolved the Diet, and the Lower House was refilled with our majority. So Premier Katsura alleged that his failure in the Diet was caused by my presence in politics. But it was merely that the Party's policies disagreed with the Cabinet's. Since the Seiyukai had the majority, the Administration's failure was a natural outcome. It was not my fault.

"But he begged me, through Yamagata and Matsukata, to give up either the party leadership or the title of Genro. I replied that the title of Genro with its privileges was bestowed upon me by His Majesty on the merits of my achievements since the Restoration days and it was not possible for me to discard it. Of course, there was a time when I would have sacrificed everything. That was when I was forming the Seiyukai. The political activity on the other hand is still my chosen activity in order to promote the betterment of our Government. And I haven't the slightest idea of dispensing with it, either."

"Huh, Premier Katsura was in a difficult position then."

"Yes, Saionji-san, I got the best of him. But he is cunning. In his

protest to my stand he performed a stunt. Katsura said that he was
going to resign because of the Seiyukai opposition under my command. No sooner had he made that gesture when Yamagata and
Matsukata finished this melodrama for him by saying that in time of
pending national crisis a change of Ministry would be most undesirable
and that Katsura must be persuaded to stay to carry on his policies.
Premier Katsura didn't intend to resign at all."

"Genro, that was the reason for his gesture, huh?"

"Yes, so in the last scene Yamagata and Matsukata in the capacity
of Genro requested a formal audience with His Majesty and at it they
recommended that I should be given the Privy Council Presidency and
withdraw from politics. The Emperor granted their request and sum-
moned me to the palace and commanded me to take your duty."

"Huh, Genro Ito, you seem to have no choice, but as to my Seiyukai
leadership, I'll leave the matter to the party executives."

After he had lighted another cigar, Ito asked Saionji: "Don't you
think I have done enough?"

He bent his fingers one by one, beginning with the thumb. "I was
Premier, one, two, three, four times, and if I serve the Privy Council
as President now—that makes three times there. And—"

"Yes, you have served more important offices than any other statesman," said Saionji.

"And the Imperial Constitution and the Sino-Nipponese wartime
leadership—"

"Huh, many other posts, too."

Genro Ito saw that his guest was bored, but he was angling for
words of praise which were hard to get from Saionji.

The Genro came out openly:

"Why is it, Saionji-san, the people don't seem to appreciate my
unselfish efforts?"

"Huh, they certainly do, but your accomplishments are so numerous
and every move you have made was vital. The public is too busy to
identify you with any of your monumental works separately."

"Do you think so?"

"Yes, I do." Saionji spoke emphatically, at last realizing his host's
purpose in recounting his tasks.

Ito was much pleased.

"Saionji-san, how about a little merrymaking with the geishas?"

"Huh, I am sorry, but I don't care much for a big noisy party."

"We can make it a quiet affair, two and two, you know. Well,
well, 'only great men are fond of the fair sex,' don't they say so?"

"Huh, I'm not that great, not like you."

"That's perfectly true. But if you don't want to go to the tea-house, how about some drinks here? I brought home from Europe whiskey, brandy, and wine enough to last for a long time. I take strong stuff and we could try every kind I have with sliced fresh raw fish, eh?"

Both Ito and Saionji were affected by the drinks.

"French wine is excellent, isn't it, Saionji-san? It is also potent."

"Huh, it's getting hot."

"Let's strip our kimonos to the waist, it's too sticky."

Genro Ito was now ready for another long recitation on foreign relations, this time directly about the Korean-Manchurian front.

The breeze from the ocean blew on Ito's goat beard, thread by thread.

"I already told you that we have been wrestling with Russia to dominate Korea and also South Manchuria, didn't I?"

"Huh, the Czar started trouble at the end of the Sino-Nipponese War in 1895 by interfering with our territorial settlements with China—" interrupted Saionji.

"Say, who is explaining this serious life and death problem of the Empire, you or I?"

Saionji just grinned. He had forgotten the boastful nature of the Genro.

Ito's face, neck, arms and chest were red. He reached for a towel, wiped his face briskly and resumed his talk:

"Do you remember that incident—my successful peace negotiations with the Chinese delegation headed by Li Hung-Chang almost ten years back? That's how I brought Nippon to top ranking in the Orient. I knew peace had to be established in Korea, which, if it fell into the enemy hands, would be like a dagger-point against the heart of Nippon. We would not know when the blade would strike through our vital part. That was my conclusion, do you see?"

"Genro Ito, your great predecessors, Councillor Kido and General Omura, were contemplating the Korean colonization in 1869—"

"Ha—you interrupt again. They dreamed of it, but I planned and carried out our Korean campaign. Because of me, China withdrew her hands from the Peninsula, though she used to claim Korea was her own outlying territory. Now Russia comes and tries to steal our game before our very eyes.

"But," Genro Ito extended his hand to an uncorked whiskey bottle and as he poured some into Saionji's glass and his own he said—"any-

way this time our competitor is too powerful to treat single-handed so
we need some strong nation to help us. We didn't expect to get Great
Britain on our side as easily as we did."

He raised his whiskey glass to his mouth and motioned to the hesitating friend to do likewise. After a long swallow Ito wiped his lips
with his hand.

"Even with British backing—you must remember that England would
not actually fight for us under the present terms of the Alliance—
every one of the forty-seven million Nipponese must tighten up his
loin-cloth to defend his country against Russia."

"Huh."

"The comparison of strength between Nippon and Russia makes me
dizzy. Think of Russia's modern weapons, vast territory, enormous
man-power, against our limited resources.

"Look here, Saionji-san, I got these figures the other day: Our
navy will reach the two hundred and sixty thousand ton mark against
Russia's five hundred and ten thousand tons; while we can mobilize
one million men, she has two million available. When I consider these
facts I believe the coming war will be the hardest one to win. The
members of the War Council are of the same opinion."

Saionji looked out frequently.

"Since the prospective battlefield will be Manchuria, far away from
the center of Russia, two thousand miles, she'll have a hard time
sending reinforcements should our army crush the Russian contingents
in Manchuria."

While Ito took another swallow, his patient listener commented:

"Huh, our men have to cross the Tsushima Straits, too."

"Don't inject such a melancholy thought into my already numerous
worries. That's why we still burn the wires between Tokyo and Moscow to settle, even put off, the difficulty by negotiations. We put two
main propositions to Russia: one is the peaceful settlement of the
Korean question and the other the execution of the promised withdrawal of the Russian troops from Liaotung Peninsula and South
Manchuria. While Russia is prolonging the peace talk, she pours
more troops into the Far East."

"Huh."

"Now, Saionji-san, you can see the background of it. But the next
point will surprise you— Why do you wave your hand?"

The Genro caught his guest looking out over the beach below
his villa.

"Huh, what is the next point?" said Saionji without looking at his host.

"Come, pay a little more attention to this, this is very important. You remember the visit a few weeks ago of the Russian War Minister, Kuropatokin, we called him 'Black Pigeon,' accompanied by his staffs from Port Arthur. He was really a spy! He came over to see whether we were getting ready to oppose his country in the Orient by force. He saw we were excited about Russia's actions in Manchuria."

"He was right, Genro Ito."

"But I know something more important than General Kuropatokin's spying."

Ito pointed his finger at Saionji and said: "The Black Pigeon, like Russia's Minister at Tokyo, Baron Rosen, is not willing to fight Nippon. But— Say, Saionji, you aren't listening to me—"

The narrator's eyes were now blinking and his head was wagging as he spoke; Saionji became bold.

"Genro Ito—"

"What? What are you beaming at, anyway?"

"Huh, we had Hachiro come over, you know, my adopted son. His university classes are in recess—"

"What of it? He is a nice young man though. You didn't make any mistake by taking our advice, did you?"

"In that case, no. See, Hachiro and Shinko are down there on the beach, walking together. They look up this way often. See, there? They are waving to me again."

Smiling broadly, Saionji left his seat and went to the edge of the veranda.

"I'm proud of my daughter and Hachiro—"

"H'm, you proud father. But your daughter is really lovely. She'll finish her college soon, eh?"

"Yes, next year," said Saionji cheerfully.

"Then comes the big occasion for the Saionji family—the wedding of Shinko and Hachiro, eh?"

"Huh, I'm looking forward to it."

"Say, Saionji-san, don't forget, Inouye and I were the *nakaudo*. Let me see the charming young couple—" Ito attempted to rise but his foot was cramped. He sat back on the tiger skin.

"Come, come back here, Saionji-san, you haven't heard my full story. Leave them alone. You are mistaken if you think that the young people like to be watched."

"Huh, you may be right, Genro Ito."

"How far had I got? What was I talking about? What was the subject anyway, Saionji-san?"

"Huh, the Black Pigeon and Baron Rosen didn't want to fight us—"

"H'm, you have a remarkable memory, haven't you? That's right. Now, when General Kuropatokin returned to Port Arthur, under Bezobrazoff's influence, the decision had been made to wage war against us. This man was the leading Russian Court dignitary and violently anti-Nipponese. He was in Manchuria during the General's absence."

"Huh, Genro, what is your personal stand? Are you for or against war?"

"Ah! I'm coming to that."

Ito shifted his feet on the pelt and said: "At Bezobrazoff's instigation, Russia is about to set up a Governor-General's office at Port Arthur under the command of Admiral Alexieff to direct Russian civil and military activities in the Far East. At the same time she is rushing to complete the double-tracking of the trans-Siberian railroads. These will perfect the Czar's preparations for a war against us.

"Do you get the idea? The country has ample power at her command, and her vanguards with fixed bayonets are charging towards us. We have our backs to the wall. What would you do, Saionji-san? You were once a Commander-General."

"Although I am against ruthless aggression, we should put a stop to the constant disturbance and irritation caused by Russia in the Far East. She has no business threatening our safety," Saionji said fervently.

"Hurrah! The future Premier and possible Genro of Nippon speaks. I agree with you. Many patriotic organizations are urging us to strike at the enemy right away."

Genro Ito's perspiring torso looked like a large, boiled red beet. Saionji, too, was drenched with sweat.

With a shout of *banzai*, they drank a toast to the continued glory of the Empire.

There was a large number of Representatives affiliated with the Party in the general meeting-room at the Seiyukai headquarters in Tokyo. They were waiting to hear an important announcement.

One with a southwestern accent said in despair:

"Well, the Seiyukai Party will be completely smashed. We depended on President Ito, but he couldn't do much last time he became Premier and now he is weak-kneed. He is going to desert us. I knew that would happen when he got stuck. These smart, thick-skinned Sat-cho politicians hide their faces when they get wrecked, like fleas putting their heads between the mat seams."

A farmer said: "I should have changed my affiliation when Premier Katsura's man approached me with an offer of a good sum for my vote in the House. Had I known that our party would go like this so soon, I would surely have taken that course. Ah, that was my mistake."

Another Diet member mourned his failure to desert in time. "What's the use of talking about party government? See what President Ito did."

"But that was our poor judgment. We knew his record very well, yet we took it seriously when he boosted the new group," the first speaker reminded the third.

The latter agreed, and continued: "That's true. He was the staunchest opponent of the party movement and then at the convenient moment he turned around and beckoned to us like a street-walker—"

"Ha, ha, ha, who knowingly followed that questionable character?" The group laughed heartily.

"But seriously, don't you think the Sat-cho politicians are selfish, and do everything to their own liking?" asked the farmer.

"Say, where are you from? Did you find that out only now? No wonder you never make money in this game of politics." A so-far silent comrade spoke with his mouth twisted.

"Well, I don't care what you say, I believed in him when he came out for the new organization. Genro Ito's henchmen told me that he, as the President of the Seiyukai, could do anything in the world by controlling the Cabinet all the time. I was made to believe that he was going to reduce taxes and force the railroad companies to lay a lot of tracks and build stations. If they wouldn't, the Government was to buy them up and build a railway station in every town in the country."

Biting his finger nail, he went on: "Instead, the tax rate went up and new taxes were imposed by the dozen every year, like mushrooms on manure piles after a long warm rain in the spring. Every time I go home the only thing I can report to my supporters is more taxes. That's all."

"Your day-dream was a fancy one. At any rate, friends, who do you think will be our next president?" Another husky-looking Representative spoke.

The first one answered: "I don't care who he may be but I hope one who will stick with us in victory or defeat. I'd like to see him picked from among ourselves, not from among the Sat-cho or other office-holders. A real fighter is my choice for Party President. But that's a vain hope, something like trying to reach the moon by jumping from the roof of my barn. What makes me mad is the fact that those few topnotch men do everything secretly and don't even let us know what's going on."

"I bet a hundred to one we get a Sat-cho man to lead us again. My own choice is that fellow, Hara, a committee member. I like Matsuda, too, but he lacks Hara's fighting spirit. Hara may break the Party, or he may really boost the Seiyukai to power. I want to see some action, anyway." Looking around, the first Representative continued:

"Too bad that crank assassinated our former leader Hoshi Toru, he was criticised by the opposition but he was an ideal leader. When he promised anything, regardless of means or methods he was certain to get it for us. And his private life was clean—that attracted me also. He was a Christian. Unlike the big politicians today, Hoshi didn't drink, he didn't chase after geishas. Really too bad he was charged with the scandals in which his friends took part."

Everyone nodded in agreement.

An elderly man came and said in a friendly manner: "Say, boys, do you know who's our next president? You would have never thought of him."

Wild guessing began. Some mentioned Ito's adopted daughter's husband and one of the Seiyukai organizers, Viscount Suyematsu Kencho, others suggested more than a dozen men.

The elderly man smiled. "Sorry, boys, you are all wrong. Have you ever heard of Marquis Saionji? But most of you are new in the Diet."

"Ah, that's an *okuge-sama*, maybe the head priest of one of the national shrines at Kyoto," one of them said.

"How can he be our Party president?" another grumbled.

"Didn't you ever hear the name of the President of the Privy Council before?" the elderly man asked.

"All we hear is the names of the Genros; no matter what happens, they run the country. Why should we care about the other men?" the farmer Representative remarked with indignation.

"Marquis Saionji was the Head of the Privy Council until a few days ago. He will succeed Ito," the informer said with an air of authority, and added: "That's what I was told by one of the members of the executive committee which accepted the Marquis' nomination."

The southwestern Representative asked: "Do you know him?"

All snickered as they observed the embarrassed expression on his face. "Well—well, at least I've heard of him. He was one of the Seiyukai organizers, too, but he didn't have time to associate with us."

The listeners laughed good-naturedly.

Bells called the meeting.

The Seiyukai members and their supporters lazily filed into the auditorium. The only well-occupied place in the hall was on the small platform.

The chairman began the proceedings but the audience paid little attention. They were still talking and laughing. Ito began delivering his farewell address.

The southwestern Representative remarked: "Ah, I have no particular liking for President Ito, but I feel sorry for him. To think he had to depart completely defeated from the Party he built."

He stopped when the retiring leader concluded with: "Gentlemen, my successor and your new leader, the former President of the Privy Council, Marquis Saionji Kimmochi!"

A commentator in the group went on: "He looks like an old rain-soaked wild pigeon, uncouth and weather-beaten, ready to fold up in a nest. Give Ito hands for the last time."

Then the farmer Representative suddenly shouted in a high-pitched voice: "Yaw! The Star Actor!" as Saionji walked to the speaker's rostrum.

The shouting threw the house into a roar of laughter with hundreds of other loud and unfriendly remarks about the New President. The chairman frantically banged the table without effect. Soon the noise subsided, but the audience didn't know what the speaker was talking about. All anyone could hear was his neighbor's comments on the style of the new leader's clothes.

President Saionji's perfectly tailored, snow-white linen frock-coat with trousers to match startled the assembly and was the subject of their wild comments. This attire, his smooth, refined face, and his poise bespoke the actor rather than the politician.

The elderly Representative, who was listening intently, poked his neighbors and whispered:

"Silence, boys! There is something new in this man. Look, he is speaking without notes. If you boys will listen to him, his diction is excellent. H'm, his enunciation and ready wit—simply marvelous." He shook his head in confirmation. He went on whispering: "Ah, now he's talking about contemporary affairs. Sh! sh!"

His neighbors, too, gradually became interested in Saionji's address.

"His piercing insight into current topics is amazing," the whispering man said as Saionji ended his acceptance speech.

The house was once more turned into a great uproar, this time the audience yelled and shrieked in acclamation of the new Party president.

The country Representative, with a joyous sigh, said: "Well, in the place of an old pigeon there descended upon us a young, brilliant and noble white crane: the sign of eternity, sincerity and prosperity, has come to us. Let us have hope!"

The Seiyukai Party soon held its Southwestern Conference at Kyoto. There President Saionji announced his principles for the organization. Publicly he emphasized among other things, the elimination of any class separating the Imperial House from the people, the operation of the Imperial Constitution in the Government to represent the popular will, the waging of war to bring the country into premier rank in the society of nations, and the cultivation of a cosmopolitan attitude.

A chilly wind accompanied by sleet blasted through Tokyo.

There were several jinrikishamen in a stand.

"Hey, brother," an elderly puller with a copy of the newspaper extra in his hand called to his young comrade, "did you see this, just came out?"

"Oh, another naval victory!" exclaimed the young one. He was a university student earning his way through by working thus at night and on holidays. His remark attracted the others, who also had newspapers in their hands and who sat on benches around a large charcoal brazier on the clay pavement.

"Student," the comrades called to him, "summarize it for us. You know so much about the background of the war and you've got the best mind, anyway. We'll read details later."

The elderly one handed the copy to the student.

"This time the Imperial Navy fought two Russian warships off Chemulpo Harbor, Korea. While on our side no casualties were sustained, the enemy ships were incapacitated after a fierce battle, and exploded. A Russian transport was also destroyed. It's a very important victory, for one of the disembarkation points for the Imperial Army is near by."

"It's great, the day before yesterday, February 8, our men-of-war inflicted heavy damage on the Czar's Oriental Squadron off Port Arthur, completely disabling a few battleships and shattering others," beamed the elderly man.

"It's the first time that we Orientals were ever successful in naval combat against the white people," the student murmured as he glanced over the pages.

"Oh, here are many heroic stories told about the Port Arthur engagement!"

Without waiting for any comments he went on: "Listen to this, 'Midshipman Kajimura on the battleship *Hatsuse* was almost blown into two, his flesh and bones scattered in a pool of blood. Despite the fatal wound he calmly requested the bystanders to pick up his own human debris and clean the deck'—Kajimura? Kajimura?" He whispered to himself, bending his head to one side.

"What a brave fellow he was! Did you know Midshipman Kajimura?" a husky *kurumaya* covered with colored tattoo on his back, legs, and arms, inquired.

"H'm-m, Kajimura?" The student was still twisting his head.

"Are there other stories like that?" the elderly one inquired.

"Well—yes, here is another one: 'In the same battle, a sailor, whose right arm was struck away by an enemy shot like a snapped-off leaf in the frosty wind, grasped it with his left hand and took it to the doctor.'—Kajimura?"

"Our men are certainly brave, are they not? What's the matter with you, student? Are you crying?" The tattooed comrade looked into the student's face behind the newspaper.

"No, I'm not!"

"But tears are dropping on the charcoal fire—"

The student bit his lower lip hard. "I, I knew Midshipman Kajimura, I knew him! He's killed. He was my best friend; we've been like brothers ever since we were boys."

"Oh!" All looked at him sympathetically. The student, letting the tears pour from his eyes, went on:

"I know his folks, too; they are my neighbors at home. When we finished high school together—his family and mine were not well-to-do —we wanted to continue our studies—we had to choose some inexpensive way to do that.

"Kajimura chose the Naval Academy because that required no tuition or other expenses—it's a government school. I came to Tokyo practically penniless. On our parting day we promised each other we'd try hard to be somebody—I finished college and just entered the university. You know what I've been doing all these years."

"Yes, yes, we do very well. Rain or shine you came to this stand regularly after classes and worked until midnight, then you studied. We often said about you that like some big men in the government offices, who went through this rikisha-pulling during their college and university days, you'd be a big man some day. We're sorry for you— you lost your best friend," said the operator of the stand, sitting on a small matted counter several feet away.

The student wiped his eyes with a towel. "I am sorry for Kajimura's mother, who loved her son so much and was kind to me, too—though I know it's for the country's sake."

He handed the paper back to the elderly comrade and murmured: "If the War Office wants me, I'll enlist immediately to fight the Russians who killed my best friend."

"I'll go with you!" said the tattooed man. There was a moment's silence. Then he spoke again: "Say, student, why is it we began fighting before war was declared?"

"Oh," the student regained his composure and began, "that's very hard to say in a few words, but it doesn't matter whether war is declared or not since our Government had sent an ultimatum. Our ultimatum read something like this: 'If you don't accept all the terms in this note within a certain period of time'—usually twenty-four or forty-eight hours—'without reservation, we'll have nothing to do with you.' That meant war, of course. The Moscow Government didn't say yes or no within the time limit—"

"I see, so Russia had her mind made up to fight—"

The elderly one commented: "Oh, student, is that ultimatum something like the signal for our *sumo*, is that it? When the umpire withdraws the fan that keeps the competing wrestlers apart, the challengers must fight to the finish. If either one wants to start the game all over again he has to step back before the umpire snaps his fan."

"Yes, that's it. Now, our ultimatum was delivered on February 6. On the eighth, when Admiral Togo attacked the enemy squadron off Port Arthur, the time limit had already expired. When the Imperial Navy and the Russian fleet met there, either could legally fire at the enemy ships. The declaration of war that was proclaimed was a mere formality—"

"H'm." The tattooed one, coming closer to the student, nodded.

The student went on. "A mere formality, telling the enemy country, 'We are fighting you.' Some say that the declaration must be made before the actual fighting begins and the others say that it doesn't matter whether its proclaimed before or after if the ultimatum has been delivered. Our Government declared war against Russia today, February 10."

"Did the enemy do the same thing?"

"Yes, Russia declared war against us today, too."

"What's that noise?" someone asked.

"Oh, a great victory lantern parade is going on in the Ginza and Kyobashi districts. When I passed there the vanguards were already turning into the square before the Imperial Palace," said a man, just returning from his rounds.

The proprietor murmured: "Unlike the last war when we first crossed swords with the continental pig-tailed brothers, this time the public has been clamoring since last summer to fight Czarist Russia."

The student went on: "Yes, there was no mistaking that bloodshed would break out any day. The coming and going of the Genros between Tokyo and Oiso, their frequent conferences at the Imperial Palace in His Majesty's presence since the early summer, the school children and students singing war songs written during the Sino-Nipponese War, the depression-wearied business world yearning to see a radical change, the newspapers and magazines carrying inflammatory articles from front to back for a war in defense of the nation's rights and safety, the patriotic organizations daily marshalling the citizenry into war demonstrations, could have only one outcome."

His comrades nodded. The tattooed man said: "Only the soldiers and the telephone posts on the roadside were noncommittal."

"In the summer of the Chinese War in 1894, ten years ago, we did not know a thing about it until the fight began. Wasn't that so?" one of the men asked.

"Yes, but this time it was different. The public tension increased as we heard about the mounting difficulties of the negotiations with Russia on the Manchurian question. On February 4, we learned that the conference of the Genros recommended to the Emperor a war measure against Russia. Two days later the Government recalled our Minister;

then things went fast. The last three days many young men who had been on the reserve units were called to the barracks."

"Look, another battalion of the Imperial Guards is moving to their embarkation point on this cold night. Let's give them a big cheer!"

A small brick building was the office and residence of the President of the Privy Council, Genro Ito, who had formed a super-cabinet at the beginning of the war. He was now the constant consultant and adviser of the Emperor and the center of all the official activities.

Saionji, the President of the Seiyukai Party, in his cream-colored linen suit was sitting opposite Ito.

"Huh, Genro Ito, everything is moving smoothly. The Imperial Navy and the Army have made a wonderful showing so far. At Port Arthur, Admiral Togo has smashed the Russian fleet on the sea, and General Nogi has advanced on land. The First and the Second Armies are pushing northward after their victory at Liaoyang. Vladivostok has been bombarded. Admiral Togo attempted to blockade the harbor entrance of Port Arthur by sinking merchantmen, as Admiral Dewey of the United States Navy did at Manila during his Philippine campaign." Saionji was in a happy mood.

"Well, Saionji-san," Ito said as he looked over a stack of mail, "the past progress was more than expected, but the future does not seem bright. We have conferences every day. The Genros, military leaders and Cabinet members are coming here today, too.

"See, we are short of man power, we have insufficient war supplies and the inevitable exhaustion of our financial resources troubles us very much. With the exception of Great Britain the Western Powers are cold to us—"

"Huh, is the United States, too?"

"That's one of the chief concerns at present, Saionji-san. We sent Baron Kaneko as our special envoy to America. See, he's a Harvard graduate and has many friends. However, so far his reports indicate that he has tried in vain to win the American public to our side. He informed me that the Russian agents have already intimated to the Americans that the conflict is a challenge of the heathen to the Christian. They say that the war is a challenge of the inferior yellow race to the superior white race, and that our opening fire was in violation of international laws dealing with armed conflicts, and so forth.

"Oh, here's Kaneko's letter!" Ito read it while Saionji commented:

"The Nipponese are unanimously for war." Saionji looked at Ito and continued: "But I'm afraid the Government is over-emphasizing the importance of our victories."

"Oh, that's excellent, excellent!" Ito burst out over the closely written pages.

"Ha, ha, ha!" The voice mingled laughter and tears. The Genro wiped his eyes with the forearm as he said: "This is unexpected good news. We must win, we must win this war, Saionji-san."

"What is it, Genro Ito?"

"It's the greatest news so far—" Ito finally managed to say: "Our special envoy to America succeeded in convincing President Theodore Roosevelt. Kaneko won him to our side! At the White House he got President Roosevelt's promise to help us in every way within his power—"

They stared at each other for a moment.

Genro Ito broke the silence: "Ha, I must inform His Majesty of this right away. But I must bring other reports, too. Well, I'd better wait for the other Genros before I proceed to the palace.—I want to talk with you. See, I want you to attend our conferences occasionally because matters are getting very serious."

Someone rushed up into the room. "Ito, is Ito here?"

It was the Chief of the General Staff Field Marshal Yamagata's voice that rang through the building. The upper sleeves and back of his khaki uniform were soaked through with perspiration.

"What has happened, Yamagata?"

"What are we going to do about this?" The Field Marshal waved several papers in his left hand. His eyes were bloodshot. "We must do something about this. Are we going to let slip our biggest chance of winning the war?" He struck the papers with his right fist and added: "Where is Oyama?"

"Tell me, what's the matter?"

"Our supply of munitions is exhausted in the Liaoyang sector. Our soldiers are at a standstill, although the retreating Russians are within a range of from three hundred to two hundred meters. It's the time to pour lead over them and annihilate them now."

Ito listened with knitted eyebrows, his head sinking lower and lower. He murmured: "We can only do our best and leave the rest to Providence."

"I cannot bear to think that at this critical moment I have to instruct the generals to check their advance because of the lack of munitions. I can vividly see, myself, how that would affect their strategies and the morale of the men." Yamagata was almost in tears.

Genro Ito knelt on the floor. His head was bent, his eyes were closed and his hands were held together before his face. He was praying to the Goddess of Amaterasu to whom the National Shrine at Ise was dedicated and where since the beginning of the struggle Ito had paid special homage.

His whisperings made Saionji and the Field Marshal bow with him until it was over. Yamagata took a chair. He was dejected.

"Yamagata, I know how it is, but what can we do?"

Someone was at the entrance.

"Katsura, what's the news?" Premier General Katsura and the War Minister, General Terauchi, who also carried papers, walked in. They did not reply to Ito's inquiry but sat down on chairs.

The Premier eyed General Terauchi. The War Minister, unfolding the papers, said gravely:

"Field Marshal, now the Quartermaster General demands a new supply of shoes; the supply on hand is practically exhausted—"

"What? Two pairs per man was your estimate. What did they do?" Ito asked.

The Premier replied: "That was true, Genro Ito, but every time they crossed a freezing stream the soldiers had to change them."

Field Marshal Yamagata added: "Our factories can't produce fast enough."

The War Minister spoke again: "Field Marshal, here is another—"

Yamagata, taking the communiqué from him, said:

"Ito, General Nogi, in command of the Third Army besieging Port Arthur, asks for final instructions as to whether or not he should delay the second attack because of the lack of artillery pieces and shells."

Another stout senior general walked in.

"Oh, all here? It's terribly hot, isn't it? It would be most ideal if we could strip everything off and dip ourselves in the basin of a huge waterfall, like the Kegon Waterfall, would it not, friends?"

The corpulent general was Field Marshal Oyama, a Genro, the Commander-in-Chief of the Expeditionary Army. He went on, rubbing his thick eyebrows with his hand: "You young men are very energetic, Katsura, Terauchi, Marquis Saionji. I envy you. But how about Marshal Yamagata, Ito—and I, a particularly fat man? I'd like to dive into ice-cold water. You know even a little sprinkle makes our testicles all shrink," emphasizing with gestures.

He was deadly in earnest about it and not in the least bit concerned about what had been going on.

"Don't you think so, Marshal Yamagata?"

"Well," the Chief of General Staff tried to hold himself, but it was too much for him and the others, too. A great laughter went up. It was the first time in many months that the harmless sound was heard in this room.

"Well, Marshal, I wish we had time to—" The stern Yamagata stopped. The fat Oyama paid no attention and pulled out a few maps and papers from his pocket and looked them over. He studied through a pile brought in by the War Minister, too, while the others went back to their heated discussion.

Marshal Yamagata was impatient. "Marshal Oyama, here are the vital problems: our soldiers have no more ammunition, no more shoes. The factories, some of which are undermanned, are running twenty-four hours a day, but we can't produce enough—"

Oyama was unmoved. Barely raising his eyes to Yamagata's, he said bluntly: "Stop the advance until we furnish them, and bring some men back and put them into the factories."

"Even so, we can't produce fast enough—" The Chief of General Staff was irritated and stared at Oyama's immobile face.

The latter went on: "Buy them from other countries."

"Terauchi!" Yamagata shouted. "What did you do with that proposal made by Vickers of England and Krupp of Germany?"

"Sir, we declined their offers to manufacture ammunition for us because we estimated at the time—"

"Our estimates were wrong. Are the offers open? Are the representatives here?" Field Marshal Yamagata asked.

"So I understand, Marshal," answered Premier Katsura.

"Get in touch with them, quick. We must order immediately," said the Chief of General Staff.

Premier Katsura asked timidly: "How are we going to pay?"

"Um—m—m!" Ito and Yamagata groaned like fatally wounded animals.

A messenger rushed into the room.

"Telegram, sir!" Premier Katsura took it. "Read it!" the two Genros shouted.

"From Takahashi Korekiyo, our Financial Commissioner to England and America, New York City, U.S.A." The Premier went on:

" 'National City Bank and Kuhn Loeb agree to One Hundred Million Yen Loan.' "

In the afternoon of New Year's Day 1905, Genro Ito was entertaining his neighbor, Saionji, at his Oiso villa.

"On account of wartime economy we'll celebrate the New Year with simple feasts, Saionji-san. But I want to congratulate you on your splendid Seiyukai support of the Government in this national crisis. My estimate of you was correct."

The host offered a few pieces of roasted dried cuttlefish after the cup of sake.

"Have you heard any more about the Port Arthur attack, Genro Ito?"

"No, Saionji-san. I am expecting some news. The last report from General Nogi was that on November 30 our army captured the two hundred and third meter height and held it. From that position our soldiers can overlook the port and the remaining enemy forts. General Nogi made a good advance after that, I believe.

"Five months have passed since the siege began. We must take Port Arthur before the Russian Baltic Fleet gets near us. The Commander-in-Chief of the United Imperial Fleet, Admiral Togo Heihachiro wants to have time enough to refit our warships before meeting the big Russian armada. Field Marshal Yamagata sent big siege guns and navy guns to Commander Nogi to silence the Russians at Port Arthur. Yamagata told me the other day our casualties there would easily be over fifty-seven thousand men. I hope it won't be long before our men plant the Colors of the Rising Sun on all the fortifications."

"The Russians are very stubborn, are they not, Genro Ito?"

"Yes. General Nogi has advised the defending commander, General Stoessel, to surrender—"

"To minimize the further loss of life and destruction of property, I suppose," Saionji remarked as he chewed the cuttlefish.

"That seems to be the idea, but General Stoessel, like our *samurai*, refused to surrender. He'd rather die fighting."

"Huh."

Through the pine trees, Genro Ito saw someone hurrying to his villa. He said: "Oh, Yamagata is coming. What now?"

"Hey, Ito, at last Port Arthur is silenced and about to fall into our hands," shouted the approaching Field Marshal.

He took his shoes off and came up from the veranda. As he sat on the matted floor with the host and Saionji he went on:

"The Imperial Headquarters got the intelligence this afternoon. General Stoessel proposed to General Nogi that they negotiate the terms of surrender. Commander Nogi requested our instructions. Have you got anything to say? Our General wants the conference to be held at a small village north of Port Arthur, Shuishinying. Of course the General will decide the details."

"I see, Yamagata. What do you think, Saionji-san? Do you have any particular suggestions?"

"Huh, the defending General was really brave, wasn't he? He deserves our praise whether he is an enemy or not—"

"True," said the Field Marshal.

"Don't you think we'd better accord him our highest courtesies? If he gives himself up he is no longer our enemy."

"But what would be the proper gesture on our part, Saionji-san?" Ito asked.

"Huh, how would this be—that at the ceremonies of the surrender we have General Nogi allow General Stoessel to wear his sword, Genro Ito? The sword is the spirit of a *samurai*."

Field Marshal Yamagata broke in: "That's right, Marquis Saionji. The sword is the warrior's spirit with which General Stoessel has won our highest esteem. Usually in a similar situation the losing general and his aides are stripped of their swords and all other martial insignia. H'm, that's a wonderful idea. What do you say, Ito?"

"That's great, Yamagata. Shall I draw up the instructions to General Nogi?"

"Yes, right away."

"Meanwhile, have a cup; it's New Year's simple formality."

While Ito wrote, Saionji and Field Marshal Yamagata conversed.

"Is it not fine, Marshal, that we can celebrate the New Year in this relaxed mood?"

"Ah, Marquis Saionji, I am sorry to cast any clouds on your holiday spirits, but I myself cannot feel free until the last Russian is swept out of Manchuria, especially when I think of the soldiers in the fields at this time. There the weather is always sub-zero during the winter."

"You feel keenly for your subordinates, don't you, Marshal?"

"I think not only of those still active, but those who already have died for the nation's defense."

Field Marshal Yamagata time and again raised his sake cup but put it back on the tray without drinking it.

Genro Ito rested the brush. He took a *sakazuki* and raised together with Yamagata.

"Do you know, Ito, I was much afraid that General Nogi might do something desperate?" Yamagata also received a piece of cuttlefish.

"What do you mean?" Ito took up his cigar.

"Well, you see, he was deeply moved because so many of his officers and men, including his own sons, were killed there by the enemy guns, bayonets and wire entanglements charged with electricity, during a series of attacks. Besides that, we were pressing him for a speedy capture. I am informed that he once or twice almost rushed out into the line—"

"H'm."

"He couldn't stand the heavy loss. I don't blame him—"

"Yamagata, do you think he will commit *harakiri?*"

The Field Marshal looked into Ito's eyes. "If I were in his position I'd feel the same way—"

"H'm."

"Yes, I would," the Field Marshal repeated. "But the capture of Port Arthur is great news, anyway."

He sipped sake for the first time and chewed the cuttlefish.

"Well, Yamagata, after Port Arthur, what is your objective?"

"Ito, there is no question of our going into a decisive battle. But we must have things put in order. Give the soldiers afield a little time to recover. I want to send as many men as possible so that Commander-in-Chief Oyama can work out his campaigns with comparative ease. General Kuropatokin will mass three hundred thousand men around Mukden, so I want to make at least two hundred and fifty thousand available for Marshal Oyama. I am anxious to see that our orders from Vickers and Krupp are delivered before the forthcoming big battle."

"Yamagata, no doubt by that time our domestic production will be quite large, too, won't it?"

"But Ito, I don't want to repeat last summer's mistake at Liaoyang and Port Arthur when we missed the already bagged game."

"That will be one of the biggest battles, Field Marshal?" asked Saionji.

"Yes, Marquis Saionji. When I have an opportunity I want to have my generals press the enemy without stopping."

Ito asked: "How far do you expect them to pursue the Russians, Yamagata?"

"Well, considerably beyond Mukden. I think if we give them chase as far as the heights of Tiehling or Kaiyuan, that will be far enough. We can't follow them too far, either. Should the war continue after we take Mukden, we must reshape our army before we go on."

"If we don't succeed in this battle—" Ito began.

"Oh, Ito, if that happens you won't see me any more. In apology to His Majesty and the people I will commit *harakiri* like a *samurai*. If we lose that decisive combat, say in the beginning of March, then in a month or two the Russian Baltic Armada will steam up into Vladivostok. Oh, that makes me shiver, Ito."

"Well, Yamagata, I hope that whether you win at Mukden or not, Admiral Togo who has been dependable so far, will trim the Baltic Fleet somehow so that they won't disturb our shores and our communication with the mainland."

All of them scowled.

"Ito, how does Korea stand?"

"Korea is in perfect accord with us, Yamagata. See, soon after the opening of the war our Minister to Korea, Hayashi, concluded an alliance with the Souel Court. Then I went there as His Majesty's special envoy last March. At that time the Korean Government and the people, who had firmly believed in Russian supremacy, were already pro-Nippon because of our continued victories over the Czar's forces. Then I went back again in July to further our friendly relationship with her. In the meantime, on May 19, Korea declared war against the Czar, too. And ever since we are growing closer to each other."

Yamagata beamed. "You mean to say that she is gradually falling into our hands."

"This latest issue of the paper states that Admiral Togo's United Imperial Fleet, between 2 P.M. yesterday, May 27, and this evening, after ten fierce battles at Tsushima Straits and the Nippon Sea, captured and disabled eight Russian battleships, five cruisers, five destroyers, three coast defense ships, three special service ships and two hospital ships. Only three Russian warcrafts, a light cruiser and two destroyers, all crippled, reached Vladivostok, the Baltic Fleet's destination."

The excited student *kurumaya* was reading to his comrades.

"That's fine," said the elderly one. The student went on:

"It is estimated that over forty-eight hundred Russians are dead and among the captured six thousand Russians was the wounded Commander Admiral Rozhdestvensky. In contrast with that our loss was three torpedo boats and seven hundred men."

"Student, tell us some more," demanded the tattooed man.

"Here are details of the great battle: See, our warships were waiting around Tsushima Straits between the northern shores of the Kyushu Island and the tip of the Korean Peninsula which forms the southern entrance to the Nippon Sea. A little after one o'clock yesterday afternoon the Baltic Fleet was sighted by one of our scouting-ships. But our Commander Admiral Togo was undisturbed—"

"He was awaiting this day and this hour for many months—" one comrade commented and another added: "The Admiral is from Kagoshima. He is a tiny fellow, grim-faced and doesn't talk much, but has an iron nerve. His flagship was the *Mikasa*."

"That's right." The student resumed: "At 1:39 P.M. the 'guest from afar' was at seven nautical miles southwest of Admiral Togo's 'reception' line, advancing in a three-column formation under a veil of thick fog—"

"H'm."

"At 1:55 the Nipponese Commander raised the message on the *Mikasa's* mast: 'The rise and fall of the Mikado's Empire depends upon this battle; every man must do his utmost!' Admiral Togo was fully ready to tackle the enemy."

"Our men were unafraid, eh?" the rikisha stand operator said proudly.

"Like the Commander, every one of our sailors was composed: the closer the Russians came the more deadly were their shots. Think, in spite of this frightful situation one of our captains from the bridge of his ship played a clear melodious tune on a *shakuhachi* flute. That calmed the entire fleet—"

"H'm."

"Admiral Togo, to make sure of his target, still leading close to the enemy formation, finally at 2:10 P.M. at six thousand meters' distance answered the Russian shot with shot. His fire was concentrated on the enemy's battleships heading the columns."

"It's exciting!"

"The better training and higher morale of the Nipponese and their freshness because of a considerable rest before this battle, resulted in their superior marksmanship and skillful manoeuvring. The Russian battleship *Osliaba* at 3:07 took the easiest way out of the unfriendly reception by sinking to the bottom of the Nippon Sea, and five Russian warships soon followed her, leaving the rest helpless, damaged and scattered.

"Admiral Togo, who had started to write a history of the Empire's first step towards her entrance into the society of the nations of the world, like many of his provincial predecessors since the country's awakening into the era of modernism in the Meiji Restoration, 1868, was thoroughgoing—"

"No doubt."

"This morning, comrades, he began again where he had left off last evening and finished that job, characteristically."

"Student," the tattooed man demanded, "give us a brief account of the Mukden battle—there two of my young cousins died and another was wounded."

Several prospective fares were listening when the student answered:

"The Commander-in-Chief of the Imperial Army in Manchuria, Field Marshal Oyama, with his two hundred and fifty thousand men, formed into nineteen divisions and four armies, advanced from the southeast. The Russian Commander General Kuropatokin's three hundred and twenty thousand soldiers of thirty divisions were grouped into three armies and a rear guard, and they formed a semi-circular armed wall around Mukden against the Nipponese advance.

"Marshal Oyama left the Fourth Army in reserve and assigned the First Army to smash the enemy's left flank at the eastern end of the battle front, ordered the Second Army to press the center and put the Third Army, headed by General Nogi of Port Arthur fame, to punch Kuropatokin's right flank in the western sector. By the middle of February the manoeuvres were completed, but the hostile armies were still relatively quiet in the sub-zero Manchurian fields.

"On February 20 the Nipponese commander ordered his armies to break camp. A bloody clash was in sight. The two hundred and fifty thousand soldiers of the Emperor pledged themselves for victory or death—"

"My cousins were among them," sighed the tattooed man.

"The tension before the cyclone was broken when on February 24 our First Army captured an outpost in the eastern area. The Russian commander quickly shifted the reserve divisions eastward to reinforce the crumbling line. General Nogi's Third Army, unknown to the enemy command, had been moving up slowly in the west and suddenly thrust themselves into the vacated sector, thereby completing the advancing formation. The Russian attempt to resume the position was of no avail after a fierce struggle.

"The fuse was set. The hostile armies numbering over five hundred thousand along the thirty mile front were pushing back and forth with all their might in the beginning of March. In the dusk on March 7, General Nogi's Third Army commenced to penetrate the Russian western front. At daybreak on the 8th, Marshal Oyama flashed the command for the general advance."

"That's when the Emperor's men began their mad dash, eh?" the stand owner interrupted.

"The next two days smoke darkened the sunlight, the firing burnt the skies at night and the explosions and battle cries shook the ground and deafened the air for many miles around. The smoke gradually clearing on the morning of March 10, which now has been proclaimed 'Army Day,' the victorious Third Army marched behind the Colors of the Empire into the enclosure of Mukden. The retreating Russians time and again attempted in vain to stem the pursuing men's advance but steadily fell back to the north.

"A few divisions followed closely behind the fleeing enemies, like hunting dogs after wounded game. Joy and sorrow mingled in the minds of the men of swords—joy for the hard-won victory, and tears for those late comrades who were wounded or killed in the battle. Kuropatokin's army left ninety thousand killed and wounded and forty thousand captured, while General Oyama counted seventy thousand casualties—"

"We celebrated the Mukden capture as usual with great lantern parades and other public demonstrations," the elderly rikishaman said.

"Well, student, what next, after our army's victory and the Tsushima triumph of our navy?" asked one of the bystanders.

"Oh, to quote an unidentified high government official, the next step will be either unconditional Russian surrender or our march to Moscow—"

"Is the Russian capital right next to Mukden?" asked the elderly man.

The student murmured: "Well, our army advanced about three hundred miles from Dairen on Liaotung Peninsula, I think. Moscow is at least two thousand miles away."

The Saionjis had spent several seasons at their Surugadai home.

Okiku was in the garden this afternoon, but her favorite iris had lost its color. She watched the withered flowers for a long time.

After sunset she had her usual evening bath and went into the living-room. She sat down before a tall mirror.

Near by, on the mat, stood her favorite, high kerosene lamp and a charcoal brazier. Okiku finished her evening make-up. She slid over to the brazier and smoked her pipe for a while.

After she looked into the glass once more, she carried it away, leaving a hand-mirror on the mat. When she returned she had on her *haori*. She sat down and lit her pipe again.

Between her puffings she looked critically at her shoulders and breasts beneath her surcoat. Her clear eyes admired the *haori*. Then she brought over a number of family photographs and turned them over for a while. She put them away and meditated anew.

From time to time Okiku looked into the hand-mirror. She counted the fine wrinkles on her forehead and a few streaks of silken gray hair. She sighed and said to herself: "Ah, age leaves its traces."

Her look brightened as she followed the outlines of her oval face, the shape of the eyes, mouth, and nose, and her Fuji-san-shaped hair-line that closely resembled those in portraits of women seen in the woodcuts of great masters.

She remembered how her beauty and talents had won her the title of *komachi* in Tokyo, and how they had impressed Saionji.

This recollection animated her, and she unconsciously sat up with her back erect. Touching her forehead tenderly with her delicate fingers, she saw a thoughtful, brooding expression on her mirrored face. She reflected again: "Why, I wonder, do taste and fashion change?"

The key word of beauty, the Fuji-shaped forehead, had given way to the voluptuous, round face, and now the young geishas danced to fast unimpressive, popular tunes more than they did to the subdued, classic music of the samisen.

"They are not real entertainers," Okiku whispered. "But young and old, high and low, the audiences are spell-bound by the new type. The patrons' taste is low."

She looked into the mirror again. When her fingers left the wrinkled forehead, she closed her eyes to avoid seeing the vision of Saionji leaning over a round face.

"I knew it, I knew it," she said to herself, grasping and shaking the ends of the surcoat sleeves on her lap. "No wonder he is staying away again these days."

Sagami came into the room.

"Sagami, I'd like to talk to you." Okiku was apparently nonchalant, but a cloud still rested between her eyebrows.

"Why such formality?" The governess shook her head.

"Yes, very formal. Don't you remember when you called on me for the first time on the Prince's behalf, over twenty years ago, you were very formal?"

"What do you mean—?" A foreboding seized the old woman.

"Yes, Sagami, I am leaving this house tonight for good. So you are the one to listen to my final words."

"My, but oh—!" Sagami's wrinkled face turned pale. "I don't know what Master will say if you leave during his absence. Can't you wait until he comes back?"

"No, I am going to make way for someone else in the house. A woman, after all, has no home of her own if even she becomes one hundred years old, as our saying goes. She has to leave the house whenever she is not wanted."

Okiku's long-restrained tears filled her eyes.

Sagami was alarmed. "I—I haven't encouraged Master in that!"

"Whether you encouraged him or not, the Prince's affection is enjoyed by a young woman."

The governess murmured: "I'm very sorry you think you have to go."

"I am sorry for you, too, for since you were our original *nakaudo* you will have to tell the Prince of my departure."

"But I don't know what to do and I shall miss you."

"Sagami, you don't need to do anything. Since you insisted that I was his mistress, not his wife, my name has not been entered into the Saionji family records. If I leave the house, that's the end."

Sagami nodded sorrowfully.

"I thank you for your association with me for all these years, though we were often at odds—but that couldn't be helped."

"That wasn't altogether your fault," the governess admitted.

"Well," Okiku continued, "under the same roof—no matter how we hide it, when two women want the affections of the same man there's bound to be a clash. You had a sort of maternal affection for him and I loved him as my spouse. You thought I took the Prince away from you. That situation was bad enough, but now another is coming. I will not share him."

Okiku stared at Sagami and went on: "Many women, especially in high society, endure an untold amount of mental suffering because their husbands keep mistresses. They do not leave because they hope to cover up their own shortcomings and those of their mates and all that. But I love my man too much to let anyone come between us. I am defeated by a young woman. I can't stay here with that knowledge. Well, it was my mistake in picking a man who would desert me when my physical attraction was gone."

"Master must provide for you."

"No, Sagami, I can support myself by teaching samisen, dancing and singing. Besides, since Shinko's wedding day is already set I want the Prince to spend his money on her. He promised me to give her husband a separate home. There will be no interference from anyone with my Shinko." For a moment Okiku was silent, and then she said: "Well, that will cost him money. And then—do you know, Sagami?"

"What?" the governess' eyes glowed in their hollows.

"There'll be another baby in the family, by the new woman."

"Oh, is that why you decided to leave so soon?"

"I'll be very candid with you at this departing hour. I am satisfied because Shinko's future is settled. I wanted to leave at the time when the Prince began this affair, but I was anxious to see Shinko become of age. Although you were very careful in her upbringing all these years, I wanted to be near her. I am grateful to you and I am proud of Shinko and her fiancé, Hachiro. My only worry is that if this war should be prolonged, Hachiro, too, may have to go to the front."

Okiku left unspoken her thought that after Shinko was married and established in her own home, she could visit her daughter freely away from Sagami's jealous eyes.

"Well, we have had harsh words, Sagami; in the early years of my life here, you were not always kind. But I realized that clever make-up, the possession of charms and the masterly arts of an entertainer fell short of making a happy home for my beloved Prince and my daughter. I resolved to take up practical training in home-making. Fortunately I had some elementary knowledge which my *hatamoto* family and well-born—remember, Sagami, well-born—made me learn."

Her eyes flashed and her old spirit gave her features a beauty that struck Sagami with amazement.

"I reached this decision after that furious argument with you about my conduct that night—you remember—I hoped to meet your requirements for a 'lady.' When I resumed the studies of the tea ceremony, flower arrangement, sewing, cooking, even poetry composition and classical literature, I think even you were satisfied with the result. You did not say so, but you were more friendly—our harsh in-law feelings disappeared.

"But, of course, we could not overcome one thing, our fundamental difficulty, our rivalry for the Prince's affection. When you said that he and I acted like a pair of manderin ducks, I knew where the trouble lay."

The governess did not look up. She said slowly: "In late years you have conducted yourself properly in the traditions of wifehood."

Okiku repeated: "When I realized that the Prince was looking for fresh flowers, I was angered, I thought I would leave the house immediately. But the thought of Shinko always checked any rash action." She sighed. "I sought peace and companionship with the Goddess of Mercy, the Asakusa *Kwannon* and my family shrine at Kamakura. There I grew to be content with life. I no longer minded your hints that the Prince must have a son and heir.

"But now Shinko is provided for. It is time for me to leave. As I said, I am grateful to you for the lessons you taught me, though they were sometimes bitter ones, and for your devoted care of Shinko. My only regret in leaving this house is that I'll not see the Prince don his full-dress uniform once more."

The governess nodded sympathetically.

"You see, he was the President of the Privy Council and when he takes a government post next time he will be the Premier. Everybody says so."

"When that happens," the old woman said eagerly, "you can't fail to see him."

Okiku did not answer. Of late Saionji's future was to Okiku secondary to her daughter's.

With a deep breath she said: "Ah, Shinko is fortunate!"

Sagami said, "The Princess is a lovely and most accomplished lady, charming, like you."

"Oh, Sagami!" Okiku exclaimed. For the first time in all these years the governess had given credit to her for Shinko's many fine qualities. The words infinitely lightened Okiku's heart. "Oh, Sagami, thank you a thousand times."

She took Sagami's hands impulsively. At this last minute of their contact, they wept hand in hand without restraint.

Sobbing, Okiku said: "It's the night of the Asakusa *Kwannon* celebration, that's why I planned to leave the house tonight. I prayed to the Goddess of Mercy especially that on my departure I should keep my temper and not have any harsh words with you. Now, you speak kindly to me." She looked affectionately into Sagami's eyes. "Sagami, I'll never forget your kind words tonight. You are remarkably healthy, but your advanced age shows plainly. Please take care of yourself. Forgive my shortcomings and rude conduct. Whenever you want my company, just call me. After all, we've lived together a long time—"

Okiku wept loudly.

Sagami, dazed, murmured: "Come to see the Princess' wedding. It's set for the luckiest day next spring. She'll miss you."

Through the calmness of the night soft easterly winds brought the sounds of the Asakusa Temple's bells to their ears.

"If these peace terms are announced, the people will be resentful against the Katsura Cabinet, eh, Ito? Premier Katsura is directly responsible, in any case." Genro Inouye spoke wearily.

His arms folded, Genro Ito replied: "No doubt about that—not only Katsura, but we, too, will be blamed by the people. The peace conference between the Nipponese and the Russian delegates has been going on at Portsmouth, New Hampshire, since early August, through the good offices of President Roosevelt. Our chief delegate, Baron Komura, I'm sure, has tried hard, but Count Witte, the Russian representative, was too clever for him."

"Should the public find out we don't get a penny for our one billion, five hundred million yen direct military expenditure, the people will just explode—" Inouye's eyes widened.

Another Genro, Field Marshal Yamagata, said: "Ah, let's face the facts. We must terminate the war sometime. It's the best opportunity. We can't march on to Siberia, not to speak of the Russian capital. I talked over the conditions in Manchuria with Marshal Oyama when I went there a month ago. We are in no position to continue hostilities—"

"Saionji constantly warned us not to over-emphasize our victories— he was right—but here we are," was Ito's mournful remark.

"Well, Ito, the Seiyukai Party will take this opportunity and attack the Katsura Cabinet, will it not?" Inouye asked.

"H'm, these days Saionji is quite independent and rarely consults me regarding party policies. I'd better get him over and persuade him to pacify the Seiyukai members."

Ito called Saionji on the telephone.

"He is at the Seiyukai headquarters. He sounds very much disturbed. He will come later, though."

Inouye picked up the note again and studied it. Yamagata had looked it over during Ito's telephone call and now said dejectedly:

"H'm, we can't get a penny out of the Russian Government after this tremendous spending. The Port Arthur section was in our hands ten years ago so that is not a new gain. So was Saghalien Island originally ours until 1875 when Russia forced us to exchange it for the uninhabitable Kuril Islands; and this time we get only the southern half of it."

Ito, too, was downcast. "The sole material gain is the South Manchurian railroad with its railway zone south of Changchun. Is it not ironical that after we risked our national life by spending one billion, five hundred million yen and causing nearly two hundred thousand casualties our accomplishment is tantamount to the recovery of Manchuria for the Chinese? But at last we'll get Korea as our protectorate."

"Our spoils of war are much less than they were ten years ago. What I would like to know," Field Marshal Yamagata said, banging his fist on the table, "when will we get Manchuria? Say, Ito," dropping his voice he went on, "do you think there is some truth in the rumors that Russia and China signed a secret treaty against us—?"

Ito's eyes spoke in agreement. "I heard it, too. But how can we prove it? We'd better not talk about it now."

There was only silence.

"Why didn't President Roosevelt ask for all of Saghalien Island?" said Inouye after a while.

"He was a mediator and he has done much for us." Ito picked his cigar to pieces.

"Where is Katsura? Why doesn't he show up and pay us his respects? We are primarily anxious to save his face." Field Marshal Yamagata's voice rasped the air.

"He's hiding somewhere; maybe at his mistress' home. He is afraid to show up. The public tension is so high. You see, that Toyama group was a great factor in modelling and maintaining public spirit for the war. Now they are furious. If Toyama finds out that we accepted these humiliating conditions, I don't know what he will do to Katsura." Ito sighed.

Yamagata was indignant. "Declare martial law, if he agitates—"

"But—" Inouye attempted to talk and was ignored.

"What do they expect? Didn't the Katsura Cabinet win the war? Keep them down by force if they rise up. Whatever the Government does is law. Why be afraid? If anyone tries to oppose the authorities by force, use force to put them down!"

The Field Marshal went on: "Let's report our decision to the Emperor and get his sanction and have Katsura announce it. Delay because of indecision may mean resumption of hostilities."

"But Katsura emphasized our victories too much and hid our losses. When Mukden fell he intimated that we were already at the gate of Moscow and when our Navy defeated the Russian fleet at Tsushima he spoke as if we had already tied the Bear up in our yard, ready to shoot it if it didn't submit to our dictation. And he boasted about his ability in the Peace Conference, too. He made the people think that we'd get a huge indemnity as in the Sino-Nipponese War; they thought that we'd get Saghalien Island, Liaotung Peninsula, and all Manchuria, besides." For once Inouye had an audience.

"That's true, Inouye, if the people learn the truth about it, in their disappointment they'll probably demand the continuation of the war. This hysteria—" Ito tried once more to light his cigar and continued. "What's the matter with Saionji? Why doesn't he come? It's only a short way from the Seiyukai Party headquarters."

"Let's proceed to the Imperial Palace." All rose wearily.

"Katsura, Katsura here?" Genro Ito gasped, standing under the dim gas light at the door of a small house. Detectives guarded the place.

A woman's voice answered: "Who is it, please?"

"It's me. Katsura here?"

"Oh! Please come right in. He's been here since this afternoon."

Ito saw the Premier cowering on the mat in a corner.

"Oh, Katsura! We recommended the peace terms to His Majesty."

"Thanks! Thanks for your kind efforts—"

Premier Katsura's lifeless face brightened at the news.

"But be quick about asking Toyama and his group to refrain from agitation against you. There are rumors and commotion. You can't tell what will happen. Should we have to spill blood at home, you'll have no way to apologize to His Majesty and to the people. Quick!"

"Do you think so?"

"Come on! You know how the public felt, and now the Russian concessions are far more skimpy than first reported."

Shaken, Premier Katsura picked up the telephone. "*Moshi, moshi,* Toyama-san, Toyama-san?"

No answer came.

Someone approached the door.

"Who is it?"

"Me, Saionji."

"Come in."

"I couldn't find you anywhere. This is certainly a hard place to locate." Saionji followed Ito to Katsura's room.

"Premier Katsura, you have accepted the peace terms, I hear," Saionji said.

"What, who told you that? We made our recommendation to the Emperor only a short while ago," Ito barked.

Saionji grinned. "Around Hibiya Park a huge lantern parade is forming in protest against the Cabinet's decision. And the demonstrators say they'll bring all the Genros and Ministers who were responsible for this to the public squares, dead or alive, to make an explanation—"

Genro Ito and Premier Katsura were speechless. They stared at Saionji.

Ito recovered from the shock. "Well, Saionji-san," he asked, "how do you and your Seiyukai Party stand?"

"Huh." The listeners held their breath. "A large number of the Party are absolutely against the terms accepted—"

"Are they?" Katsura was shaking visibly.

"And some will lead the demonstration." Saionji's faint smile tormented them.

"Help me, in the name of the Emperor and our country!" Katsura begged.

"Don't you agree with us? It's the only way, Saionji-san."

"Yes, Genro Ito. I personally agree with you."

"You do?" Ito sat back on the mat. "Despite the Party majority?"

"What of it? Can we go on with this war indefinitely? It would mean our sure ruin. I'd rather let the Party go to ruin than my country. I debated with the members all afternoon and I convinced some of them. I, as the Seiyukai President, support the Katsura Ministry in this instance."

Just then a group of people rushed past the house towards the Hibiya

Park section, shouting a demand for more war and Katsura's resignation.

"Oh, they are shooting!" said Saionji with a sigh.

Katsura and Ito shut their wearied eyes.

Saionji got up and opened the sliding wooden doors to look down towards Hibiya Park. The others came to his side. "Ah, after a great loss of lives in Manchuria, now this tragedy within sight of His Majesty." Ito moaned. Katsura was silent.

Looking at Saionji, Ito continued: "Oh, look at that! The mobs are now setting fire to the police boxes and the pro-Cabinet newspaper building!"

Katsura shut the wooden slide. He stood like a statue and murmured: "It's September 5. I'll have the Imperial Rescript of the restoration of peace issued after I formally present the peace conditions to His Majesty. That'll be the middle of October."

"Marquis Saionji, it seems that a great task lies ahead of you this year," Takekoshi, Saionji's former Councillor, hopefully said to a small gathering at the Surugadai home. He went on: "Four years and seven months of Katsura's Cabinet is too much. People are tired of it. A new spirit must be injected."

"Yes, there'll be a great disturbance in the forthcoming Diet session if Katsura stays in office. To start with, some of our Seiyukai members, who were mistreated by the police authorities when they protested against the acceptance of the Portsmouth Peace terms, will certainly criticize Premier Katsura," commented Hara, one of the leading Seiyukai members and ex-Minister of Communications.

Saionji looked at him earnestly and said: "Hara-san, we must suppress that agitation even if it is from our own Party men and could be made an effective weapon against the Cabinet. We must turn people's minds from the last war and emphasize other issues, instead."

"That's right, Monsieur, we can find countless charges against the Cabinet," an elderly friend began. He was Matsuda, of the *Oriental Liberal Newspaper* days. He had already been Cabinet Minister twice, one of the Seiyukai organizers like Hara, and the President of the House of Representatives. He went on:

"Look at the present Cabinet's six-million-yen loan to a private bank during the war. The Government had just secured loans of one hundred million yen in England and America at six per cent interest. Think, the people, even the destitute, were contributing their share of real blood and tears to the war funds. Yet the Katsura Cabinet loaned six million yen at two per cent to the Osaka bank. We suppressed the question as long as we could but now it's time to demand an explanation."

The aggressive Hara was solicitous. "Marquis, what will you do if Katsura makes overtures to you to succeed him as Premier?" He leaned over to the host's side.

"Huh," said Saionji with a broad smile.

Matsuda took it up: "Let's not be too hopeful of Katsura's hypothetical overture or resignation. This younger Choshu Premier is very clever. If we aren't careful we'll make fools of ourselves. Now our former leader, Genro Ito, is in Korea as Resident-General; his mentor, Field Marshal Yamagata, is too old to do active service; Genro Inouye cannot command enough influence to take the Premiership, while Genro Matsukata is retired because of ill health and Field Marshal Oyama has no political ambition. Katsura may perform another trick as he did almost three years ago."

"Do you mean that he might offer Marquis an opportunity to succeed him? And that if the offer is not accepted at once he may, with that as a pretext, retreat into the Premier's chair like a badger into its den when it discovers the approaching hunter?" Hara asked heatedly.

Saionji was meditating.

Just then they heard a cry of the girl-baby lately born to the host's second 'wife,' Otama. Saionji had named her Sonoko. A fatherly smile came to his face. Otama's entry into the Saionji household had been a quiet one, as Okiku's voluntary departure was known only to a small circle of family acquaintances.

"Monsieur, the mother and the baby are doing fine, I suppose?" the President of the House asked, bowing slightly. "Monsieur, you never get old. You look young and active. Is it because you always associate with young people?"

"Huh, I have some gray hair on both sides of my head." The host put his hand to his temple.

"See mine, the top is completely bald, ha, ha." Matsuda was in good humor.

Hara turned to Saionji and asked: "If you become the Premier, will you have only members of our Party in your Cabinet?"

Matsuda answered by saying: "That's impossible. If we announce that the Seiyukai will form a ministry without the Sat-cho henchmen, Genro Yamagata will put obstacles in our way. Don't you remember, even Genro Ito was forced to resign when Yamagata manipulated the Upper House against him? We must take several Yamagata men into the Cabinet."

Saionji nodded in assent.

Seeing the jovial spirit subsiding, Takekoshi again spoke up: "Anyway, the Marquis' Premiership is now merely a matter of days. The Saionji house will be busy this year. Besides his political advancement, his daughter's marriage is also set for this spring."

"Monsieur, Lady Shinko is really charming like her mother—"

Saionji beamed as he accepted the compliment.

"Oh, her mother was pretty. When we came back from France everybody talked about her. Didn't they, Monsieur? What has Shinko been doing since she was graduated from the women's college?"

"Huh, my governess insisted that she should be taught the arts of homemaking, such as the tea-ceremony, flower-arrangement, sewing, cooking, and *biwa* music, some of which I also think necessary—"

"H'm, Monsieur, after we returned from Europe you used to play *biwa* music occasionally at a drinking party. Do you still have the instrument in the house?"

"Yes, Matsuda-san."

Saionji's servant announced that Genro Inouye had arrived to see him.

"Marquis and friends, good evening!"

"Marquis Inouye, I am very pleased to see you." Saionji bowed.

Inouye was somewhat at a loss. Matsuda got up and said: "Monsieur, we'll see you tomorrow at Party headquarters. We'll bid you good night."

The visitor gently wet his lips. His eyes travelled from his host to the departing friends.

"Marquis Saionji"—his tone was serious—"with your permission, I would like to state the purpose of my mission in the presence of your friends, since they are your high lieutenants—"

"Let's hear it." Hara returned to his seat. Important news seemed to be on Genro Inouye's tongue-tip.

"Certainly, Marquis Inouye; if you consider it appropriate and desire it, certainly!"

The friends watched Inouye and Saionji intently.

"Since your Party has regained its membership—"

He was careful. Saionji's smooth undemonstrative face showed determination. "Yes, the Seiyukai Party did drop to slightly over one hundred members, but of late it has regained its membership. At the present rate I have no doubt it will reach record size in a short time, commanding once more an absolute majority in the Diet."

Saionji's slender arms were firmly planted on his lap.

Genro Inouye saw no need of beating around the bush and came out with his message. "Katsura desires to know if you will accept the Premiership if he should resign."

"May I know whether that is Premier Katsura's own wish?"

"Yes, yes; I was officially entrusted with this mission."

Saionji readjusted his kimono in front and thrust up his chin.

"Genro Inouye, if I should be commanded by the Emperor, I shall be glad to assume the duty, not only for the sake of the Seiyukai Party of which I am the President, but also for the sake of the country, to settle the minds of the Nipponese and to stabilize the nation's affairs. However, it is my feeling that if Premier Katsura intends to resign he should submit his resignation to His Majesty."

Inouye stared at the host, his lower jaw sagging, and uncontrollable signs of joy and satisfaction showed in the faces of Saionji's friends.

With a deep sigh Inouye said: "So, you are ready."

"Yes, I am ready. I shall act promptly when I am appointed as His Majesty's Premier-designé."

On the morning of January 7, 1906, Saionji was called to the telephone.

"Monsieur? It's Matsuda talking from headquarters. Will you come over right away? It's urgent. Something important has happened this morning!"

"Huh. See you soon."

Saionji beamed at his governess.

"Oh, Master, a messenger from the Imperial Palace!" She bowed low to the Imperial crests of the Golden Chrysanthemum on the horse-carriage stopping at the gate.

"Sagami! My full-dress uniform!" he said after the messenger had left.

The governess bowed low again and said with tears of joy: "Master, it's the greatest day of my life. It was about this time thirty-eight years ago when you left for the Tamba front as the Commander-General of the Imperial Expeditionary Army. If the late master and your real father could witness this glorious day of the Saionji family—" She was overcome. She saw her master, too, was moved.

"Sagami, will you see to it that Otama and Shinko get my things ready for me?"

A few minutes later Saionji was dressing; his new 'wife,' the pretty round-faced Otama and his daughter Shinko busily assisted him. The bent, old governess sat near by, directing them with her forehead.

"Otama, bring out my hat—"

"Yes, my darling—" She was about to walk away.

"My MASTER!" came from Sagami in a low but penetrating voice. Otama jumped. Her pretty mouth was open and her round, brown eyes bulged as she turned to Sagami.

The gray head nodded meaningfully. " 'Master'! Say, 'MASTER'!"

Otama reddened, then she shrugged her shoulders.

The jinrikisha, bearing Saionji, rushed through the streets in the cold morning air and turned towards the Seiyukai headquarters. At home Sagami knelt before the family altar to inform the departed souls of the good tidings.

Saionji was soon at the Party office where the prospective ministers who had been decided upon the previous night were waiting for him.

"Friends, I am designated by His Majesty to form the Cabinet," Saionji announced when he came into the committee room which was packed to capacity.

Amid the thunderous cheers and applause, Matsuda replied: "Monsieur, we are ready!"

Then he read off the list of the names and their portfolios:

> "Premier, Marquis Saionji Kimmochi,
> Foreign Minister, Baron Kato Komei,
> Home Minister, Hara Kei,
> Finance Minister, Sakatani Yoshiro,
> Navy Minister, Admiral Saito Makoto,
> Justice Minister, Matsuda Masahisa,
> Agriculture and Commerce Minister, Matsuoka Yasutake,
> Communications Minister, Yamagata Isaburo,
> Education Minister, Makino Shinken, and,
> War Minister, General Terauchi Masaki, of the previous
>   Cabinet will remain with us."

A deafening noise went up when Saionji, accompanied by his colleagues, emerged from the room into the street.

Matsuda raised his voice and said: "Let's follow the President to the Palace in the order I have just read!"

When Matsuda had mounted his jinrikisha he shouted once more:

"Let us go down the Ginza, then turn to the left towards the Sakashita Gate of the Palace Grounds."

The milling partisans, yelling and shouting, followed the caravan of jinrikishas on both sides, front and back, with the Party banners and placards high in the air. It looked from afar as if the frenzied crowds were carrying the would-be Ministers on their shoulders. They surged through the streets, completely blocking the traffic and the electric tramcar line which had just begun operating.

Along the Ginza and Kyobashi sections, Tokyo's 'White Light' districts, men and women, old and young, in kimonos and European suits, cheered from the sidewalks, prosperous stores and office windows.

Now and then the Premier-designé put his right hand to his hat in response to the greetings.

Suddenly he jumped up on the carriage seat and shouted at the top of his voice: "Okiku! Okiku!" waving his hand.

The tumult drowned his cry, but Okiku, who was among the crowd, lifted her handkerchief in response.

"Prince! Prince!" She tried in vain to reach the carriage. Saionji often looked back to Okiku who was holding her handkerchief now to her eyes and now in the air, waving frantically with the crowd.

The parade was approaching the Sakashita Gate, beyond which ordinary people were not allowed to go without a pass. With great confusion the crowd dropped back before the sentries, and the Saionji party proceeded slowly.

Many times before he had entered the Palace Grounds, but now in a few minutes he was to be appointed the *Soridaijin*.

Since the last quarter of the sixteenth century the Palace Grounds had been the site of the governing seat. They included the Fukiage Imperial Terrace in the hilly northeastern half, covering nearly four hundred acres of select land in the center of the Capital.

Its records dated back as far as the fifteenth century. When one of the *samurai* castle-builders, Ota Dokan, chose the place in 1462 and erected his stronghold, the present Capital was less than a fishing village on the northern shore of Edo or Tokyo Bay. The selection was made because of its strategic value. The builder, who also was a poet of note, was accredited with a famous stanza expressing the atmosphere of his chosen spot.

Saionji on the jinrikisha readily repeated: "*Waga-iho wa Matsubara tzuzuki Umi-chikaku Fuji-no takane-o Nokiba-ni-zo-miru.*"

The builder's hut was in the pine grove near the ocean, and from

there above the 'eave's edge' he could admire the view of Fuji-san. This
Edo Castle was built on a revolutionary principle of Ota's time. Contrary to the prevailing ideas, which looked for such sites on the high
hills, Ota planned the fortification on the flat land, but at the rear it
was protected by the extended hills, which now formed the Fukiage
Imperial Terrace and its adjacent heights. The marshy land and the
ocean protected the front to the south, thus making the new fortress
'easy to defend and hard to take.'

Since that time its occupants had changed and the formation had
been altered, chiefly by a series of natural disasters, earthquakes and
fires, and by the new war strategies.

In 1572 Iyeyasu, the founder of the famous Tokugawa Shogunate,
then a local chieftain, captured it. In the ensuing twenty-five years, he
rose to the dictatorship of the Island Empire, and his descendants held
that position until his fifteenth successor in the 1860's.

The changing world and the decline of the statesmanship of the
Tokugawa oligarchy in 1868 forced it to relinquish the vested privilege
of national leadership and Edo Castle in favor of the Imperial Family.

In May 1873, Edo Castle suffered from a fire. Emperor Meiji did
not authorize rebuilding for many years because of the government's
increasing outlay. Finally the present Imperial Palace was constructed
at the cost of four million yen and finished in 1888 when Saionji was
at the court of Wilhelm II as the Nipponese Minister.

The Emperor and the Imperial Household returned to the new
Kyujyo in the following year, leaving the Akasaka Detached Palace
where they had found shelter meanwhile.

In the new arrangement the actual Palace Grounds covered over
some two hundred and fifty acres, while the Fukiage Imperial Terrace
extended some one hundred and thirty acres.

Many miles of deep inner and outer moats circled the grounds. The
zigzag masonry works stood as high as forty feet on the inside of the
outermost moats, topped with a row of old pine trees and filled with
deep, blue water. It must have been impregnable when the bow and
arrow was the fighters' arms and the *Masamune* sword was the regular
weapon of the warrior. Now the combination of the evergreens, the
gray stones and the blue mirror-like water seemed to heighten the
beauty.

The *Kyujyo* were outwardly shrine-style, constructed mostly of
native cypress wood, *hinoki*, two stories high, with elegant sloping

roofs of copper tile. Among the structures, the Inner and Outer Palaces were the largest buildings.

The Saionji group was to arrive at the East Vestibule of the Outer Palace. This was designated for the passage of government officials and prospective appointees, while the South Vestibule connected directly with the Main Gate, or *Niju-bashi*, Double Bridge, was the entrance for the diplomatic corps and the Emperor and Empress.

The Outer Palace embraced nearly twenty large halls and rooms. The *Seiden* was the place where all the ceremonial functions of State were performed. This Hall, one of the largest and most luxuriously decorated buildings, was seventy feet long and fifty-six feet wide and surrounded on three sides by wide corridors with glass windows. Among the features were the tall wooden pillars placed fourteen feet apart covered with heavy dark brown velvet tapestries, large chandeliers hanging from the coved brightly colored ceiling and the floor artistically laid over with hardwood. A pair of the golden Imperial thrones with the crests of the sixteen-petal chrysanthemum stood near the north end of the Hall.

Besides the *Seiden* there were the Homei Hall, Phoenix Hall, where nowadays the usual appointment ceremonies are conducted, the Paulownia Hall where the Empress held her Audiences, and the Bamboo Hall.

The Saionji party approached the buildings on the higher ground. Ahead on the right and left the tips of the Fukiage forest showed through a thin veil of purple mist.

From the early days of Edo Castle the Terrace had been famous for its flowers and preserved monuments, its ponds and waterfalls. There between the forests were many acres of flat space for general horticulture and bridle-paths.

In the wooded section was a group of 'Three Sacred Palaces' and several other small buildings housing the historic relics of Emperor Meiji's reign. The Waterfall Arbor, the Spring Arbor, and the Ancient Arbor could be seen through the columns of cryptomaria, pine and other trees.

Saionji meditated while the passage ahead was being cleared.

The gnarled branches of the old pine trees on the side of the road stretched out to him like an old man's arms; the whispering winter wind, piercing through the pines and leafless trees to his ears, sounded like congratulations from the sky on his ascendance to power; the cold, grayish, heavy stones, lying still for hundreds of years in the masonry work, appeared to offer a helping hand to push and pull the wheels of his leisurely carriage moving towards the East Vestibule.

Now the winding hilly roads ahead seemed to presage hardship; the blue water in the moats on both sides of the passage coming into his view hinted at the depth of his task; the cold clouds hanging low forecast the stormy course of Saionji's first administration.

He shut his eyes. Suddenly he noticed a sweet odor in the air.

He nodded to himself. "That fragrance comes from the early plum blossoms on the terrace already blooming because of the warm weather this winter. That blossom signifies perseverance and virtue. I shall be serene."

The caravan at last was in front of the East Vestibule. All alighted from the jinrikishas. Led by the ceremonial officials, while the others waited, the Premier-elect entered one of the halls where the officiation was to take place in 'standing' style, in imitation of Western ceremonial manners.

The Lord Keeper of the Privy Seal, Tokudaiji, Saionji's own brother, stood at the left of the Imperial throne. When Saionji halted at a short space from the Imperial seat and bowed, His Majesty entered the hall from the side door.

Saionji stood before the Sovereign, his head slightly forward. He heard the Emperor's clear, melodious voice.

Looking up, he received a large sheet of parchment, fixed his eyes on it, read his office and the Imperial Seal, and also in fresh black ink the counter-signature of his brother Tokudaiji as the Lord Keeper of the Privy Seal.

His mental strain turned to joy. An expression of great satisfaction appeared on the face of Tokudaiji, who stood rigid. When their eyes caught each other's, the Emperor, with a smiling countenance, looked upon them as if he were going to speak to them.

The ceremony ended as the Sovereign followed by Tokudaiji retired from the hall. In the meantime, the other Ministers were ushered in and the Sovereign returned to install them as the new Premier took his brother's place beside the throne.

The relaxed new Ministers emerged through the main doorway. The sun had just broken through the clouds. As they were about to get into the jinrikishas for the return to the Party headquarters, there was a voice calling:

"Kimmochi, Kimmochi! His Majesty wishes to tender you his personal congratulations."

It was Tokudaiji. His long white beard waved gently in the winter breeze, his solemn features broke into a smile. Saionji's beardless face was radiant in the sunlight. The brothers walked arm in arm through the corridor towards His Majesty's study. The onlookers smiled at the sight of their fraternal affection and pride.

Beyond the study door, Emperor Meiji congratulated the new *Soridaijin:* "I feel personally very proud of you, Kimmochi. You are the honor and the pride of our native town, Kyoto."

VI

❧

ELDER STATESMAN

CHAPTER VI

ELDER STATESMAN

"Since this is our first cabinet meeting, i'd like to outline my fundamental policies."

Premier Saionji was speaking from the head of a long table in the 'cabinet room' of his official residence at Nagata-cho.

On the Premier's right sat the Minister of Justice, Matsuda the eldest among the group and chief strategist of the Seiyukai Party. On his left was the Minister of Home Affairs, Hara, the Party's field general. These three Seiyukai men were the central figures in the Administration.

Saionji first addressed the Minister for Foreign Affairs, Kato, the son-in-law of the founder of the Mitsubishi Financial House: "Minister Kato, I want you to negotiate an agreement with Russia to confirm our neighborly relations, especially with respect to our mutual rights resulting from the Portsmouth Peace Treaty so that we may eradicate the bad memories of the last war."

He went on: "And sound out France on an agreement to support the peace and welfare of China. We want to maintain the *status quo* and the territorial rights of both the French Republic and the Nipponese Empire in the Far East. The third major task I'd like to lay on your shoulders is the problem involving us and the United States. There have been rumors of agitation against the Japanese immigrants on the Pacific Coast. It has been and still is hard to deal with the problem. It is a local one, but the trouble is increasing and something must be done. The wisest thing we can do is to propose to the Washington Government that we enter into an arbitration treaty under which the signatories would refer to the Hague International Tribunal any disputes arising between the two countries.

"The next matter concerns the Departments of Home Affairs and of Justice. I am speaking of the control and suppression of the Socialists. The previous Cabinets took extreme measures against them, but we'll reverse that attitude. I noticed that there is something worth while listening to in their contentions. Minister Hara, I wish you would instruct the police authorities to grant permission, if the Socialist group should present a petition to form a political party, as with any other political factions. The Government's new attitude toward the Socialists will, of course, necessitate a little modification of the Police and Criminal Codes."

Saionji also addressed the other Ministers individually, and finally said: "General Terauchi and Admiral Saito, we must keep the outlays just large enough to cover the already settled expansion programs. Economy is our aim."

He turned to the Communications Minister, Yamagata Isaburo, the adopted heir of Genro Yamagata. "That may be difficult in your Department, with many new railway projects started by the retired Cabinet, but the budget does not permit any increase. The total amount of revenues will not even reach the minimum limit of the necessary programs. However, we'll expand our educational facilities, Minister Makino." He looked towards the Education Minister. "Through your efforts we shall cultivate a cosmopolitan outlook in the minds of our young people."

Laying both hands on the table, the Premier looked around.

"The foremost among my remaining suggestions is this—" The listeners sat up straight as he continued: "The nationalization of railroads, in which project I want your utmost co-operation. We must achieve this great undertaking during this Administration. It may seem socialistic to some, but although we shall be reasonable to the stockholders, we will force it through for the benefit of the future economic development and strategic needs of the country."

The elder Matsuda caught the Premier's eye after a short period of general comments from the Ministers, and rose. "Gentlemen, in behalf of the Seiyukai Party, I am requested to extend its invitation to you all to attend our congratulatory dinner immediately after this meeting at the Koyokan Hall."

The Ministers clapped their hands in unanimous acceptance.

"Monsieur, come, come, one more *sakazuki* and we'll say finis."

Matsuda offered a sake cup to Saionji. "Our, our first meeting was in Paris over thirty years ago, was it not, Monsieur? After our newspaper experience we were separated for many years until the formation of the Seiyukai Party."

The Premier, with a strong alcoholic breath, said: "Huh, it's like a dream—to think that Komyoji is no more—and Nakae, too—"

"Ah!" Matsuda opened his wide, moustached mouth and waved his hand uncertainly. "In my mind, Komyoji was always associated with drenching perfume, ha, ha, ha! Too bad he died so young when he was about to make a name for himself as a Justice of the Supreme Court after his return from Paris and short experience in the Diet," he added in a low voice.

"Chief, here comes another French-trained colleague, I want you to give him your *sakazuki* in blessing, so that one day he may be Premier, too."

"Huh, Hara, you'll be a Chief Executive soon, and you—General Terauchi. You studied in France also? Good! Here's to your success! General, you have a great Choshu provincial heritage, you have your Russo-Nipponese War record, and above all you have executive ability. Your pointed bald head, your sparkling eyes, your massive eyebrows slanting upwards, your bearded jaws, all bespeak power and courage. You'll be a Prime Minister, no doubt," Saionji said as he extended his cup to the General.

When the Premier received the returned cup filled with warm sake, he asked: "May I offer you a suggestion? It is silence. Keep your mouth shut. Talkativeness is most undesirable in the military organization."

The War Minister took the advice amiably.

"Huh, Matsu-Matsuda, let's get Saito. He is very quiet, drinking like a whale, and monopolizes all the pretty geishas."

The round-cheeked Navy Minister bowed. "Premier Saionji, this is the fourth time I come for your blessings."

"Good, Admiral Saito, sit down—what's that, Matsuda? What are Hara and Kato arguing about?" Saionji asked.

The young Foreign Minister's voice rose: "The idea of nationalizing of the railways is unacceptable, for it is socialistic, contrary to the theory of *laissez-faire* upon which the business practices of Nippon have so far been conducted."

Hara retorted: "Let me remind you of these facts: first, some years ago, when our Government purchased the Korean railways, you supported the project; second, the present railway question is out of your jurisdiction, which is restricted to the foreign affairs; third, your argument has a bitter taste of personal interests. If you persist in opposing this program, it will look as if you did so because you are related to the Mitsubishi House, which may suffer a set-back under the new scheme. And lastly, whether you object to it or not, this Cabinet will carry it through."

"I admit," said the Foreign Minister, "that I'm personally interested in defending the Mitsubishi. That is usual in other governments, too. If one represents any economic group, he protects that interest. Heretofore, Genro Ito and Genro Inouye have given my wife's House most careful consideration—"

Saionji and Matsuda listened.

The Foreign Minister continued: "I'm not a bit ashamed of my stand. Frankly speaking, Minister Hara, you yourself are most closely connected with the Furukawa mining interests, and our Chief is related to the Mitsui and Sumitomo. All these Houses may cut into the sphere of the business interests so far fostered by the Mitsubishi, particularly in Kyushu. I oppose the nationalization of railways for the same reason and motives as you support it. If the Cabinet does not alter its attitude, I shall resign my post."

"Hey, what's happened to our merriment?" Matsuda's coarse voice boomed.

At Saionji's Surugadai home on a late afternoon, Shinko was meditating on the veranda. The late winter sun shone down on the garden before her. Idly she watched an old plum tree with a few early blossoms.

A sparrow flew from its nest in the eaves to a low-hanging branch. The bird looked around, twittering. That brought a smaller sparrow of lighter plumage. They rested a few inches apart. The older one flew down to the ground, the younger followed. They hopped around together in search of their supper. To Shinko they appeared to be mother and daughter. Every now and then the larger bird found a crumb for the smaller one.

"Oh, Mother!" Shinko murmured to herself—her mother, Okiku, had left the house many months ago. Warm tears rolled from her pretty eyes.

"Princess, Princess? Oh, you're there. You must take a bath and have your hair rearranged to get ready for the evening—it will take much time."

It was Sagami's voice.

The bow-shaped governess came nearer and stretched herself, with her hands on the back of her hips. "Oh, Princess! Oh, Princess, you must be confused. Don't you worry, everything will be all right. Your father has arranged everything. There'll never be a wedding as dignified as yours." She shook her gray head. "See, Princess, you are the descendant of a celebrated Fujiwara line, your fiancé is from an equally noted family. Your father is the nation's Prime Minister," Sagami went on exultantly.

"Although your father demands simplicity in every respect, your uncle Sumitomo has provided everything you might possibly like to have for your wedding. Genro Inouye and his *okugata* are coming as your fiancé's *nakaudo* and Genro Ito and his *okugata* as yours to officiate at the ceremony. They and Lord Hachiro's elder brother, Prince Mori, and his *okugata* will accompany the bridegroom. Your uncle Tokudaiji and aunt will represent your relatives." The governess became greatly excited. "Wedding gifts are piled high in the recess of the guest-room. And you have so many dresses! That lovely white silk European dress—I don't know how you'll get it on—is to be worn when your father takes you and your husband to that fashionable Koyokan Hall and presents you to the hundreds of relatives, friends and acquaintances of the Saionjis and the Moris. But for the ceremony you'll wear that white satin dress with your pretty hair combed down your back and your teeth blackened, like the portraits of ancient court ladies. And Lord Hachiro will be attired in a black silk *montsuki* and a *hakama*."

She kept on: "Oh, there's that orchid-design purple silk kimono with the Saionji family crests in white. That is your father's special gift. I love that light purple, it's the family's Court color for a lady, and the design is Master's favorite flower."

Sagami's enthusiasm brought only a faint response from Shinko, but she continued with a joyful gesture: "Princess, did you see the guest room? It's decorated for the ceremony. I had a pair of scrolls hung in the alcove—very suitable for the occasion. The figures are God Izanagi and Goddess Izanami, the first married couple in mythology. That is a part of the long-established Kyoto wedding customs, I suggested it to your father."

"You insisted, I suppose." Shinko's faint smile inspired the servant to go on.

"Genro Ito and his *okugata* conferred with your father and the chef the other day so as to have the rest of the things in Tokyo fashion. Anyway, Princess, you must come and see the room. Well, I can tell you what there are, too.

"Near the alcove is the *Shimadai*, or Elysian Fields, on a large and high lacquer tray with picturesque branches of pine, bamboo and plum. The diminutive old man and his white-haired spouse, together with a pair of cranes and a tortoise, are placed under the imaginary forest. You see, Princess, these plants and animals are supposed to prophesy a long, happy and healthy family life for you. The pine symbolizes eternity, the bamboo, virtue and propagation, and the plum, perseverance and feminine grace, and that bird with its lovely figure like yours is said to be most self-restraining about its appetite for its health's sake.

"On the veranda side of the room, a folding screen is placed so that nobody can peep in through the paper screens during the ceremony. I also had a pair of high candle-holders brought in there.

"Then, at the first wedding feast, which you and your husband must attend as the host and hostess for the sake of formalities, you will serve warm sake to the guests. There you will, for the first time, serve your husband also.

"Princess, you'll be very happy. Occasionally you must retire and change your costume to show the company your different outfits. Ito-no-okugata will know all that. It's all confusing. Before the festivities begin with the geishas and others, you'll have your hair dressed in *marumage* style, to show the new life. Then you can retire—you retire to the room which is provided for you and your husband—"

Sagami grinned to herself like a contented cat.

"Sagami." Shinko turned to the governess.

"Yes, Princess." Sagami raised her head as high as she could.

"Sagami, you've never been married?"

"No, Princess, but I can imagine from my reading and witnessing many like affairs in the past how confused the Princess is."

Shinko kept her eyes on the sparrows. "You had no children, of course—"

"Well, no—you seem to be looking into the future. That would be a happy occasion for my master and me."

"Sagami, I can't think so far ahead." Her voice began to tremble.

"Princess, what has happened?"

"Look at those two birds on the ground, mother and child, I suppose. They are picking crumbs out of the dirt. But don't they look happy?" She pointed at them with her slender finger.

"Princess," Sagami said in a low voice.

"I was like that little bird with my, my—" she stammered.

Sagami whispered: "—Mother?"

Shinko nodded and sobbed.

"And, Sagami, you also told me often that to avoid tragedy my mother's position here had to be anomalous, because if the heir to the

Saionji family married legally, misfortune would befall his lady, according to the *biwa* legend."

"Oh, Princess!" the governess gasped as if shocked by an electric current, and her face turned pale. "Oh, that?" Then she said in a whisper: "I, I wouldn't—I wouldn't think of that, now, Princess."

"Sagami! Sagami! Where are you? Is everything ready?"

"Yes, Master!" The governess composed herself and turned to Shinko. "Princess, your father has come home from the office and he'll be here in a minute. Please, hide your tears—"

"Sagami— Oh, Shinko is there too, huh?"

Saionji, who was cheerful, came close to them. The governess put the edge of her kimono sleeve to Shinko's eyes to wipe her tears away.

"Oh, I think you are excited, Shinko. Come, come, you'll be the happiest girl under the sun. Is something else still lacking?" he asked, putting his hand gently on her shoulder.

She turned slightly towards her father. "No, Father." Her sobbing began again.

"What, why is this, Shinko, my dearest child? What is this—Sagami? Do you want something more, Shinko?"

There was no answer. Shinko hid her face and shook her head.

"Oh, then, come, come. Brother Tokudaiji told me he and his wife will be here early in the evening to help us receive the guests. He is formal and doesn't want to see tears on the wedding day. Let's not show him any signs of disturbance." Hearing the sound of a voice outside, he added quickly: "Huh, that sounds like Brother now,—that's Brother's voice. I'll meet him. Genro Ito and his wife will also be arriving soon—"

Another sparrow flew down from the eaves and joined the two on the ground.

"That's the father sparrow," Shinko murmured as she walked towards her room.

The calm but cold winter evening fell around the Saionji home on the Surugadai Heights.

Every room in the building was brightly illuminated. The passage between the gate and the *genkan* was covered with fine pebbles showing the clear straight lines of bamboo garden rake.

"Genro Ito, what is the matter with the party—"

"Ah, don't you worry about it, you are a bit too anxious, Saionji-san. They will be here shortly; it's only a little after midnight."

"Genro Ito, I'd like to speak to you later—" Saionji left the room.

The white-bearded Tokudaiji beamed. "Genro Ito, my brother seems excited tonight."

"I don't blame him, Marquis Tokudaiji. Saionji-san is very fond of his daughter, and the governess is also much moved. Anyway, it is a great occasion for the Saionji family."

"Genro Ito, as Shinko's relative, I must, on her behalf and that of my brother's family, thank you and Genro Inouye for your efforts to bring about this marriage," the Lord of the Privy Seal said with his usual dignity and formality.

"Don't mention it! Marquis Tokudaiji, you and your brother have been my best friends for many years, and it's a small thing—"

"This time you had to come home from Korea to honor us."

"We, Inouye and I, must thank you for Saionji-san's trusting us to promote this happy union. As you know, the bridegroom, Hachiro, is our former lord's son. By this act we render our humble services to the Mori family and to your brother's."

"A most valuable and personal help to us, indeed, Genro Ito. Our traditional system of arranging matrimony is not bad after all, is it?" The elderly Tokudaiji was contented. He continued: "We delegate wise and experienced married couples to select brides and bridegrooms whom the matchmakers can honestly recommend to their friends, subject to the approval of the families and their immediate relatives."

"In this case the principles were given opportunity to associate with each other for many years. For that reason I have no fear that the newly-weds will quarrel and then dump the settlement on our shoulders, as often happens." Ito smoked leisurely for a moment and then said: "Oh, the bridegroom's carriage is approaching the house."

Now Matchmaker Ito was excited. "Let's take these new paper lanterns that have the Saionji family crests and go to the gate to welcome the party," he suggested. "Marquis Tokudaiji, you stand with the others on the left side of the passage and I'll head the line on the right side. Now, everybody get busy, but don't get confused. Oh, the first cock is already crowing—"

"Genro Ito! Genro Ito! Shall I come too?"

"Oh, no, no! Saionji-san, you see if everything is all right in the house. Leave this to us. Come, come, we mustn't delay!"

The quietness of the Saionji estates yielded to a subdued hum of voices. After the exchange of formal greetings in the reception-room, the bridegroom and his attendants retired to a chamber.

Ito whispered to his wife and the Inouyes.

"Now, Inouye, you'll lead the bridegroom into the ceremonial room, and your wife will follow on the right side, and we'll escort the bride. Then when we are all in the proper positions, we'll sit down—"

"Yes, yes, Ito, we understand. There isn't any change since we discussed things the other day, is there?"

"No, but I don't want to make any mistake," said Genro Ito, beaming. "I'd like to make the ceremony as formal as possible."

Ito's wife and Inouye's wife excused themselves frequently to see what progress had been made as to the make-up of the bride.

As Ito's wife returned to the room, her husband asked: "Is everything going all right with Shinko?"

"Yes. It'll take a little more time to get fully ready, however—"

"That's fine." He didn't notice her worried look.

Genro Inouye interrupted: "Well, no matter what you do, a wedding ceremony can never be completed before daybreak—"

"Did you practice chanting your *utai* sufficiently? I don't want you to stumble on it at the crucial point, and don't sing the whole stanza—"

"Oh, Ito, have you and Marquis Saionji decided whether the bride's real mother or the Marquis' new wife should appear with the Marquis tonight?"

"Ah!" Genro Ito's face darkened. "I'd completely forgotten about it," he said, dropping his voice to a barely audible whisper and leaning over the Inouyes. He cautiously looked around the room. "Say, Inouye, Saionji-san asked me to do things any way you and I thought best, but you see, it is a ticklish proposition. Let's go somewhere. Shall we take the women along, Inouye?" he asked as he got up.

"Yes, that's a good idea. They may have some suggestions."

The women rose, laughing.

"Something must be wrong. I have never before been consulted about anything," said Ito's wife.

"The same is true of me."

When they were alone Ito said: "See, Shinko's mother is not living in this house any more, as you know."

"So I understand—"

"And like Shinko's mother, Otama, although she gave birth to a child, has not been—probably never will be—registered as the wife. In ordinary cases there would be no question. The new one should take part in the ceremony." Ito waited for his friend's comment.

"Marquis Saionji and Okiku didn't quarrel, did they, Ito?" Inouye asked.

"No, that's the strange part of it—I can't understand. Okiku just went away when she found out that Otama had become pregnant."

"Okiku is a most courageous woman," said Ito's wife suddenly, and Inouye's wife smiled.

Inouye said with a gesture: "Have the couple, Shinko and Hachiro, any choice?"

"I don't think so, Inouye. I'm sure they haven't."

The women looked at each other for a moment.

Finally Inouye's wife said: "I don't know what Ito-no-okusan thinks, but I am sure it makes a great difference to the bride."

Between puffs of the cigar, Ito said: "H'm! H'm!"

She continued: "Shinko would be infinitely pleased to have her own mother tonight. You men can't understand a bride's feelings on her wedding night."

"Though she looks calm, Shinko is very sensitive, isn't she, Ito?"

"The choice is left in our hands," Ito said to himself, "and if the bride wishes it that way—"

His wife said: "Maybe Shinko's mood has been caused by the thought that—"

They turned to her.

"Early this evening, the hairdresser, after some hesitation, told me that the bride seemed to be worried. A little while ago, too, she remarked that no matter how hard and how many times she had put make-up on Shinko, it all came off. She thought Shinko wiped away her tears."

"Ha, ha, do they think Shinko has a hidden sweetheart, eh?" Ito interrupted.

Under the direction of Genro Ito, the wedding rites in the candle-lighted room had been progressing solemnly.

The master of ceremonies with the thinly-bearded chin conducted the procedure systematically. The formal exchange of the earthen saucer filled with cold sake between the bride and the bridegroom was about to be completed, the bride receiving the last serving of the nuptial cup.

Ito nodded to the other *nakaudo* to begin his *utai*. The subject of the chanting for the happy occasion was, as usual, *Takasago*.

Inouye raised his half-opened fan before his mouth; all eyes were on him. He, in turn, glanced through the room which in the meantime had been enlarged by removing the slides so that it now included the adjacent one. The relatives and close friends of the newlyweds who had waited in the ante-room watched the concluding part of the ceremony.

Inouye noticed the sake cup trembling in the bride's hands as he began: "TA—KA—SA—GO—Y-A-A! Ko—no—ura—fune—ni—"

He could not go on.

The listeners, who took his pause as a dramatic gesture, waited expectantly. Inouye struggled hard to go on. His throat was dry and his tongue stiff.

Just then the governess ushered Shinko's mother into the ante-room. Okiku was almost pushed to Saionji's side in the first row. She sat and bowed low.

The slight disturbance made the bride look up. Her eyes flashed as her mother raised her face. Shinko was radiant and lifted the cup to her mouth.

Genro Ito took a deep breath and Genro Inouye's *utai* went on melodiously.

"Is it not great that at last we can discuss any problems freely in the light of Socialist principles? Hurrah for the Nipponese Socialists!" shouted a young student waiting for his liberal associates to gather in an old tenement house in Tokyo. An instructor in sociology at Waseda University, named Abe Iso, replied: "But, my comrade, the present situation seems so unreal. Think, until just a few months ago, the Government made us miserable by applying strict measures of suppression. We couldn't publish our pamphlets, we couldn't hold meetings, we couldn't speak in public squares, and we couldn't openly organize our political groups—"

"This new Premier Saionji must be either tremendously broad-minded or knows so much about the liberal theories that he is un-afraid of the Socialist movement. Wasn't he the fellow who was once interested in the French School of Socialism?" the young man in-quired.

"Yes, but for the last twenty-five years the people thought Saionji had quite forgotten his liberalism. Although he kept radical young men close to him all these years, we certainly did not expect him to lift the ban against our group over-night."

Looking steadily at the young friend he said: "The only thing I am afraid of is a reaction to the present status—"

"Why?" the young comrade demanded.

"Because we get this freedom without paying a price for it. It comes as a surprise. Our influence didn't amount to much, for our group is negligible when compared with the entire population of the country. There may be two to three hundred people who understand Socialism in Nippon. Our sympathizers included, we are like a dewdrop in the Pacific Ocean. Unaided, we were in no position to sway the national policy towards liberalism.

"The more I study the situation, the more I'm convinced that the sudden change is due to the Premier's own initiative. The Seiyukai Party he heads has been considered the most conservative regarding all social and political changes which we have advocated. Then, too, think how powerful those Sat-cho Genros are. If they decide to interfere with officials or their policies, nothing can stop them. Should the Genros become resentful of the Cabinet's new attitude towards us, they would replace Premier Saionji with someone else like a magician pulls a live rabbit out of his sleeve—with someone who would kick us and beat us."

"Let's not be pessimistic, Professor. Let's do something. What can we do now?"

"Well, in the past it was easy; whenever we opened our mouths or picked up our pens we attacked the authorities. That's over. Now we must give the public a constructive program in our speeches and writings, besides pointing out the injustice and willful mistakes of the officials and the political parties," the Socialist professor concluded.

"In a way, your argument sounds true," the young man, concurring, went on. "When we used to meet secretly and published our leaflets under cover, ever so many people expressed their sympathy and willingness to join us if we should have any opportunity to form a regular party. Now that everything's free and open, we don't see those would-be Socialists any more—"

"That's human psychology. We like to pity other people and hear something new, fearful and forbidden. When all is open, that dies down and the curious stay away."

"Well, then why don't we take advantage of that weakness and play up something?" Grinning, he continued: "Say, by making our speeches terribly difficult to understand by the listeners and having our usual gatherings big noisy affairs—"

"Those tactics are necessary to attract the audience and to keep it intact, but over-emphasis on the point will do us no good in the long run. We must educate them rather than excite them about our principles, and we must explain to them our constructive programs in simple terms so they can grasp something."

"That will take a long time. What can our new Nippon Socialist Party do now, Professor?"

"There is one thing we can do for the people of Tokyo. It will give us great credit and publicity whether we succeed or not. That is our protest against the contemplated seventy per cent increase in carfares in the city. The newspapers and politicians are silent on the question. If we carry on a vigorous campaign the citizens will wake up and follow us. Even if we can't defeat the plan, we may be able to force the companies to reduce the expected increase."

"I wonder whether the other members will ever show up," the young man said after a hearty yawn. He sat down beside a large, old charcoal brazier which had a tiny fire.

"Well, Professor, I have somewhat lost interest in this movement, too."

Yawning again, the young Socialist stretched out on a shabby mat. A black cat with eyes glaring into the dim light came out of the brazier and shook itself heartily.

"Get away! Get away, you! You rascal, you put ashes into my mouth and eyes!"

The small fishing boats were slowly sailing homeward; a flock of sea gulls circled over the surf.

"In appreciation of your great service, Genro Ito and Genro Inouye, I had intended to have you here before, but as you know, hundreds of things came my way at one time." Saionji was in his Oiso home, entertaining his guests at a dinner.

"Ah, don't say that, Saionji-san, that was a pleasure for us. Don't you feel that way too, Inouye? As we said before, we couldn't do anything better for Lord Mori and for you than by arranging that wedding."

"Very true, Ito. But the hardest part of the wedding ceremony was—"

"I know, Inouye, that was your *utai*." Ito laughed indulgently.

"No, I mean the quick decision we had to make whether to have Shinko's real mother or stepmother for the ceremony."

Ito recalled: "The other day we had the new couple to dinner at my home. Shinko didn't say it in words, but it was plain to me that she was happy that her real mother had been present at her wedding. My wife tells me that your wife and she were the ones who actually saved the situation—

"Well, this is a perfect spring afternoon, with the best wine and the best friends. What more can we expect? In Korea I felt homesick for this relaxation. And yet I was glad to be there as the Resident-General and serve my country and her new protectorate. This may be my last active service to His Majesty," Ito added.

"Ito, you don't think we will annex Korea, do you?"

"If we want to we can, but I believe the present relationship is more satisfactory to the natives of the peninsula than outright annexation."

"Are you beginning to speak for the Koreans?" Inouye was dissatisfied and with the influence of drinks they were as usual conversing freely.

"I am, Inouye. I thought I could force anything Nippon wanted, but I begin to perceive that high-handed approach was a mistake. Although we must by no means relinquish our hard-earned rights over that country, we must see things from the native's point of view, as far as we can. Otherwise, even if we annex that old kingdom, our Korean administration will be haphazard."

Saionji agreed, but Inouye grumbled: "I don't see why we must come down to their level."

"If we disregard their rights, there will be constant conflicts between the governing and the governed. With the exception of a small number of irreconcilables and religious fanatics, I think the Koreans will co-operate with us if we deal with them with care—"

"Well!"

"Ha, ha, leave it to me and come to see the Korean belles." Ito beamed characteristically, "You'll be surprised to find how lovely and delicate is the texture of their skin. Their complexion is something like that of our Kyoto girls—"

"So that's what kept you there, huh?" the host broke in.

"Ha, you should come over, Saionji-san. I'll be your guide—"

"Tisk, tisk! When you two get together you talk openly about everything." Inouye was disgusted.

"It's our chronic ailment, Inouye, like your irresistible desire to do something for other people even if you are not asked for help, ha, ha.

"But our liking for the fair sex is different from most people's. Like yourself, we are honest so we let it out, while other men keep their affairs secret and pretend that they wouldn't look at any women except their own 'gods of the mountain' at home."

"You always find some excuse all right, Ito."

"Ha, your wife says the same thing of you, Inouye—you are always able to find some excuse to help other people."

Inouye couldn't help laughing, too.

"Anyway, leave Korea to me. You know and everybody knows my past records. Now in—"

Genro Ito's lengthy recounting of his meritorious accomplishments was interrupted by Inouye: "Among my own past achievements the one enterprise of which I am still proud is—"

"I know, Inouye, your part in presenting the *kabuki* drama—but how many times did I hear you tell about that?"

"That 1887 affair was a noteworthy one. I made the great classical actors, Danjuro, Kikugoro, and Sadanji and their followers perform in the presence of the Emperor and the Empress and other high personages for four days at my new mansion. The theatrical people still appreciate my favor—"

"I was the Premier and you were my Foreign Minister—"

"Marquis Saionji," Inouye ignored his friend's remark, "you are well-versed in drama, literature and all that. How many centuries was it since actors, whom we used to call 'Riverbeech beggars' and whom we excluded from society, had been accorded such a great honor?"

"I don't remember, probably never before. By your efforts, our actors were elevated to social equality with other people. You know I am fond of Danjuro. He is simply superb." Saionji soothed Inouye's feelings.

"Yes, Danjuro IX and Kikugoro V are rare artists."

Ito grumbled: "You are both alike!" Changing the subject, he said: "Saionji-san, you've dismissed Foreign Minister Kato, I hear. I brought him into the limelight—"

"Yes, I did. I believe you know the reason for my action."

"We didn't think you would act so quickly and daringly in that respect. You are getting increasingly bold. The purchase of railroads by the Government is at variance with Nipponese practice, too. Many people say it's socialistic." Inouye frowned at the term.

"The Government already owns the navy yards, arsenals, iron foundries and telephone and telegraph systems. In a country like ours, I believe that the average man is better off when the Government either owns or controls the key industries, including the railroads. But

Foreign Minister Kato strenuously objected to our policy in spite of the fact that the railroad question was not in his province—"

"He had to protect the Mitsubishi interests in Kyushu, which were threatened by your radical action," said Ito.

"So you dismissed him," Inouye sighed.

"No, he resigned. Did you hear anything strange in that connection?"

Ito commented: "I know of no other Minister who retired because he disagreed on a question outside of his jurisdiction."

"That is not what I mean. See, he wrote a lengthy thesis explaining his resignation—"

"For what, a magazine or a newspaper?" Ito asked.

"No, in his resignation presented to His Majesty—"

"What did you do with it, Saionji-san?"

"I presented it to His Majesty when I got it from the Minister."

"My, did the Emperor accept it without questioning the lack of precedence?"

"He did, saying that so far, whenever a Minister resigned, his reason for it had always been 'ill-health.'"

"That's an established custom." Genro Ito was much concerned. "Then, what did you reply?"

"Huh, I explained to the Emperor that Kato's action was also in order because whenever any responsible appointee tenders his resignation without actually being ill, there must be some definite reason for it. If he, on his retirement, freely expresses his views on the question, His Majesty will be informed as to how the matter stands."

Ito shook his head. "That's ideal, but I created a contrary precedent."

"Marquis Saionji," Genro Inouye spoke out, "I have heard that the Socialists are very active in the Capital these days. And they are greatly increasing in number and strength."

"What, Inouye? Socialists?" Ito laid his *sakazuki* on the tray. "That's outrageous, Saionji-san. Before they become stronger, put them out of existence at all cost."

"Don't get excited, Genro. There aren't many real Socialists in Nippon—"

"Oh, but the Metropolitan Police Headquarters has stated there are about twenty-five thousand in the country. Of these, fourteen thousand are in Tokyo alone. The figure includes three thousand, two hundred working people, seven thousand, five hundred students, fifty politicians, one hundred and eighty military men, sixty religious people, forty-five physicians, and ten justices."

"Huh, you know very well that such reports are always magnified for obvious reasons—"

"But, Marquis, the proof of the Socialist strength was revealed in their protest against the attempted increase of carfares in Tokyo last March. As a result, the companies' petitions to raise the three-sen fare to five sen were rejected by the Department of Home Affairs and the Municipal Assembly of Tokyo enacted laws so that the city could purchase the systems."

"Huh, had I known that the companies planned to raise the fare from three to five sen for no good reason, I myself would have had the Home Minister refuse to consider the application. Socialists or no Socialists, don't you think the car line owners were outrageous?"

Genro Ito played with his goat beard for a while. Then, with the air of a 'big brother,' he said: "Well, the companies were too greedy, but it's better for the country and for you to smash the radicals before they get too strong."

"You must remember, Genro, that the free play of discussions and thoughts is the only way to revitalize and rejuvenate our minds and keep us constantly moving forwards—"

"What?" Ito raised his eyebrows.

"Let me finish this." Saionji was stubborn. "Now, as I look back on the Restoration and immediately afterwards, our amazing progress was chiefly due to the same practice. In the name of His Majesty, the leaders, representing people of varied conditions, mental attainments, origin and ability, merged to push their country forward.

"You must admit that those Four Sages, as you call our great leaders, for instance, could not have done as much for the country had they been selfish, prejudiced and unco-operative."

"Are you telling us Genros what to do?" Ito said sardonically.

"No, I'm not— Now, I'm afraid that we are once more becoming politically, socially and economically stereotyped. You Choshu and Satsuma leaders—I'm one of your henchmen also—with but one political and social outlook, the totalitarian concept, despite the Imperial Constitution, have held the country in your grip for a generation. For the sake of His Majesty and for the average man, this must be modified—modified gradually—but we must begin now—"

"That's exactly what those radicals advocate. It's Socialism, no doubt," Inouye insisted.

"H'm," Ito snorted. "The average man, the ordinary person, doesn't know what's good or what's bad. He doesn't know anything, anyway. He can be booted around—"

"Genro," Saionji smiled, but answered firmly, "I'm sorry, but there you Genros and I differ as heaven and earth. I may be mistaken—"

"You must be, Saionji-san," Ito said amiably.

"Under your leadership a new class has been created in our country. These people enjoy exceptional privileges, they control the nation's affairs, they exploit the masses, and they monopolize social opportunities to gain closer contact with the Imperial Family—"

"Why not?" Ito thrust out his chin.

"My idea is to bring all Nipponese subjects and the Imperial Family closer together, thereby creating a really strong father and son, or considerate master and faithful subject, relationship."

"Inouye, I think you're right, Saionji-san is becoming a Socialist. He is ready to accept radical ideas and willing to shake the *status quo* we established with such effort."

"Huh, I did not 'accept' anything. That idea was almost born with me."

"Ah, you mean that radical ideas were born in you while you had a sweet dream with a Parisian beauty over thirty years ago, eh?"

"No!"

All smiled.

"However, don't you ever imagine that you can fool us Genros, particularly me, Saionji-san," Ito warned him.

"Me either. What is your next move?" Inouye asked.

"Huh, the Diet session has been successfully concluded. Genro Inouye, I shall take a short trip to Manchuria—"

"What, you, the Premier, plan to leave the country to go to Manchuria?" Ito was again puzzled.

"Yes, Genro, why not? The South Manchurian railway, south of Changchun, and its branches, which came to us as spoils of the recent war must be reorganized. We must administer the strip of land on which the railroads are laid and manage Liaotung Peninsula. As Premier, I'd better have first-hand knowledge of the acquisitions before tackling the situation."

Ito said: "You can't break every political precedent I have established."

"We'll not allow such unprecedented action," said Inouye with authority.

"Huh, this time your 'we' is broken. The other day I mentioned it to Genro Yamagata, who, though he was first reluctant, supported my plan."

"Hu'm, Yamagata has already agreed—"

Saionji said, laughing: "Supposing Premier Saionji sneaks out as a private person, who's to stop him? What would you say?"

Ito shook his head: "I'd say you were a rascal."

The gentle easterly wind brought a melodious, "Ho, ho, hokekkyo!"

"Ah!" Genro Ito smiled broadly. "That nightingale is singing in the grove of plum trees around my Four Sages' Arbor on my estate. Is it not sweet? Listen!"

"Huh, spring is here again," Saionji said.

They beamed amiably.

Premier Saionji, dressed in Nipponese clothes, a toothpick in his hand, stood in the garden of his official residence at Nagata-cho, which was not far from the southeastern end of the grounds of the Imperial Palace. He was looking at a few orchid plants he had brought over from his Surugadai home.

"Sir, the Honorable Matsuda, the Minister of Justice, and the Honorable Hara, the Minister of Home Affairs, are here to see you."

His face clouded.

"Huh." As he turned around he saw the two Cabinet colleagues greeting him.

When the host and the visitors were seated around a large charcoal brazier, Premier Saionji said: "Huh, friends, we seem to be heading for a Cabinet crisis. How shall we solve the impending problems?"

The ever-composed Matsuda replied: "Monsieur, can we hear your opinion first?"

The Premier smiled. "Huh, we must settle this budget quarrel between Finance Minister Sakatani and Communications Minister Yamagata. I am for the Finance Minister, but their difference even became personal—"

"Hard to dismiss one and keep the other, is it not, Chief?" Hara scowled and went on: "The Communications Minister has powerful political backing through his adopted father, Genro Yamagata. The Finance Minister through his father-in-law, Shibusawa, brings the Cabinet the tremendous support of the financial group."

The Ministers looked at each other. Saionji puffed at his cigarette and said: "I'll try a radical operation, if you approve—"

"That's fine!" Hara moved closer to his host.

"I'll dismiss both at the same time—"

"Do you have any successors in mind, Monsieur?"

"Huh, Matsuda-san, I have hope of persuading certain people, but during the present Diet session I want you to take over the Finance Post and Hara-san to look after the Communications Department besides your present assignments. That will keep the opposition in suspense."

"We'll act as you command, but, Chief, whom have you in mind to replace the quarrelling Ministers?" Hara asked.

"Huh, two influential members of the House of Peers— If this scheme succeeds, it will startle Genro Yamagata, who thinks the Upper House is completely in his hands."

"Monsieur, that'll kill two birds with one stone." The Justice Minister relaxed.

"Well, Chief, by that method we keep the Lords on our side, then in May the general elections will come. I'm certain that after the election we'll have a greater majority in the Lower House than we have now, because the public hailed our nationalizing the railways. And I'll get the Prefects and the police authorities throughout the country to work for the candidates nominated by the Seiyukai Party."

"Hara-kun," Matsuda objected, "your cherished idea of abolishing the county system, the subdivision of the prefecture, will enrage Genro Yamagata, who originated the plan many years ago, don't you think?" He glanced at Saionji.

"It will, Matsuda-san. The measure passed the Lower House last time, but was defeated in the Upper House. I still think the county system is outdated. It must be done away with in order to economize on governmental expenditures and accelerate the political and administrative co-ordination of the central and local governments. I'll push that measure until I succeed."

Matsuda looked uncomfortable.

"What do you think of the Socialists now?" said the Premier.

"Oh, Chief, I think your original idea was excellent. When we lifted the ban against them, they deflated like a punctured balloon. We didn't hear any more of their abusive complaints."

"But," Matsuda interjected, "now the Genros are terrified, and our liberal policy and the failure of the budget retrenchment irritates the businessmen."

"So you recognize that the business group is already restless, huh?"

"But, Chief, was it not fine that we pushed every measure through? We'll not have to increase taxes until the coming general election is over. Facing the electorates with a new tax proposal or a higher tax rate would be suicidal to the Seiyukai Party."

"Yes, there is a way to finance the next fiscal years," Matsuda remarked. "As Finance Minister Sakatani contends, we can increase paper currency to meet the expected deficiency."

"Huh, but that will inflate the money market still further, will it not?"

"No doubt, Monsieur—"

"Oh," Hara spoke again, "Premier, are you aware of the fact that our former Foreign Minister, Kato, seems to be active in organizing a political party under cover?"

"Huh, I've heard of it."

"That's something we must watch very closely." Hara continued: "That may mean that his backer, the Mitsubishi House, is ready to discard its long-established tradition of getting what it wanted through the manipulation of the Genros. Perhaps it will put its strength behind Kato. But first he may work under, say the ex-Premier, General Katsura."

"It may also mean that the Genro power and prestige has diminished in the eyes of the business world," said the cautious Matsuda with a smile. "The truth of the matter is that the financial magnate is willing to put money directly into the hands of its own man instead of dealing through the Genros."

"Huh, it's logical, Matsuda-san. The Genros are old; ex-Foreign Minister Kato is young. The strength of the Mitsubishi, like that of several other big business families, has been growing at an amazing rate, particularly since the war. When its interest is at stake, the House will give any amount of material support to the man who will look after it."

Hara clapped his hands. "If the Mitsubishi should put its own man up, we wouldn't have any difficulty in convincing its business rivals, the Mitsui, for instance, to back our Seiyukai Party. That's a new departure in politics, Chief. The fight is in its initial stage, we must get busy in that direction."

Saionji was smoking. "We must not commit ourselves to any business group."

The Justice Minister agreed with him.

"Sir, ex-Premier Katsura, is here. I informed him that I had been instructed to show him in—" the secretary said.

Saionji and his two Ministers looked at each other. The host murmured: "Huh, I meant these two gentlemen—"

The stout and erect kimono-clad General Katsura was already behind the secretary. "Oh, Premier Saionji, and friends," Katsura greeted them with an expansive smile as he walked in, "it's nice to see you. I lived here for over four years, as you know, and I still feel quite at home in this building and in the neighborhood. I often take a walk up in this direction, so I thought I'd drop in."

Katsura showed no trace of his characteristic military Satcho hauteur, though at heart he was anxious to gain power, prestige and dignity, like his provincial seniors. His ambition brought him into frequent conflict with the Genros, but he managed somehow to smooth matters over. His cleverness won him not only the favor of many politicians, but of businessmen, as well.

"We are glad to see you, too," the host welcomed Katsura.

After commenting on general matters, the ex-Premier remarked casually: "I understand that although you have followed my major policies, you are lenient towards the Socialists. And from what I gather from the Genros, your Cabinet's life was originally for a year. You have already successfully steered through two years."

The listeners were at a loss to know whether Katsura was making compliments or hinting for something.

Hara, a moment later, said: "The Seiyukai Party will carry on."

There was a silence.

Then Katsura said politely: "Premier, will you do me a favor? I'm in a predicament." He looked around at the company and continued: "It is not hard, it's a trifling matter for you to grant my humble request—"

"What is it, General?" Saionji asked lightly. The others leaned forward.

"Will you recommend to His Majesty the granting of a barony to Yasuda Zenjiro, the head of the Yasuda Banking House? See, during the recent war when the One Hundred and Thirtieth Bank of Osaka was on the verge of bankruptcy, I advanced government funds to rescue it at the request of Genro Matsukata and Genro Inouye who were personally interested, and asked Yasuda to restore the bank to its original condition."

Matsuda and Hara seemed eager to comment on the notorious case, but waited for their superior to speak. Saionji was unmoved.

Katsura continued: "At that time, the Genros promised that financial genius a peerage as the reward if he should succeed. Because of Yasuda's efforts the Osaka bank became solvent and prosperous. Since that was a private institution, I hesitated to comply with the Genros' wishes to get him the peerage. Then I resigned from the Premiership."

"Huh, so now Matsukata and Inouye want you to keep your promise—" Saionji murmured in his soft monotone.

"That's exactly it, Marquis Saionji."

The Justice Minister said: "It seems to me that it would be somewhat irregular if the Seiyukai Cabinet should act in Yasuda's behalf. Furthermore, that will put us in a difficult position because the Seiyukai Party protested in the Diet against your six million yen loan to the Osaka bank during the war—"

"I know it, Matsuda-san, but if the bank had crashed it might have resulted in a general financial panic in the midst of that titanic struggle. The grant of a barony won't hurt the dignity of the Saionji Cabinet."

"Some years ago," the host said reminiscently, "when I was the Director of Imperial Decorations, Genro Inouye commanded me to grant honors to his acquaintance who apparently deserved no public merits. Naturally, I refused—"

"So in the present instance, too." Hara interrupted.

"Yes." Saionji turned to the ex-Premier and said: "I am sorry, but I cannot comply with your request. It is my opinion that if you believed Yasuda deserved the honor you should have done the job yourself, while you were in the office."

"I see," Katsura murmured, while Saionji's colleagues nodded in confirmation.

"Sir," the secretary announced, "a telegram for the Home Minister—"

"Oh, from whom, I wonder!" Hara said as he accepted it. "Hu'm, from the Prefect of Tochigi—"

"What's up, Hara-kun?" Matsuda asked nonchalantly.

"Oh!" the Home Minister groaned, and then said rapidly: "Think, the miners at the Ashio Copper Mines have called a strike. They resisted the local police and there was a series of bloody conflicts. It is now out of police control. The Prefect asks my immediate instruction."

General Katsura, with a cynical smile, said: "Isn't that the famous copper mine of the Furukawa Company of which you are the adviser?"

Saionji and Matsuda stared at Hara, who took no heed of Katsura's comments but asked: "What shall I do, Premier?"

"Naturally—" Matsuda paused.

Katsura said coldly: "If I were you I should order a military unit to be mobilized, that is what it is for." Turning his contemptuous eyes to Saionji and Matsuda, he added: "Well, when a fire begins to burn one's own eyebrows it's different, is it not? It's needless to remind you"—he emphasized his final remark with a jerk of his chin—"that this is the direct result of Socialist agitation which you have encouraged—"

The Premier replied: "Not necessarily."

"Come, Little Princess." Thus Saionji's aged governess called Sonoko, her master's second daughter.

The girl was playing in the garden. Otama, her mother, wearing a simple house-kimono, sat near the baby in the warm spring sun.

Sagami's head shook at Otama. She repeated: "Come, Little Princess."

"She can stay with me," said the mother. "It's lovely here—so warm—"

The governess was no longer agile. When Shinko, her 'Big Princess,' was Sonoko's age, Sagami had often played with her. Now she contented herself with telling the other members of the household, especially Otama, how to conduct themselves.

Her scarcely visible eyebrows knitted and her lean chin stuck out toward her. "You must not interfere with my way of training Little Princess. You don't seem to realize it, but you—I must look after Princess."

Otama asked: "Why? Do you mean I'm unfit to bring up my child?"

"Oh, you have the wrong notion altogether." The governess shook her gray head rhythmically and scowled. She explained at length the views on the relationship between Otama and Saionji, and Otama and the child.

"See, you are my master's mistress, just a mistress. You cannot claim to be his *okugata* or Little Princess' mother. No, no, that's a mistaken idea—"

Otama's round eyes were fixed on the governess.

With a swing of her chin, Sagami continued: "And furthermore, even when you're with Little Princess, at home, you must conduct yourself decently—"

"Well, why? What do you mean?" she asked after a long sigh.

"Let me remind you, a young woman like you must always dress properly and have her hair combed and keep her make-up right, so that whenever your master comes home you will be pleasing to look at—"

"Oh, what's—"

The aged woman persisted: "Do you ever think of that?"

"Well, I know, but what's the use of all that trouble? He doesn't come home, he doesn't take me anywhere any more, and I'm simply a nurse-maid," said Otama.

"My, my, this young woman! What do you think your master is? He is His Majesty's Prime Minister. The welfare of fifty million Nipponese depends upon him. Why should he come to see his fading mistress every night? Little Princess is different, of course. He must entertain and meet statesmen at his official residence, besides his ordinary social contacts in the evening."

"He promised me hundreds of things, but here I am left alone. I could have gone to one of the richest men in the country had I known I was doomed to be a kept woman. There I could have had luxury without being constantly told to do this and that and not to—"

"If you don't like it here, I suppose you could just walk out, that's what Big Princess' mother did. She, too, was very stubborn, and misbehaved at first, but under my instruction she became a perfect housewife. It was too bad the Saionji tradition did not allow her to be my master's *okugata*—"

"I don't care what she did. How can I return to my geisha life or find a suitor able to give me luxury? I no longer have my former beauty. My contact with you has robbed me of my gay disposition and charm—like the heavy, frosty night air smothering a greenhouse rose."

The governess shrugged her shoulders. "It's because you don't take care of yourself—you don't know how. Big Princess' mother was always dressed up whether the master was here or away. Besides, she learned everything a woman should know."

Unmindful of the heated argument, Little Princess trotted about the garden, talking unintelligibly and laughing to herself.

"Ah, Master is home!" the governess exclaimed with a big smile.

"Come, Little Princess." She caught Sonoko. "See, your honorable father has come home."

"Oh, Sonoko, come to Father." Saionji took her into his arms and carried her to his room.

Tenderly laying his daughter on his lap, Saionji said: "Sagami, Takekoshi-san may come to see me."

"Yes, Master!"

After Saionji looked through a pile of letters on his table, he turned to her again.

"Sagami."

"Yes, Master."

"I had intended to relieve you completely of your duties here, but—" he hesitated—"as you know, Otama has enough to do with the baby and can't help direct the household. And you don't have Shinko to help you. Shall we engage a regular housekeeper to succeed you?"

"Master, I am still quite able to work. Since you often remain at the official residence, there is little to do at home, but O—"

"Otama is no help, huh?"

"It may be the way with young women of her age and profession today, but Okiku was different," she said rather mournfully.

"Huh, she was a good companion, too," Saionji admitted.

Sagami, beaming, added: "Master, I met her at Big Princess' the other day. The Princess sent for her. Oh, we had a nice long chat together. It was such a relief to see her there."

"Huh, after all, you and Okiku like each other—"

"You like her well also?" She looked into his eyes.

"Huh—Sagami, do you know how soon Shinko expects her baby? Is she all right?"

"Oh, Master!" The governess leaned over to him and said: "You'll be a grandfather any day now. Big Princess is quite all right and it's lucky to have her experienced and kindhearted mother looking after her—"

"Huh, she pays much attention to Shinko?"

"Master, you should see Okiku and the Princess together. Okiku told me that she prayed every morning and night to the Asakusa *Kwannon* for the safety of the expectant mother and the child and to the Tsurugaoka Hachiman Shrine that the first grandchild might be a son and heir to the Saionji family."

"Huh."

"Have you considered the first grandchild's name, Master?"

"In my spare time at the Cabinet desk I jotted down several names for the daughter's first born—I'm sure Hachiro will ask me to name his child. If he is a boy I'll name him Ko-ichi. The first letter of my name can be read *Ko*, and the character denoting first is *ichi*, so that his name will mean my first grandson."

Otama came in.

"Huh, Otama!" Saionji smiled, but Sagami glanced at her critically.

"Will you take me somewhere today?" Otama began. "Take me to a moving picture show—I hear that new amusement is very popular—or to Uyeno Park for the night view of the cherryblossoms. I have been home all these days." She spoke peevishly.

"Huh, I will, but wait awhile. I have to attend to a few things before we go out." Then he turned to Sagami and said: "I'm tired and wanted to rest at home. That's why I left the Nagata-cho residence for an evening."

The governess sympathized with him; Otama turned her sulky face away.

"Huh, Takekoshi's at the door!"

The dutiful Sagami tried to get up immediately. Otama sat motionless. The aged woman put her hands on her knees, pulling them up one at a time, to get to her feet. She stood up, bowed briefly to her master and murmured as she went to receive the visitor: "Takekoshi-san is a gentleman—"

As the governess' bow-like figure disappeared, Saionji said to Otama: "I didn't know you were acting like a spoiled child at home, letting Sagami attend to everything here. I wish you would go to the door when we have a visitor. Sagami is very old—"

"She doesn't like my way of doing things," Otama snapped back at him. She took little Sonoko and went away as they heard the visitor and Sagami returning to the room.

Takekoshi looked down at the bent figure. "You always look strong. It's amazing."

"Thanks very much. Excellent health is my pride and my privilege, so that I can serve my master without failure," Sagami replied.

"Marquis!"

"Huh, Takekoshi-san, sorry to bother you—"

"Oh, no, it's a pleasure, sir. I've been wanting to visit you for a long time."

"You must be busy these days. My Cabinet colleagues, and I particularly, are deeply thankful for and elated at your brilliant editorials and feature articles in your Yomiuri newspaper, supporting the Administration's policies."

"Not at all, sir. It's a great honor to be considered useful. It is a partial repayment of my long and heavy indebtedness for the favors I have enjoyed from you in past years."

Sagami retired; both lighted their cigarettes.

"Huh, Takekoshi-san, will you help me to carry out a little plan of mine?"

"Whatever I can, Marquis." The newspaper editor was smiling.

"Although I want to become acquainted with more literary people, I don't know many of them because I have been so absorbed in official duties. I'd like to invite some here."

"I see, Premier Saionji. About how many?"

"As many as you think reasonable. I'd like to have interesting people of every school of the contemporary literary world. I'll leave it all to you—you know my house and everything. I want to have a really informal gathering here. Oh, by the way, Takekoshi-san, what became of that Kunigita, the novelist who lived here for a while?"

"Marquis, I am terribly sorry for that genius. He is not feeling well. He has lung trouble now, I am told. Since he left here I haven't seen much of him. A novel he wrote at your house, entitled *Police*, just appeared on the market—"

"Huh, I received a complimentary copy."

"It is gaining much popularity."

"Huh, that's good news. I suppose he is still drinking."

Smiling, the host continued: "Takekoshi-san, I must tell you about that picture-scroll. Do you remember the one we worked on together? At His Majesty's request we described the life of Sanjyo Sanetsumu, the father of the late Premier Sanjyo. You made drafts in twelve sections out of the historical material furnished us by the Department of the Imperial Household, and I made a few revisions and had a Court artist fill in the drawings."

"I do, sir."

"Huh, my brother, Tokudaiji, told me this. One day, not long ago, he was with the Emperor in the Imperial study. His Majesty called my brother to his desk to see the scroll. The Mikado was in good humor and said to him: 'Look at this picture-scroll illustrating Sanjyo's life. I knew that if I had Kimmochi handle this undertaking, he would begin with this type of opening remark. Here it is, exactly as I thought it would be, "The Trend of Affairs in the World." ' His

Majesty slapped his knees and laughed heartily, Tokudaiji told me."

"His Majesty knows you well, Marquis."

"I guess so, Takekoshi-san. You see, whenever I am received in audience, I recommend to the Emperor the urgency of marching forward with the general trend of the times."

"I beg your pardon, sir," the voice behind the paper screen said. "Telephone from Lord Hachiro—"

"All right. Excuse me, Takekoshi-san. I don't know what my son-in-law wants," he said to his young friend as he rose to go to the phone.

"What?" The Premier's voice was excited. "What did you say, Hachiro? What? Fine! I'll be right over. Oh, no, I was exhausted; that's why I came home to rest, but nothing can stop my coming over."

Never before had Saionji been so excited; he forgot his visitor, Sagami, Otama and his weariness, and hastened to the bedside of his daughter and first grandson.

For some time it had been an established custom for the Premier after his succession to office to hold a banquet to entertain influential people at his official residence at Nagatacho, the chief guests being the Genros and the Cabinet members.

Premier Saionji gave such a banquet in the summer of 1908.

Elaborate preparations were in progress. Among other things, a stage was erected in the garden for the presentation of *kabuki* plays as a unique part of the entertainment.

The Premier had supervised the plans until late in the afternoon, when a messenger arrived.

Saionji sat for a while with the letter on his lap. Once he was about to call his chief political lieutenants to come immediately. Then he left the telephone with a deep sigh and picked up a cigarette. He looked over his official documents and stayed at his desk until just before the earliest arrivals came.

The cheerful guests conversed in the waiting-room, with Foreign Minister Hayashi as the center of attraction.

A business executive was saying: "The recent achievement of your office, Foreign Minister, is the elevation of our Legations in Berlin and Washington to Embassies—now we have Ambassadors there instead of Ministers."

Another commented: "Well, Foreign Minister, we outsiders aren't affected much, but your subordinates at home and abroad must be greatly pleased with the change."

"No doubt. A Minister at a foreign court is treated like a distant cousin, but Ambassadors are received as honored guests on all state occasions. While the former represents the Foreign Minister of his Government, the latter speak for the Sovereign, so that the Minister can only meet the Foreign Minister, but Ambassadors can ask an audience—" Hayashi explained.

"How is it that this German Government so quickly copied the United States in receiving our Ambassador? Many years ago, when we had great admiration and respect for the Berlin Government, she slapped our face often. As a result our newspapers and magazines were unfriendly to Germany."

Hayashi answered: "Well, we are not at liberty to speak about the actions of another government, but when Ambassador Inouye was received in audience at the German Court, Wilhelm II pointed out the hostile attitude of our newspapers towards Germany. Our diplomat was consulted as to what could be done to create more friendly feelings between the two countries."

"Is it a mere rumor or is there some truth in the story that a revised commercial treaty is to be concluded between Nippon and America in which the United States will give us full power to adjust the tax rate on goods coming into our country from abroad? What do you call that in your legal phrase—tariff autonomy?" the businessman asked.

The Foreign Minister dodged the question by saying: "Other people seem to know much more than I do."

Another group, surrounding the Minister of Home Affairs, Hara, was congratulating the Seiyukai Party on its victory in the last general elections.

"It is a fact that in our Cabinet the Minister of Home Affairs wields enormous power, is it not? In ordinary times he has direct control over all the Prefects or Governors in the country, including the power to appoint and dismiss them, and through the Prefect his authority reaches to the lowest political subdivisions. But, Home Minister Hara, how did you influence the general elections and how did you carry the last one so successfully?"

Hara replied quietly: "By carefully mobilizing the Prefects and their subordinates for the Government Party, the Seiyukai, and by the Party's own campaigns."

"But, if the Governors don't co-operate with you?"

"Well, candidly, they'll be dismissed. Like my predecessors, when I came into office, I weeded out the unfriendly Prefects and promoted prefectural Bureau heads in their places. In addition, during the general elections, a strong pressure was exerted upon them from my office. They are something like horses pulling a heavy load, and the Home Minister is the driver. If they slacken, the swishing whip descends upon their backs. Some, of course, will be laid off if they fail to show results."

"H'm."

"See, since our Prefects are career men, they dread a dismissal note from Tokyo—"

The former Justice Minister, Matsuda, strolled into the room.

"How is our Finance Minister these days?" A man began a conversation with him.

"Well, I am somewhat at a loss with my Portfolio, do you know? I headed the same Department ten years ago, so I'm not a stranger to the job. My present difficulty is my unfamiliarity with businessmen. You see, soon after the Sino-Nipponese War, when I directed the Department last, there were only a few influential and wealthy people. It was easy to get to know them and get their co-operation with the Treasury."

"I see."

"But now our last war with Russia created many millionaires or so-called 'get-rich-quick' people—and those who had large holdings in the pre-war period became multi-millionaires. They became politically minded, too. While the Cabinets rose and fell, the money people grew steadily more powerful. If they oppose the Finance Department's policies, for instance, I can't do a thing—"

The sound of conversations and laughter filled the room. Then the announcement was made that the guests were to take their places at the dinner table.

Genros Yamagata, Matsukata, Inouye and Oyama were singled out from the crowd and led to the head of the table on either side of the host. The others took their seats.

Premier Saionji made his simple speech of greeting and, after the thunderous applause, Finance Minister Matsuda, representing the guests, responded briefly. For the first time the Genros were not called on to make speeches, nor were they made the center of attention.

Various drinks were offered to the guests; pretty geishas were at their service; the merriment was kept up in the liveliest fashion until the company adjourned to watch the actors on the temporary stage in the garden. The Genros left unusually early, but no one missed them.

When the actors bowed for the last time to the enthusiastic audience, the moon was already pale, and from afar the crowing of a cock broke through the sleepy, summer-morning air.

After the other people had left, Saionji persuaded the Cabinet Ministers to sit down and drink a little more before they departed.

"Gentlemen," the Premier said slowly, "I intended to report to you tomorrow, but I want to tell you now that I had to make a rather sad decision this afternoon—" The Ministers pricked up their ears. "I shall resign from the Premiership—"

"What!" the men were startled. But no one dared to speak again for some time.

Then Home Minister Hara, breathing audibly, mumbled to himself: "Why should we retire? The people have just given us an indisputable mandate by electing an absolute Seiyukai majority to the Lower House of the Imperial Diet."

He raised his dreamy eyes to the Premier and asked: "Chief, may Matsuda-san and I be allowed to hear the reasons for your sudden decision?"

"As I see it, the country needs different national policies, which should be formulated and executed by another Cabinet. We have remained in power much longer than the average Administration—which was about a year and a half."

"We don't mean to dispute your decision, Monsieur, but what has led you to decide so abruptly? To my mind, the only people who can shake your confidence and threaten your future are the Genros. I noticed that they did not enjoy the evening here tonight, but why—?"

Matsuda saw that the Premier was not willing to elaborate, but the aggressive Hara was still inquisitive: "Is it our tolerance towards the Socialists?"

At that moment they saw a glint in the Premier's steady brown eyes.

"You have added another star to your brilliant political skies, Genro Ito," Saionji said.

"It's great to be at home, Saionji-san, after my long absence. I went to the Korean Capital immediately after the Russo-Nipponese War in 1905."

They stood before the Four Sages' Arbor on Genro Ito's Oiso villa. The morning sun shone on them through the thick branches of plum trees whose fruit was already grown to the size of a bean.

"Your last task must have been an arduous one. The wrinkles on your forehead have deepened, your hair is thinner at the temples and in front, and your beard is gray, Genro Ito."

"Ah, it took much out of me. But don't you think I did a good job in Korea? No other Nipponese could have done what I did." Ito raised one shoulder, and said: "Don't you think I look much more dignified than I used to?"

"Yes, you do. An increased frosty touch in your appearance has given you a more elderly look—"

"I'm not talking about that. Don't you remember I was elevated to princehood last year? I am Prince Ito—"

"Huh, that's right."

"Ah, you're disgusting. You don't pay any attention to titles. In your eyes a title is something like a gold coin before the eyes of a cat, as we say—doesn't mean a thing. No Nipponese subject can rise higher than Prince. I rose from the lowest to the supreme rank. In the Imperial Court I am allowed to sit next to the Emperor because I was honored with the 'Collar of the Grand Cordon of the Chrysanthemum,' too. Now that I'm home again, Oiso will once more be the center of politics. I expect a lot of visitors today."

"I hope they will call you Prince Ito," remarked Saionji.

"Well, they can address me as Former Resident-General in Korea, Genro Prince Ito—"

"Huh, but where is the title of the Privy Council Presidency to which you have been reappointed?" Mischievously, Saionji added: "If a slow-talking man like Matsuda is required to say all that, it will take him a half hour—"

"You are as cynical as ever. Your hair is getting gray—much more so than mine. I may get bald-headed, but you'll be totally white, as if you had a cotton cap!"

"Huh, I guess you are ready to remain quiet from now on!"

"Well, yes, Saionji-san, I have one more trip." Ito swallowed his words with his cigar smoke.

"Do you have a secret plan or something?"

Saionji lighted his cigarette.

After a short silence, Ito said: "In a way it is secret. Confidentially, yes, I have a plan. It's an exceedingly ambitious one. I'll explain it to you later. After all, you are my best friend, and also a leading statesman—next to us Genros. You should know about it."

Saionji gazed at Ito for a while. "Huh, I see, you are planning a trip to other countries, with a definite purpose—"

"Anyway, Saionji-san, shall you and I have a good and leisurely talk here, with a little drink? Later we may go to the Gunkaku-ro. It's our reunion."

"Not a bad idea, Ito, or Prince Ito, rather, ha, ha."

After ordering the servants to prepare a few dishes, Ito asked Saionji: "Did you know I had a foreign-styled room made of the annex? I want you to see it. I don't have much use for it, but a man of my standing—"

"Huh, it is still largely a matter of satisfying one's vanity to have a European room, is it not?"

The Genro ignored the remark.

"Ah, the cook has prepared my favorite menu," the host said sometime later. "You know, Saionji-san, there are many things I want to say to you." Ito was sitting on the tiger skin.

"Huh, I expected that."

"You are the only one I can talk with intelligently on important subjects."

"So you think I'm an intelligent man?"

"There are a few other clever men in Nippon besides you, though—"

"Huh?"

"Yes, a really intelligent man—or at least one who is my equal—is Okuma. He has never been out of Nippon, but he knows much of other countries because he reads widely and meets everybody, young or old, enemy or friend, or even a stranger, if he has something to offer him."

"You are broad-minded, too."

"Yes—I, in that respect, may surpass him, but candidly, Okuma is intelligent. When I returned home from my last Western trip and visited him at his Waseda home, I told him a lot of things I had seen in America and Europe. After he had listened to my talk patiently, Okuma asked me if I had seen an automobile in America. I replied affirmatively—"

"And you gave another long lecture on it, I suppose?"

"Ha, ha, ha," Ito laughed aloud. "I think, Saionji-san, he knew more about American automobiles than I did. Then he also asked me if I had a ride in a car. I said, 'Yes.' He thought for a while and praised my venturesome spirit and all that, saying even the daring Americans hesitated to ride in a car because the automobile was so slow and poured out smoke from the radiator—ha. He embarrassed me." He paused. "See, I saw the car, but I didn't ride in it."

"How did you answer him?"

"So I said I got into it to have my picture taken, ha, ha."

Saionji choked with laughter over his sake, and long afterward said: "Huh, you are a clever one."

He raised the sake jug to serve Saionji. The latter waved his hand. "Pass me up this time. I have had enough. Let's talk for a while."

"Oh, you have weakened these days, Saionji-san; it may be because of your advanced age. If you get tired of sake, here is this drink I brought home from Korea, it's made of *kaoliang*, something like our *shochu*. I am sure you can stand a little of it."

As he poured the new drink into Saionji's cup Ito whispered: "Say, I heard you found another pretty geisha, is that true? I've got to get busy in that direction myself."

The guest just smiled. "Huh, what do you think of your disciple?" He looked into the Genro's eyes.

"I was coming to that—so far, so good." Ito stroked his beard and continued: "In general, you have upheld my policies and have done a good job, too, in both domestic and international affairs. But you ignored my warning. I told you not to leave the Socialists free. That made Yamagata mad—as a matter of fact, all the Genros were against your social policies."

Saionji was unmoved despite a barrage of sharp comments from his mentor; his eyes twinkled in the reddish expanse of his face.

Ito shifted his legs and went on: "In the future, too, Saionji-san, if you listen to those unpatriotic radicals, we, the Genros, will throw you out again. Some of those Socialists were against the war during the Russo-Nipponese conflict, you remember? You see, the civilized Western nations are tending towards what they call 'armed peace' with their armies and navies expanding as fast as possible. Nippon is about to enter the arena. The Socialists are against that program—for the sake of the 'average man.' "

Ito lighted his cigar and continued: "If we want to have membership in those enlightened circles, we must act as the others do, that is, expand our national defense—"

"How are we going to meet the bills?"

"Taxes!" the Genro barked.

"The common people have enough tax burden to bear."

"Forget the 'common people' or 'average man,' your favorite terms! No matter what happens to them, armament must go on, do you understand, Saionji-san?"

Saionji merely grinned.

Ito drank another cup of *kaoliang* liquor. "Otherwise you are all right, but you always get frightened when it comes to the question of military preparedness. There Katsura is far better than you are. That fellow shows his true statesmanship there, he can take strides unafraid—that's also true of his measures against the Socialists, he simply grinds them under his heels, and he can raise money—"

"Huh, I'm not so sure about that—"

"Why not? How dare you contradict me?"

"If you tax the average man so heavily in peace times as to hurt his productive power, don't you think in the long run you will kill 'the goose'?"

"Don't you dare preach to me, that's your bad habit."

"Wait, Genro Ito, huh, Prince Ito." Ito smiled at that. "Let me say a little more—"

The Genro raised his hand to stop Saionji. To shift his cramped legs, Saionji put both his hands on the floor in front of him as if he were bowing to the Genro.

This movement pleased Ito.

"Huh, this Korean liquor is potent. It makes me dizzy," said Saionji, wiping his forehead.

"Come, come, take some more, you rebellious *Okuge-sama*—that title of the old order is no good now. You dare talk back to me— Remember, I and you were both Marquis until a few months ago, but I'm above you now. I'm a Prince and you are not."

With an unsteady hand Genro Ito poured more liquor into Saionji's cup and his own.

"Huh, Marquis or Prince or what not," Saionji murmured, "I'll feed the title to a dog, a-ha-ha-ha!" He raised his cup.

"Here's to Prince Ito and his ambitious new plans!" He gulped the liquor.

"I was going to tell you. I, Prince Ito, you understand, the greatest living statesman of the Nipponese Empire, will leave for the continent to carry out my schemes on the now disintegrating China. There is no way of rescuing that Old Empire; sooner or later the Dragon will be cut up among the Powers. We've got to act quick, now—"

"Huh, that—that's what I thought you had in mind."

Saionji's eyes were shut; Genro Ito blinked. The two men were swaying sideways.

"Nippon, Nippon alone can't bite a chunk out of the Dragon. Prince—Prince Ito, what country will you invite to co-operate with us? Can you tell me, whe—whether your plan is worth anything?"

Ito rubbed his smoke-filled eyes and started to talk: "Russ—Russia—Russ and us must co-operate, not fight—"

"Now, now, Prince, Prince Ito, I—I say, we must co-operate—not fight, let's rest awhile." Saionji stretched on the mat on his side, using his arm as a pillow.

The host lay flat on the tiger skin, with his arms around the animal's head.

He murmured: "H'm. Your Okiku used to call you Prince, but that was from the old order—but I earned my title." Before each word he had to lick his lips.

A second later, the country's two leading statesmen were snoring side by side to the rhythm of the droning waves below the villa.

It was late afternoon when they woke up.

"O-o-o, a-a-uh!" Ito stretched on the pelt. "A-a-uh, bring us water!" he said and added, "It looks like rain soon."

Saionji yawned heartily and asked: "Why is it, we used to take a lot of liquor without having it affect us. Today we went down so fast—?"

"Well, Saionji-san," Ito yawned once more with his arms up over his head, "I suppose it's chiefly because of our advanced age; you'll be sixty soon—I'm eight years your senior."

"But there is another reason for it." Both drank their glass of water. "We're both out of practice."

Genro Ito grinned and went on with a serious look: "See, while I was there in Korea, I was busy and had no time to relax, nor had I a really intimate friend like you, for instance, to drink and talk with, without reservation."

"Huh, that gives our poor brains a rest—"

"That's right, Saionji-san. There was still another reason for my self-restraint."

"Huh?"

"As we know from history books, political murder by poisoning has been popular there. I was constantly warned against that notorious practice which is mostly carried out at drinking parties. I may have been over-cautious, even timid, and probably unfair to my good Korean friends. On the other hand, not a single minute did I ever forget that I was representing His Majesty, to assist our neighboring country in the administration of her national affairs."

"Huh, your good old spirit as a true servant of our Sovereign."

"Anyway, my conscience restrained me from carelessness and over-indulgence and all that. See, I don't want to perish for nothing, though I'm ever ready to die for the country and for the Emperor. By the way, what were we talking about before we went to sleep?"

"I don't remember. But why did you mention death? You have a great deal more to do, Genro Ito—"

"Ah, ah, that's right, we were on the subject of my scheduled trip to the continent—I remember now. But, Saionji-san, that's really confidential, for I don't want any premature publicity about it. I'll first confer with the Russian Minister of Finance whom I expect to see in Manchuria in the fall and I'll sound out what he thinks of my idea of Russia and Nippon standing together on the questions concerning Eastern Asia, and China in particular."

"How about England, our present ally, Genro?"

"Well"—Genro Ito again licked his dry lips—"the Anglo-Nipponese Alliance is a good thing and has yielded us some benefits, but we must co-operate with our neighbors, China and Russia. But since China is undependable at this time, we must take Russia into our confidence and work with her. Did I tell you of my plan for a big army and navy?"

"Huh, you did!"

"At last we've discovered that might is right; we must back up our words in international affairs. We used to think when we first heard of international law that it was a code like civil or criminal statutes. It doesn't exist. International law is merely the stern voice from the Foreign Office of any big Power.

"In that connection, that American President, Theodore Roosevelt, who has just retired from office, is a foresighted man. He has done everything on such a big scale. His big navy program is something to think about, not only as a model of fine statesmanship, but also as possibly an initial move by the United States towards telling us what to do and what not to do—"

"Where?"

"On this side of the Pacific Ocean, including China. Don't you know, last year a rumor was prevalent that the United States and the late Empress Dowager Tsu Tsi had concluded an alliance?"

"Genro Ito, I'm more interested in President Roosevelt's new economic policies, breaking up big monopolies and—"

"Don't you ever let such a misleading ideal for our country grow in your head. You are susceptible to that sort of thing. We must keep our common people as they are—contented—as long as possible. That's our national strength."

Saionji shrugged his shoulders. With a smile he asked: "By the way, Genro, is this scheme about China your idea; did you think it out?"

"Why do you ask such an insulting question? You've got a hang-over from drinking. You can't think straight—but just a second, I have to go to the water closet."

When the host staggered back, Saionji was shaking his head. "Huh, my head is heavy, all right."

Genro Ito resumed: "I have had that scheme in mind for some time and then that Goto Shimpei, that conceited fellow you appointed President of the South Manchurian Railways and who's now Katsura's Communications Minister, urged me to do something."

"Huh, I think Goto is one of the most enterprising and courageous men we have."

"He did not ask my approval before accepting the post. He dared to slight a Genro."

A faint smile quivered on Saionji's face.

Ito's servant returned.

"Oh, bring a couple of jugs of hot sake!"

"Sir, here are many visiting-cards left by people who were here during your nap."

"Ah, leave them and bring hot sake first. If we take a little hot stuff to counteract the hang-over, we'll feel better, eh, Saionji-san?"

"Huh, I'll take just a bit to warm up my system."

"Well, well. Oh, speaking of Goto, don't let him sway you with his big talk on 'Great Asia Principles.' I warned him on that. That will irritate other Oriental peoples and create misunderstandings with the Western Powers. Even without that as a pretext, some politicians in America, for instance, are already making a lot of fuss about our people on the Pacific Coast and about our increasing influence on the Asiatic Continent."

"That immigration problem is a very difficult one. My Foreign Minister has spent a great deal of time on it, but the Washington Government seems unable to cope with the local agitations in California and Washington." Saionji showed concern. "What would you do with that immigration problem, if you were the Premier or the Foreign Minister?"

"Well, we could lodge a stronger protest if it gets worse, but—but I think we've just got to forget our people there. How many are there, one hundred or one hundred and twenty thousand in America?"

"Huh!" Saionji stared at his senior. "That's most unbecoming of you. On what grounds do you make such a bold declaration?"

Ito, stroking his beard down to his throat, said: "Well, those big business people who deal with American merchants, particularly in raw silk, our most important export commodity, don't want us to displease our best customers under any circumstances, you see.—Let's have this hot one." He served sake to his friend and was eager to change the subject.

"Huh, after a few cups of this I've got to be leaving. It was nice to see you once more at your home."

"Don't hurry, you are my neighbor."

"Huh, I'm no longer your neighbor—"

"What? What did you do with your house?"

"I sold it soon after I had you and Genro Inouye for dinner following Shinko's wedding."

"You sold it. Why?"

"Huh, with you away in Korea, Oiso meant little to me, and that farmer next to my house became disagreeable. He began to use some fertilizer with horrible odors in the adjoining vegetable gardens. I could not stand it any more."

"Probably he wanted you to buy it at a high price," Ito snickered.

"He made a mistake, Genro."

"Why didn't you do something?"

"No, never thought of it—I packed up and left."

"Who bought your estate?"

"Huh, the buyer was one of the directors of the Mitsui Banking House, Ikeda Seihin."

"Fine, you must have charged him plenty, eh?"

"I did not."

"You didn't? Who handled it for you?"

"My young friend, Takekoshi."

"Why didn't you let a clever go-between do it for you? Inouye, for instance. You should have asked for his help; he's dying to do something for somebody."

"I didn't want to make money on it. Even Takekoshi was surprised when I made the evaluation by the Hypothec Bank of Nippon the basis for the transaction."

"My, that kind of bank usually figures very conservatively. Their estimate would give you a third of its market price at best—"

"That's all I got and I'm satisfied."

"I don't know what to say, you are an extremely queer person when it comes to material things. No matter how long you are in power, when you retire from active political life, I bet you will not have a penny to your name. Ah—" The Genro shook his head.

"Huh, anyway, I don't want to get mixed up with big business people like Ikeda or any other financiers."

Ito presented his sake cup to Saionji and said: "Where do you spend your time besides at your Surugadai home?"

"Huh, here and there, at hot springs and Kyoto, and also at Kozu where Yamagata and Katsura have their summer homes."

"I suppose you don't stay any place any more than a few years?"

Saionji snickered. "You may be right. On the way home from Kyoto last time, I stopped over at Okitsu. I was fascinated by its surroundings. Okitsu is a small fishing village."

Ito pulled up the lacquer tray of visiting-cards left by his servant and looked them over. "H'm, so many fellows came to pay me their respects." He smiled contentedly. "Oh, Saionji-san, here is Katsura's card. H'm, he wrote something on the back; he says he'll be at the Gunkaku-ro waiting for me and you. He has some very urgent problems to discuss with us."

"Huh, he will probably suggest another compromise with the Seiyukai Party. Ever since he succeeded me, since we had the majority in the Lower House, he has always modified his policies to suit us. Otherwise he would have been blocked in the Lower House."

Ito's face saddened. "That reminds me, Saionji-san, that besides Katsura, we don't have prospective successors to the Premiership from Satsuma and Choshu Provinces to continue our policies. Well, there are Admiral Yamamoto Gombei of Satsuma, the Minister of the Navy from 1898 to 1906 under three Cabinets, and General Terauchi Masaki of our Province, the Minister of War, since 1902.—He served under you, too."

"Huh, Makino Shinken, my Education Minister, is also from Satsuma. He is an able and upright man with experience in diplomacy."

"Ah, Saionji-san, I think he is too honest to be a politician, something like yourself. We'll give Admiral Yamamoto and General Terauchi chances to be the Premier, but after those fellows, I don't know who could be picked from our Sat-cho group for future national leadership."

Genro Ito threw the visiting-cards back into the tray. "You see, Saionji-san, there are two other men, we, the Genros, have our eyes on, General Nogi of Choshu, of Port Arthur fame, and Admiral Togo of Satsuma, the conqueror of the Baltic Fleet in the Nippon Sea."

"Huh, they proved their leadership in their respective fields and are known not only in this country, but also abroad."

"Yes, but they are single-minded, and don't want to capitalize on their brilliant military background."

"Even you can't move them, huh?"

"Both Admiral Togo and General Nogi refused to take our good advice on almost identical grounds, by saying that their chosen spheres of service to His Majesty and the country happened to be in the navy and the army, so that they liked to remain there and do their best. They don't want to meddle in politics. What can we say?"

Genro Ito puffed at his cigar for a while. "We are partly responsible for the exhaustion of the Sat-cho supply of military leaders, because none of us Genros put our sons and heirs into the fighting profession. Instead, we trained them for other fields where life might be easier for them."

"Huh, that's a natural parental impulse, is it not?"

"No one can deny that. I love my adopted son and heir so dearly that I want to give him all possible material comfort and enjoyment in life. I have him in the Department of the Imperial Household, not that there is a large salary, but the position may be easier for him— easier than what I came through without a moment of real rest during the last forty odd years. Often I was even followed by assassins."

Saionji watched him with sympathetic eyes.

"But the minute I realize that I have dedicated my life to His Majesty, my private matters become secondary. I'd walk into an enemy camp or go through fire or water, if it were for the country's sake." The Genro's eyes glared into the space, then his features softened.

"Oh, Saionji-san, that General Terauchi has his son, Juichi, in the Military Academy. It's gratifying for Nippon, but we did not think one day able Generals could come from other Provinces than Satsuma and Choshu."

"While the young sons of your Sat-cho leaders stay away from the military profession, the talented young men from other sections step in, huh? In another decade or two our national defense units will be headed by men from various sections. My Navy Minister, Saito Makoto, is one. He is a native of Morioka, one of the northeastern provinces. He was a close follower of ex-Navy Minister, Admiral Yamamoto, but as you say, as far as his birthplace is concerned, he is non-Sat-cho."

They paused for a moment to listen to the rain.

"Huh, how about Premier Katsura? He is still waiting at the Gunkaku-ro, is he not?"

"Well, yes, but," Ito said, biting his upper lip, "no hurry on account of him. Say, how about your staying here with me tonight and having a leisurely chat—? We haven't had a knee-to-knee talk for a long time. And if I should go to the continent this fall, we may not be able to meet for another long period—maybe never."

"I'm willing to listen to your glorious reminiscences, but you sound sentimental tonight."

"Somehow, I don't want you to go. I feel that this may be our last meeting. Of late I have odd illusions."

"Huh, I'll stay with you overnight and listen to the sound of the drippings from the eaves."

"Ha, you become poetic." He smiled slightly.

"Do you know, Genro, I have learned to compose that *haikai*, the seventeen syllable epigram, which I used to think no poem at all? I've written a lot of them—as you compose *shi*, your Chinese-style verse."

"You are talented in the thirty-one syllabled *waka*, so you must be good in *haikai*, too. Do you keep them? I preserve all my compositions."

"No, I destroy them all. They aren't worth anything."

"Ah, there you go—your hermit-like practice!"

After a moment the Genro said: "Saionji-san, you certainly do peculiar things. You invited novelists to your home, I was told. I never heard of a Premier's mingling with those people—"

"Why not? I like them, and I think they like me. They honored me by forming a club called the 'Voice of Rain.' I have much fun with them whenever the club meets."

One afternoon, the ex-Premier, Marquis Saionji, was debating with himself on the Tokyo-bound train. There were various problems that his Seiyukai Party had soon to face in the next Session of the Imperial Diet. He had to decide whether the Party should block the measures reported to be introduced by the Katsura Cabinet or support some bills and reject others.

Lost in thought when the conductor announced: "O-o-i-i-s-s-o-o! O-o-i-i-s-s-o-o!" he got off the train from force of habit. Suddenly he realized that he had sold his house and that the master of the *Sorokaku*, Genro Ito, was in Manchuria for his supposedly secret mission, having left that very station on October 14.

Saionji said to himself: "Huh, I'll go to Ito's and visit his Four Sages' Arbor to get some inspiration."

The next moment the idea seemed ridiculous, but then he thought he would pay his respects to the Genro's family.

When he descended to the platform he did not notice that the station master and his subordinates were absent. A gloomy-faced young man who collected his ticket was the only one near him. The others stood behind the windows around the station master's desk.

He strolled on and saw a few *kurumayas* in the front of the station, reading a newspaper together. They didn't recognize the lone customer strolling away. As for Saionji, it was rather a pleasure to take the short walk to his destination, for he loved the town, the road with a row of old weather-beaten pine trees, the beach, the fishing village, and the simple folk of his former retreat.

As he went along, he saw small groups of people, shabbily-clad fishermen, a few farmers and merchants, their wives and children gathering in the warm October sun around their hut-like houses. Some were going towards the town registry office, where all official business was transacted for the inhabitants, and where governmental announcements were posted on a small billboard.

Saionji was disappointed because of the unusual quietness.

Soon he saw more and more townspeople moving towards the registry. He hurried to join them.

He thrust himself forward. The people, young and old, whispering, "Ah, Saionji-sama, Saionji-sama," stepped aside and made way for him.

He clutched the bamboo fence separating the yard from the road, and read the notice, blinking doubtfully.

GENRO PRINCE ITO HIROBUMI WAS SHOT BY AN ASSASSIN AT HARBIN STATION THIS MORNING.

He shook his head as if he were trying to awake from a nightmare.

"Hey!" he called. The registry clerk recognized him.

"Yes, sir!" The young man bowed low.

"Do, do you have any other in—information?" he asked, his face pale and his voice shaky.

"Here is the latest—" Another clerk brought a second bulletin with black ink dripping from the letters.

Saionji held his breath. THE LATE GENRO PRINCE ITO HIROBUMI SUCCUMBED AT 10 A.M. THIS MORNING FROM PISTOL WOUNDS INFLICTED BY A KOREAN NAMED AN CHUNG KEN—

The tears in his eyes prevented him from reading further; he removed his hat and bowed before the notice. The crowd around him became silent and bowed with him.

His thoughts were darkened.

The *hinomaru*, the national flag with the symbol of the rising sun, was raised on the flagpole and left at half-mast.

A few seconds later the noise of a newsboy's bells broke the silence.

He emerged from the crowd and stood at the roadside, thinking whether he should proceed to Ito's home or turn back to the station.

A fisherman's wife near him whispered to her neighbor who had a baby at her bosom: "Did Saionji-sama come to break the sad news to the widow?"

The woman with the baby said: "Let's follow him to the late Genro's house.—We can't say much, but we can go there and show Ito-no-okusama our sad feelings for the death of her great husband."

Dawn was reddening the sky above the Higashiyama Mountains.

Saionji was reading the morning newspaper at the *Seifuso*, his home in Kyoto.

"Huh, Takamaro!"

His younger brother left his automobile and walked towards him.

"Good morning, Brother Saionji! Am I disturbing you? I wanted to pay you a visit since I was driving up this way."

"No, not at all. I have been up for some time. It's my recent custom to get up at sunrise and take a little walk before I read the papers. Huh, you—"

"I was worried about your health, but you look well," Sumitomo observed through his eyeglasses as he sat down on the edge of the veranda.

Saionji pushed the paper from his lap to the mat and moved towards his brother. "You bought a large automobile." Then he said, staring at Sumitomo, "You, too, are looking strong—and full of vigor. How old are you, forty-seven or eight?"

"About that. Yes, I am active now. During the Russo-Nipponese War inflation I got in on the ground floor, so even the present post-war depression does not shake me as hard as it does the average or smaller businessmen. I am even expanding my enterprises by purchasing some defunct companies at a reasonable figure, and so on."

He wiped his neat moustache with a handkerchief.

"Brother Saionji, if there should be another great boom like that during the last war, I'm almost certain I will come close to the Mitsui and the Mitsubishi, who have also increased their tremendous holdings."

The sunrays began to beat on the Seifuso.

"Huh, I guess you are busy."

"Well, yes, I have already done practically a day's work this morning. With the automobile, travel is faster and easier than by carriages. The only obstacle is the narrow roads. I was inspecting some plants and properties.—Wasn't Genro Ito's death tragic?"

"Huh, as they say, 'man's life vanishes like the morning dew'—he has gone."

"In every nook and corner of the land the loss of that statesman is felt, Brother. He was aggressive and constructive."

"He was interesting, too, Takamaro. He rarely admitted his defeat, probably never did in public. Once he compared himself with Toyotomi Hideyoshi, that great peasant-born dictator, and said that Hideyoshi could never have been his equal because he was illiterate. But his conceit was a trifle, in contrast to what he accomplished for his country."

Sumitomo looked at Saionji during a brief silence. "I'd like to talk to you."

Saionji nodded.

"I have several things in mind. I don't know whether you would like my suggestions or not, but I want to mention them to you, Brother."

"Huh."

"I have bought some properties at different summer resorts and hot springs—"

Saionji smiled. "I sold out my Oiso home."

"I heard of that, Brother." Sumitomo was amused. "If you would like any of them— Another thing, I have an automobile in Tokyo too, so whenever you want it, the car will always be at your service. Big business people and ranking statesmen are using cars more and more. I believe you are often in need of a private automobile."

"Huh, that's very nice of you to have arranged it for me that way. I have something I'd like to talk over with you, and that is the arrangement of my household."

"Hu'm."

"I want to leave Sagami, my governess, here in Kyoto this time. She is old and clings to the ancient capital."

Sumitomo understood the whole situation before his brother elaborated. "If Sagami remains here in her birthplace, I will see to it that she has a servant and is well provided for. I'll instruct my Kyoto branch office to look after her affairs. What will you do about a substitute?"

"Sagami has been looking for one to take her place or to help her—"

"Brother Saionji," Sumitomo said with a cheerful voice, "people are again hoping for your return to power. Is there any truth in the report that Premier Katsura is ready to hand the Cabinet over to you?"

"Huh." Saionji put his hands into his kimono sleeves and smiled. "General Katsura urges me to come back to Tokyo as soon as possible to discuss the matter—I have his letter. By the way, the last time I met him he confided to me the news that before he retires he is going to recommend you and three or four other businessmen for the grant of a barony for your services to the country during the Russo-Nipponese War."

"Oh!"

The cranes in the garden became alarmed when the electric car, passing through the one corner of the estate, screeched against the rails.

The Saionji household stirred; the neighbors opened their wooden slides.

Sumitomo, who stood ready to leave, asked his brother: "Brother, do you lack anything here? If you do, please tell me—"

Saionji gazed at him. "You'll be surprised, I do miss something."

Sumitomo looked up; in a laughing voice Saionji remarked: "I miss the singing of the *kajika*. The modern improvements, like the electric car lines, seem to have driven the frogs away."

"Oh, Marquis, you look refreshed after your visit to your Kyoto retreat," the ex-Home Minister Hara greeted the host as he entered Saionji's Surugadai home. Like his host, Hara was clad in a cool Nipponese summer wear.

"How were things with you? I heard you returned to your native place during the summer—that was after your Chinese trip?"

"Thanks, Marquis, I'm very well—but many things disturbed me."

"Huh." Saionji motioned to his visitor to take a seat on the mat near the veranda of the room looking out on the small garden.

"Up in my home district, Iwate Prefecture, as in the neighboring prefectures, the local people are in bad shape. Every once in a while an early frost or a typhoon or a drought kills off the rice crop. Then nothing is left for the poor farmers. This year it's the drought again. With no other industries to speak of, the inhabitants in the northeast are miserable." Hara shook his head as he sat down.

"Is Matsuda-san coming, Marquis?"

"Huh, yes."

Hara began to discuss the affairs of the Seiyukai Party. "The members and supporters are asking: 'How soon will Saionji be Premier again?' Three years have elapsed since you resigned in the summer of 1908. Don't you think, Marquis, if you decide to wrest the power from General Katsura there is a possibility of success? The Seiyukai still control the majority in the Diet, the present Administration is weary and the public is tired of the same pro-industrialist policies."

Hara saw that his persuasion was no more than a summer breeze passing over the water.

Saionji asked: "What impression did you get from your trip to China?"

"My tour was too short to get an authentic insight, Marquis, though I had an interesting time with many Chinese officials in Tientsin and Peking."

"Huh, you are careful, Hara-san. Many people speak authoritatively of a country or a place after just one peep at it. A constant rumor is being circulated as to an eventual nation-wide revolution in China. You won't commit yourself on the question, huh? You were in China many years ago, too, weren't you?"

"Oh, yes, Marquis, that was in 1883-4 as Consul at Tientsin—two years before I met you in Paris in 1886."

"Huh, those days were happy ones, were they not, Hara-san?"

"You were our Minister Extraordinary and Plenipotentiary to the Austrian Court and I was a secretary at our Paris legation. You spent most of your time at Paris, didn't you?"

"With good wines and French beauties it wasn't bad, huh? I had little to do, for the countries had no problems at all, so I devoted my time to the betterment of Franco-Nipponese relations."

Just then Matsuda came in with his expansive face pale and his gray moustache untrimmed, looking much older than his sixty-seven years. But the half-moon of his bald head shone with good humor.

"Well, what's going on here?" he said after he sat down.

"Oh, talking about my Chinese trip and a few reminiscences—"

"You took a trip to America and Europe after we resigned, too, didn't you, Hara-san?"

"Yes. That was interesting and informative save for my experiences with the immigration officials when I entered the United States."

"Huh, how did they treat you?"

"Well, Marquis Saionji, the petty officials treated me like 'just another one of those poor Orientals.' But when I came to London, I was respected in every way. *The London Times* carried my interview story and all that."

Matsuda said: "You wouldn't dare say you were mistreated in our old home, Paris, would you?"

Hara's heavy eyebrows unknit.

"It was different there in the French Capital. I still managed the language pretty well and things were familiar to me."

"Oh, your American experience reminds me, do you think that the Western people will ever treat us as their equals?"

"Yes, Matsuda-san, I believe so. To do that, we Nipponese and Chinese and other non-white peoples must improve ourselves and show our unique qualities, and the whites must discard the idea that they are superior racially to other human beings."

Hara shook his head. "Chief, you're idealistic; it is not likely that prejudiced people will ever admit us as their equals—"

"I don't know about that—" Matsuda began, but Hara interrupted him.

"Many, many years ago I thought it was possible when I was young and lured by the appeal of a Christian, but that was an air castle. I originally trained under and worked with this foreign missionary to Nippon, before I decided to enter a college, after which I went into newspaper work and government jobs. The Westerners talk about human equality, but that is in a religious sense, not socially or politically. No, they'll never think us their equals unless we make them by force."

"I was thinking," Matsuda interrupted, "of the diplomatic history of our position. In the 1870's Nippon was nowhere. Until the Sino-Nipponese War even China had imposed her extraterritorial rights on us. After that war the Westerners retracted their unreasonable privileges over us little by little. Great Britain made a monumental departure when she signed the Anglo-Nipponese Alliance for the first time in 1902. Along came the Russo-Nipponese War in 1904-5 with the result that the United States and Germany were the first to agree to exchange Ambassadors with us instead of Ministers. In another generation they'll yield their remaining unreasonable rights."

Matsuda had a patient audience, but Hara could not wait longer, and said: "That was correct, but it was because our big guns spoke, which is not true to Christian teachings."

"Huh, Hara-san, we can't deny the historical facts he has pointed out, can we? At the same time we see many contradictions between their religious teachings and their diplomatic policies and practices. As Genro Ito used to say, we have just come to realize that, and we must also admit that might is still right. We are now reaping the fruits of our patient learning from the West, our annexation of Korea last summer was the first practical lesson."

"That gave Premier Katsura a pretext to have himself raised to the Princehood—"

"Some newspapers were bitter about it, weren't they? They even went so far as to say that Katsura helped himself to it. Huh, my brother, Tokudaiji was also made Prince."

"Oh, your brother, Lord Keeper of the Privy Seal deserved the reward, for he has been at Court ever since we first heard of him and has held that post since when, Monsieur?"

"Since 1871, I think. And this was his first promotion. Although it is General Katsura's usual practice to take all credit to himself, what impressed me was that the Premier presumed to ascribe our Korean annexation to his own efforts, entitling him to a rich prize."

"Nonsense," Hara mumbled.

"It was due mostly to the long devotion of our people who waged the last two wars for that single purpose," said Saionji.

"Furthermore," Hara took the argument up quickly, "the Katsura Cabinet was responsible for that horrible and infamous incident, the Socialist plot against the Sovereign. The Cabinet should have resigned when the plot was discovered last year. Well, somehow, those Choshu and Satsuma politicians are greedy for honors and titles. I can't understand their craving for them. I may be the extreme opposite, but in my will, which I renew on January 2 every year, I have a definite stipulation that my heir shall not accept any title offered after my death for my services."

"Huh."

"For, Marquis, I believe my adopted son should not accept the Imperial grace expressed in the form of a title because of any duties performed for His Majesty during my lifetime. Should he be found unworthy of such an honor, he disgraces not only my family, but the bestower, the Imperial Family. I shall remain a commoner and I'll keep my adopted son in the same station, unless he earns titles by his own merits."

"That sounds reasonable," Matsuda nodded.

"Huh, I have heard that Premier Katsura and Field Marshal Prince Yamagata are at odds."

"That's conceivable."

"After Genro Ito was gone, Yamagata was the only Sat-cho leader who held the highest rank. That gave the old Field Marshal great pride and satisfaction. Then General Katsura, Yamagata's junior, got the title, too."

Matsuda spoke gravely through his moustache. "That being the case, Monsieur, the time has come for you to get ready for the next Cabinet. Don't you think so, Hara-san?"

"That's what I have tried to say to the Marquis, Matsuda-san."

"Since the Genros' personal feelings still sway the Cabinet and since Genro Yamagata is the most powerful among them, we must get in touch with the Field Marshal to ascertain his real attitude towards Premier Katsura. What do you think?"

Matsuda was just as eager for action as Hara was.

After a considerable time, Saionji said: "We'd better remain inactive for a little while longer."

The visitors frowned.

"But we can, among the three of us, make our selection of the prospective Ministers." Saionji smiled at them.

Hara, moving nearer to the host, cheerfully asked: "So, Chief, you have some reliable information and have made up your mind. Matsuda-san, is it not wonderful that the Seiyukai Party banner will once more fly in the happy morning sun?"

Still calm, Saionji continued: "In the last Cabinet I had to have some men of the Genros' choice and recommendation, but this time we can do the selecting of Ministers."

"It couldn't be better." Hara was jubilant.

"I believe you have already some men in mind."

"Huh, besides you two, I want to have more party Ministers. And I want an expert for the Treasury post."

Approvingly, Matsuda said: "That's a new approach and a wise one."

"Huh, I have another novel idea. What do you think of this? I'll invite a non-Sat-cho General to head the War Department and Admiral Saito to lead the Navy Department."

"H'm, for the first time the Choshu domination in the War Department will be broken." Hara was enthusiastic.

"But, we've got to be careful not to incur the ire of Field Marshal Yamagata."

Saionji grinned at Matsuda and kept on: "And also, I'd like to introduce a new spirit in the Foreign Office, where in the past men of European background, that is, our former envoys to European Capitals, were installed as Ministers."

"Whom are you going to invite, Marquis?"

"Uchida Kosai, our Ambassador to the United States."

"How about the War Minister? Whom have you in mind?" Hara was eager to learn everything immediately.

"Huh, General Ishimoto Shinroku of Himeji. I'm almost certain I can get him because Field Marshal Yamagata some time ago greatly praised the Lieutenant General; so I'll ask Yamagata to help me draft his favorite follower. He couldn't possibly go back on his own word."

Saionji turned to Matsuda once more. "Matsuda-san, do you remember a young *sous-lieutenant* we met in Paris in 1874 or 5, attending the French Military Academy? Huh, you do? That's General Ishimoto."

"Well, after all you have everything worked out a step ahead of us. In the meantime, however, what are you going to do?"

"Huh, Matsuda-san, I am leaving for some hot springs after I arrange my personal matters, and see my grandchildren."

A smile brightened Saionji's face.

"*Go-inkyo-san*, how do you do?" a little maid greeted the new guest at the inn. It was at the Ikaho Hot Springs, about ninety miles west of Tokyo. As refreshments, that late summer afternoon, she had brought a tray of warm, green tea, pickled plums and crisp rice cakes.

After she served him, she brought out a ledger.

"*Go-inkyo-san*," she smiled, "may I ask you to register? We ask every customer to write down his original domicile, present address, age, occupation, and from where he has just come and so forth." The girl went on phonographically.

"Can you put them down for me? I'm tired. Mine is simple."

"Well, I can write it all right, for I went to school, but—"

"But the innkeeper told you not to, huh?"

"Oh, no"—her brown eyes twinkled at the customer—"Big Sister is sweet, but, oh, if the police officer should find it out, we'd get into trouble." She went on with lark-like eloquence. "Every day we bring this book to the officer's place, he looks it over to see if any bad man is at our place or in this town. Sometimes a bad man asks us to write his name in the book, but he tells us somebody else's name, so that he can get away from the police. You see, the officer says he can see the difference in your writing and mine even if we both write the same name. That's why you've got to write it. But often the police give it back without looking into it carefully."

Teasing her, the customer said: "If you write it for me, I'll give you a big tip."

"No, Big Sister says that kind of a man is never a good one."

She became suspicious, saying: "You didn't tell me your name and other things yet. But if you can't write them I suppose I've got to do it for you—but no tip."

She picked up a pointed, dry brush with its long bamboo holder. She chewed the brush point a little before she dipped it in the black ink.

"What is your name, please?"

"Huh, you'll write it for me? All right, my name is Saionji Kimmochi."

The maid looked at Saionji, and still busily chewing the brush, said: "I never heard of such a name before. It sounds like a Buddhist temple."

"That's right, but that's my name. You want my real one, don't you?"

"Sure! But spell it for me."

"*Sai*, west, *on*, garden or terrace, *ji*, temple. Did you get it?"

"Well, it is not nice writing, but the police officer is very kind and can always read my writing, so I think it's all right. That's your family name—"

"My given name is Kim-mochi—"

"That's too hard for me. What are we going to do? If it is too hard for me, my aunt surely can't make it out."

"Now, let me have the book and brush. I'll save you the trouble."

"Can you do it? Why didn't you say so?"

When the book was returned to her small hands she opened it and read the lines.

"Ah, it's so stylishly written, I can't read it, but I can guess at the rest. You were born in Kyoto, live in Tokyo. You don't say at what number and on what street. Age sixty-three, and the occupation is government official. This is not good. This does not say whether you are the head man of a town or a man working at a town office or somewhere for a long time until you got gray-haired. You do look though, very much like the *Go-inkyo-san* of the drygoods store in the town. He gave everything to his son and he doesn't do a thing now. He has a pretty young mistress." Innocently she prattled on before she retired to the downstairs counter.

A little later she reappeared with a clean kimono and towel and other things for the bath. She told Saionji gravely: "Big Sister said your information in the register was not enough and if the police officer should think the same way, she would have the police come over and make you write more in front of him. But I said," she gestured with her hands, "that you, *Go-inkyo-san*, were a sort of good man and might be afraid of the police so that she should ask the officer as a favor to overlook your case and she should some time later invite the police for supper in exchange for the favor."

"Huh, that's very kind of you. What is your name?"

"My name is Ume, plum, you see."

The maid sat down and chatted with Saionji. "How did you come, *Go-inkyo-san?*"

"Huh, by train, stagecoach and mountain palanquin."

"Oh, I'd like to ride on the stagecoach and the train. I know them because I read about them in schoolbooks, but my mama tells me that a girl born here shouldn't hope for such adventures. Once I went down with my teacher and classmate on the long mountain path to the town, over seven or eight miles, to see the stagecoach come."

"Huh."

"But I know Tokyo and Kyoto—they're in our schoolbooks. Kyoto is the ancient capital and Tokyo is the new one. *O-Tenshi-sama*, the Emperor, and the Empress, many other high people, the Prime Minister and other Ministers, the Generals and Admirals live there. Have you ever seen any of those big men? When I was in school my teacher used to tell me the Premier was General Katsura. I suppose you didn't know that. After I quit school that Premier gave up his job, so I don't know any other statesmen." Looking earnestly at Saionji, she asked: "What did you come over here for? Do you have rheumatism? This hot spring is terribly good for that ailment."

"Huh, a little, and I want to rest here. I like this place because you people are kind and it is pretty and quiet."

"Oh, we are all good people and the town is lovely all through the year. Did you see the sights? The houses are all on the slope and the river runs at the foot of the slope. If you climb up this hill you'll find the Ikaho Shrine," she said impetuously. "Did anybody tell you how high this hot spring is, *Go-inkyo-san?*"

"Huh, do you know, Ume? What is the elevation above sea level?"

"That's it, that's the word that slipped out of my mind. It's twenty-one hundred feet. We've got to remember everything there is here so we can tell the customers, you see."

"Huh, huh."

"Ume! Ume!" The innkeeper's voice called her. As she went out of the room, she added: "Did you hear the robin twittering? It's lovely. I'll tell you more when I come to serve you supper. Can you read newspapers? We get the Tokyo morning paper in the evening. If you want me to, I can borrow it for you from the counter. Big Sister reads love stories and so forth, but she skips the first page. That's too hard for her—for me too."

"u-m-e!" Another call. The girl rushed out.

When the maid later brought the simple meal, she had recalled whatever information she had omitted before.

"Do you know, *Go-inkyo-san*, that this hot spring is one of the most famous?" She beamed with importance.

"Huh." Saionji's hand with the chopsticks rested on his lap for a moment. "You seem to know so much."

"Through schoolbooks—" she said proudly.

"Now, tell me what the books say about the hot springs. Do they mention your place as the best or don't you know any other names?"

Ume was slightly hurt. "Things I know from my primary school studies and from this business information are different." Then she admitted: "When I first came here last spring, Big Sister told me to remember all about the place. I argued with her that many things she said weren't so, because the books didn't say that they were. She scolded me terribly. She said she would send me home—I can't go home because my father borrowed money from her, that's why I'm here. My father makes charcoal, he works hard but makes little money. And she even frightened me by saying that she could sell me to a prostitute-house if I'm so stupid as to believe schoolbooks—the *joroya* in this town were taken away but the geisha houses are still here."

"Huh, so you think this is the best one in the country?"

"Well, of course."

Every now and then she assumed the manner of a mature person. Her expressions and gestures amused Saionji.

"You see, *Go-inkyo-san*, I'll tell you—don't you tell this to Big Sister —there are the Hakone, the Kusatsu, and the Beppu hot springs which people knew better than this place. This place became famous mostly because of that love story, *Hototogisu*, by Tokutomi Roka."

The maid went on eagerly: "The summer is almost over and many people are going home but it's the best time for you to stay longer because there'll be no crowd. And in the fall, along the river and up yonder, the maple leaves turn a lovely, glowing red; in the winter, those high mountains—see them?"—she pointed to the overhanging peaks—"will be all covered with snow, and in the spring there'll be something else to enjoy."

With the cooked-rice box under one small arm and the empty supper tray under the other, she was about to leave.

"*Go-inkyo-san*," she assured Saionji, "if you want to retire, clap your hands at any time. I'll come up and spread your beddings for you on the mat. If you want to look around the town tomorrow, I suppose Big Sister would let me take you around—not with a young gentleman she says though, and also I can help in your bath if you want to have somebody rub your back in the bathroom. That, too, is not for a young gentleman, Big Sister says. The water closet is at the end of the veranda—"

Many harmless days came and passed at the hot spring, then still remote and inconvenient. Saionji enjoyed the simple life. His whereabouts were known only to his family circle and to the two political associates, Matsuda and Hara.

One evening when Ume came into his room to wait on him for his supper, she had a copy of a Tokyo newspaper.

She doubtfully told him: "The young gentlemen staying here in our downstairs rooms were talking about you when they read this." She pushed the neatly folded paper over to him.

"Huh, what did they say?"

"One of them said the old man, meaning you, looked very much like the newspaper pictures of the former Premier. I told him he was mistaken—I said you were the *Go-inkyo-san* of a drygoods store or something—as far as I could make out. Another one said I'd the right idea because if you were such a man, there would be lots of detectives, policemen and other big people around. You are alone, you dress in a simple kimono, you don't shout at us to do this and to do that, and not to do this and not to do that, and hundreds of other things. But that young man thought the man they had in mind was not like the other big men in the country and had no moustache. You don't wear a moustache. You aren't the former Premier, are you?"

"Huh." Saionji smiled.

"I'd like to see such a big man in my lifetime, though."

"Ume, would you really like to meet him?" He had the paper unfolded in his hands and his eyes glanced at his full-dress uniform portrait and through the columns.

"Yes, yes. But I suppose the best people I could meet here are like you, with nothing to do any more."

While the maid prattled on, Saionji's brown eyes were fixed on one column. She noticed the dishes were getting cold.

"*Go-inkyo-san*, why don't you eat first as you usually do, and read the newspaper after supper?"

There came a loud noise from downstairs.

"Oh, our police officer's here!" Ume was excited.

They heard voices. "These dignitaries are from Tokyo to see the former Premier, who is supposed to be here, in your place—"

"What? A *Soridaijin* in our place?" the hysterical landlady answered.

The maid jumped up. "*Go-inkyo-san*, I want to see that big man, too. I'll come back later to clean up your room, your supper tray and all." She headed for the staircase leading to the ground floor.

"Ume!"

She stopped and looked back meekly.

"Put these things aside first," said Saionji.

"But I want to see that *Soridaijin!*"

She was about to obey. Then, headed by the innkeeper who was trembling with excitement, several men, shoeless, but wearing high hats and frock coats which had never been seen in this mountain resort, appeared one by one at the top of the staircase and politely filed into Saionji's room. Taking their hats off, all sat down in a row on the mat, facing the *Go-inkyo-san* in his simple kimono. They bowed very low.

The bewildered girl, with the tips of her kimono sleeves tightly clutched in her little fists, stared at them.

Premier Saionji, who organized his second Cabinet on August 28, 1911, called his Ministers for the first meeting.

The men were experienced in their Portfolios with few exceptions: the Foreign Minister, Uchida Kosai, who had represented his country at Washington, the Finance Minister, Yamamoto Tatsuo, one of the most brilliant financial experts in the country, who resigned from the Presidency of the government Hypothec Bank to take the Cabinet post; the War Minister, Lieutenant General Ishimoto Shinroku, and the Education Minister, Haseba Junko, one of the leading Seiyukai Party men.

"I'd like to state my views to you briefly," began Premier Saionji, "on the main issues. During this Ministry I wish to carry into effect two of the primary Seiyukai objectives: administrative reform and the reduction of administrative expenditure. These measures are inseparable."

"Monsieur, what is your expectation, to what extent do you want us to retrench?" asked Minister of Justice Matsuda.

"At least ten per cent of the Departmental outlay; it would be better if we could make it fifteen per cent."

The Ministers nodded in agreement.

The Premier went on: "Since this is an ambitious undertaking and the Twenty-eighth Session of the Imperial Diet is so near at hand, I'd like to ask every Department to devote its time and energy to it after the forthcoming Session.

"Another important matter to which I'd like to call your attention is our stand against pressure from some quarters that we intervene in the Chinese Revolution which has spread since last October. To me, it is China's own affair whether she establishes a republican form of government or whether Emperor Hsuan Tung suppresses the rebellion through General Yuan Shih-kai. We must remain neutral as long as they respect our vested interests there. Should there be any change, the question can be considered anew."

All eyes focussed on the Foreign Minister, the Minister of War, and the Navy Minister as they expressed their accord with the Premier.

A momentary silence was broken by Matsuda. "Have you other general instructions, Monsieur?"

"Huh, before we adjourn, I'd like to ask the War and Navy Ministers how their Departments stand on our retrenchment idea?"

General Ishimoto answered mildly: "Not popular," and looked at Admiral Saito, who nodded, grinning. The General added: "Some people want not reduction, but two new divisions."

The Premier said: "We trust you to do your share. I will ask the voters to decide this question in the general elections next May. We have the mandate of the Emperor and if the people should endorse this issue, the Cabinet will carry it through."

Home Minister Hara voiced hearty agreement with the Premier and asked the Finance Minister: "We are spending quite heavily for national defense, are we not, Yamamoto-san?"

"Yes. Before the Sino-Nipponese War, the ratio of expenditures of the War and Navy Departments was from twenty to thirty per cent of the national outlay, and since then it has been over fifty per cent. For the next fiscal year in co-operation with General Ishimoto and Admiral Saito I expect to bring it down considerably, but we may still need ninety-five million yen for the Army and ninety-three million yen for the Navy, of the total five hundred and seventy-six million. That means slightly over thirty-two per cent of the budget total."

"Marquis Saionji, it is almost the first anniversary of the organization of your second Cabinet, is it not?"

"Huh, doesn't time fly, Takekoshi-san?"

They were at Saionji's Surugadai home.

"Once more the Seiyukai Party swept the country in the last elections. I congratulate you and your Party. Your Cabinet will effect the reform programs in the fall, I suppose?"

"Huh, the May election results showed two hundred and fourteen Seiyukai members elected to the three hundred and eighty Diet seats.

I must compliment you, too. You have been elected to the Diet again, it's your third term."

"Thanks, Marquis. Anyway, the Seiyukai's success indicates that your economy measures are popular with the people. The newspapers and the associations of the Chambers of Commerce and other groups back your moves."

"Huh."

"It will be interesting to watch how the Army Department goes about the problem of the two-division increase, which disrupts the original Seiyukai plans. Your new War Minister, General Uyehara Yusaku, who succeeded the late General Ishimoto, has one of the best minds in the defense unit, they say. Well, Marquis, are you going away this summer?"

"No, I'll remain in the city. I am much concerned about the Emperor's health. Although it has not been made public, the court physicians informed me some time ago that he was not well. Also, a few days ago, Genro Yamagata called to my attention the fact that the Emperor seemed weary. On July 15, when the Privy Council was in session with Field Marshal presiding, His Majesty was present. During the deliberation the Genro was not far from him. All of a sudden, the Sovereign seemed to be napping. Yamagata said that he had never seen him so wearied during a discussion of state affairs."

"Oh!"

"But, as you know, His Majesty possesses tremendous will power and doesn't reveal his condition. The other day, when I went to the Palace to present a report on a national issue to the Throne, he showed no symptoms of illness at all. Before I left, without any explanation he gave me a landscape scroll which was on the desk."

"His Majesty has enjoyed most extraordinary health all these years, has he not? He will recover, Marquis. Your forebodings are groundless."

"Huh, Takekoshi-san, I beg your pardon. Look, a horse-carriage from the Palace is coming into my yard."

Saionji went out.

Imperial Household Minister Watanabe, his face pale, emerged from the carriage. As soon as they had exchanged brief greetings, the Minister announced: "Premier Saionji, His Majesty has been gravely ill since last night. The court physicians agree that his condition has become worse this morning." His voice was trembling. He went on: "They say it is due to the ailment in his urinary system. I conferred with Genro Yamagata before I came over here. What shall we do?"

"Oh! What did Genro Yamagata say?"

"He was of the opinion that the matter must be made known to the public—"

"That's what I think, too. Issue bulletins regarding every change of his condition. Does my brother, Tokudaiji, know?"

"Yes, Premier, Prince Tokudaiji has been at the Emperor's bedside since midnight."

"I shall go to the Palace immediately.—May I ride with you?"

In one of the halls of the Imperial Palace there were assembled the worried Genros, the court dignitaries and high government officials who had been informed that the Emperor's end was near.

When Premier Saionji and Tokudaiji returned there from the Sovereign's bedside, Privy Council President Yamagata approached Saionji. Gazing at each other, they shook their heads sadly and sat down side by side. Tokudaiji and the Imperial Household Minister joined them.

The Field Marshal said in a low voice: "In spite of all human efforts and the desire of his fifty million subjects, as the days go by his condition becomes gradually worse. Throughout the country at the Shinto shrines, Buddhist temples, Christian churches and other religious institutions, and in their homes, the Nipponese, in their beloved Emperor's behalf, continue to offer the most heart-felt prayers to the superhuman power—" He swallowed hard and added:

"Day and night, since the first announcement of His Majesty's grave illness was made public on July 20, the great square before the Imperial Palace has been filled with hundreds of thousands of people from the city and from the countryside around the Capital. They kneel reverently on the lawn and bow low, their foreheads touching the ground in prayer for his speedy recovery."

Looking at the Premier with tearful eyes, Yamagata resumed: "We must be prepared for the worst!" Then he turned to the Imperial Household Minister and the Lord Keeper of the Privy Seal. "Should the worst come—is everything ready?"

The Imperial Household Minister replied: "Yes, Genro Yamagata. Without delay Crown Prince Yoshihito as the New Sovereign will succeed to the throne, should the necessity arise. Chief of Rituals, Iwakura, is here. You, the President of the Privy Council, Premier Saionji, Lord Keeper of the Privy Seal Tokudaiji, the members of the

Privy Council, the Ministers of the Cabinet and the court dignitaries, who should witness the occasion, are also present."

He turned to Tokudaiji and continued: "The Lord Keeper of the Privy Seal at the Binden will offer the New Ruler the Sacred Sword and Jewel, then the Imperial Seal and the seal of the State. In the meantime the rites at the Sanctuary, then at the Imperial Ancestors' Shrine and the other places will be performed by the Chief Ritualist to announce the accession of the New Sovereign."

The clock struck midnight.

"It's the 30th of July," Premier Saionji whispered.

"The Presentation Ceremony will take place on the following day with civil and military officials present?" Tokudaiji asked.

"Yes, His Majesty will issue the Imperial Rescript to which the Premier must respond in the presence of the officials and dignitaries in the *Seiden* of the Palace," concluded the Imperial Household Minister.

Perfect silence prevailed.

At 1:43 A.M. on July 30, 1912, Emperor Mutsuhito passed away at the age of fifty-nine.

The deceased Sovereign's son, Yoshihito, born August 31, 1879, succeeded his father as the one hundred and twenty-third Ruler of Nippon.

The new era of *Taisho*, Great Righteousness, was declared to begin on July 31.

The Imperial Funeral for the late Emperor, posthumously named Meiji, the title given the period of his reign, was announced for September 13. His remains were to be buried at Momoyama, near the old capital, Kyoto, his birthplace and the scene of his accession to the throne forty-six years earlier at the death of his father, Emperor Komei. He himself had selected his last resting place, because of its scenic beauty and its nearness to his native city.

The national mourning period of one year for the late Sovereign was proclaimed. In the fall of 1915 the coronation ceremonies for Emperor Yoshihito were to be held at Kyoto.

Premier Saionji returned to his Surugadai home. Going wearily to the room where the family altar was placed, he lighted the new candles. Stepping back a few paces, he sat down on the mat to offer a prayer for the eternal peace of the soul of the late Emperor.

The yellowish beams illuminated his short-cropped gray hair, the deepened lines on his forehead, his lower lip, and his ash-colored complexion. He closed his eyes in meditation.

Sagami came into the room and joined him in prayer. They were speechless and motionless, like bronze busts in an ancient sanctuary, with their heads bent forward under the wavering light.

Through the echoless summer evening air resounded the mourning bells of the Buddhist temples in Tokyo.

After a long while Sagami whispered: "Master, our great Ruler has gone. The Emperor with whom you had the honor to associate as a boy, by whom you were appointed as the Commander General, and who finally elevated you to the nation's highest political office has now joined his Ancestors."

Her thin voice went on: "The late Emperor gave you the picture scroll because of a premonition—" She wiped her eyes.

"Yes, Sagami, when I attended his bedside a few hours before the last breath, His Majesty was unconscious."

Saionji's words were equally faint and reverent. Bowing again, he said: "The sadness of the Nipponese people, who attribute the country's progress during the past years to his leadership, was greater at the late Emperor's passing than at the death of any other person in the nation's history, save perhaps that of Prince Shotoku. He died in the year of 621 at the age of forty-eight in the midst of his great reform administration. According to the historians, his countrymen grieved over his death as if even the sun and the moon had lost their radiant light and Heaven and the earth were come to an end."

In the semi-darkness the governess saw tears trickling down Saionji's cheeks.

"Kimmochi! Kimmochi! Are you at home?" The caller was the Lord Keeper of the Privy Seal.

"Yes. But why your unexpected visit at this time?"

"Kimmochi, I cannot go on with my court duties. Although I feel greatly obligated to serve the new Sovereign, the late Emperor's death has shattered my spirit and physical stamina."

"I understand, Brother Tokudaiji, you were closer to him than anyone else—I sympathize with you."

When they had sat down, Tokudaiji said: "I want to retire and pray for his soul. I have spoken of the matter to Genro Yamagata and to the Imperial Household Minister. You, as the Premier, are also concerned. Relieve me from the office as soon as possible. My deep sorrow and advanced age—I'm seventy-three years old—"

"Brother, you have done a great service. I'll see to it that your request is fulfilled."

Tokudaiji held his bearded chin in one hand and shut his eyes: "It was in 1871, the year you left for Paris to study, that I entered the court service." He sighed.

"Yes."

"I'm satisfied, Kimmochi, for I was with the Emperor Meiji until his last hour. Even if I die now, I have nothing to regret."

Then a faint smile softened his lips. He said: "I witnessed your appointment as the Premier too, Kimmochi, that was one of my greatest moments when I saw you bowing before the Sovereign." After a deep breath he continued: "It was our deceased father's and then my concern that you might disgrace the name of your adopted family, Saionji—"

Looking at his brother with satisfaction, Tokudaiji added: "What more can one ask than to have his son, real or adopted, twice honored as the Emperor's Premier? Kimmochi, you have already equalled, if not surpassed, the ranking ancestors of the Saionji and also of the Tokudaiji family. I shall be proud to inform our parents of your achievement when I join them."

At eight o'clock in the evening of September 13, 1912, a solemn cannon boomed. In cities, towns and villages throughout the Empire, thousands of religious ceremonies began.

It was the hour of the Imperial Funeral in Tokyo.

Mounted detectives headed the procession. Three thousand army and navy guards of honor, four abreast, and a long line of functionaries followed on foot.

From the East Vestibule of the Palace the Imperial coffin was borne on a vehicle thirteen feet high, fourteen feet long, and eight feet wide. Its two wheels and lower part were of black lacquer, and its body was chestnut color. Two pairs of black oxen with white cotton reins drew it at a slow, uniform pace.

Immediately around the coffin were the military and civil officials who had ever attended the late Sovereign. The first dignitary who preceded the vehicle was the Master of Imperial Ceremonies and the next was the Minister of the Imperial Household; both were clad in the traditional, black ceremonial garb and leaned on white canes of paulownia branches.

Close behind the coffin were the attending civil and military servants to the new Emperor, his representative, and the surviving members of the Imperial Family and their relatives.

The Lord Keeper of the Privy Seal, Tokudaiji, Premier Saionji, and the President of Privy Council, Field Marshal Yamagata, followed the Imperial group a few paces apart. Saionji and Yamagata were in full-dress uniform. Then came the diplomatic corps, among whom was the American Secretary of State, P. C. Knox, Prince Connaught of Great Britain, Prince Heinrich of Germany, and General Lebon of France. Another three thousand army and navy guards of honor brought up the rear.

These ten thousand official mourners marched to the subdued music of the ancient Oriental *sho* and *hichiriki*.

Thirty-five pairs of torches distributed in the line blazed the way. In the vast square in front of the Imperial Palace many huge bonfires that had been built as the procession began, were reflected in the water of the moats.

Soon after the march was under way, through the heavy night air one hundred and one guns of condolence boomed from the artillery unit of the Imperial Guard Division located behind the Palace, synchronized with the minute-gun fired from the Imperial Navy Squadron anchored off Shinagawa in Tokyo Bay.

The coffin proceeded through the thick walls of sorrowful people from the Nijubashi Gate to the Aoyama funeral grounds.

Premier Saionji, marching, heard the faint bells of a rushing newspaper boy. The noise came closer to the slow-moving procession. A few blocks away the shouting became clear: "General Nogi and his wife commit suicide immediately after the cannon signal for the funeral!"

Saionji stood still with shock and looked back at Genro Marshal Yamagata. Their eyes caught through the dim torch light.

In accordance with the old custom of expressing the highest loyalty to one's master by committing harakiri at the latter's death, the Nogis had followed the Emperor to the world beyond.

Only the hissing sounds of the wheels of the ox-drawn coffin recalled Premier Saionji to himself.

The aged governess said amiably: "Master, it is gratifying to have you at home with us for a change," as she came into the room.

Saionji was lying on his side, supporting his head with one hand and leisurely smoking a cigarette. Sallow and listless, Otama sat not far from him. Her round eyes gazed at the old woman in amazement because of her friendliness since the early afternoon.

"Huh, sit with us for a moment and be our companion. I have been busy for many months. The moon is full— The air is calm—"

She beamed from ear to ear at her master's kind words.

"Before I sit down I must go back once more to see if the new housekeeper, my understudy, is doing things properly."

"Too much hustling may harm your health, I am afraid. You are growing old," Saionji objected.

"Master, I was never ill and never will be. You, too, are getting old. You used to smoke strong cigars, and drink much with every meal." She glanced fondly at him. "You never used to lie down like that after a meal. It is a pleasure, it is a pleasure to be of service to you. I'll be as active as always until I shut my eyes for good, my Master."

"Ha, ha, you don't approve of this idleness, huh?" Looking at Otama for a second, he continued, smiling: "Sagami always thinks of me as she did when she first took me into her arms over sixty years ago."

A flush came over her lean face. She expanded her chest—her typical expression of pride and satisfaction.

They watched the serene figure hobbling off, with both hands clenched behind her back.

Meditatively Saionji puffed his cigarette smoke towards the ceiling. He recalled Otama's question before Sagami had interrupted their conversation.

"Huh, you asked why General Nogi's wife took her life when her husband did. Some people revere her for her act and others do not. She was devoted according to the *samurai* family tradition that in joy and sorrow, grief and pleasure, the wife is to follow her husband."

"She didn't need to die, did she?"

"Huh, I suppose ordinary women, particularly young people, can hardly comprehend such a high sense of duty, Otama. But every mother can understand her second motive. You see, her two sons, both army officers, were killed in the Russo-Nipponese War. With her husband gone, she would have had nobody to comfort her last years. If a mother becomes suddenly childless—"

Otama nodded, her eyes filling with sympathetic tears.

"And her husband, broken by the loss of his sons, determined to follow the late Emperor whom he had faithfully served. Some people believe that in the next life we will continue to act in the master-servant relationship much as we do now.

"She felt the greatest devotion for Emperor Meiji, too. Now that he had passed away and her husband had decided to end his life, she did not hesitate to share death with the General. The Nogis committed the traditional *seppuku*. He, dressed in his military uniform, severed his abdomen and throat with his war sword, and she, attired in a kimono, drove the family dagger into her heart. They were found dead, sitting composedly side by side at their home."

Otama shut her eyes, saying: "They always did rather strange things, didn't they? I heard that she once bought three bottles of the best perfume and packed them in her sons' and husband's baggage when they left for the front."

"Huh, that sounds ridiculous nowadays, but that was true to her *samurai*-like upbringing. You know, in a classical play, the pretty widow of a noted warrior establishes the identity of her slain husband by the helmet her spouse wore in battle."

"How strange! How does she do that?"

"Being a warrior's wife, who does not expect him to return, before her husband's departure the woman perfumes his martial attire, particularly the helmet, with good incense. When he dies on the field and his head is taken away by the enemy, it will not emanate a bad smell because of the scented helmet.

"General Nogi's wife feared that her sons and husband would die in Manchuria. So, like the classical heroine, she told her sons that they should use the perfume every morning whenever they were ordered to lead their companies in the field."

"Master—" the governess returned to the room—"everything has been put in good order. The new housekeeper is young, but is amenable to my authority. Little Princess is in bed, sleeping like an angel—"

"Did you go to Sonoko's room?" Otama asked.

"Yes, yes, I looked the whole house over."

"Huh, why so ambitious, Sagami?"

"Nagiye will be here shortly, Master." She sat down, and began a recitation of the master's childhood and rising career. She was as proud as if his honors were her own.

Saionji merely smiled at her remarks; Otama was slightly bored, for of late Sagami had too often subjected the household to the familiar tale.

The governess said: "I must tell these people who used to stick out their tongues at me and my dearest charge." She glanced at her master. "They criticized because I always defended his acts—I taught him many things of which the neighbors disapproved."

He was amused. "Huh, Sagami, how can you tell our old neighbors who were shocked by my mischief? They have all been dead for many, many years—"

Ignoring his remarks she continued with an additional version of Saionji's achievements: "It is a rare honor and accomplishment for a servant to follow his master like the Nogis, but it is equally great, if not greater, for a subject to see his master's burial—my master as the Premier, saw the Imperial coffin of the late Sovereign put peacefully to rest for ever and ever."

It was already late when Sagami paused. Nagiye had just come into the room. Saionji saw the new servant for the first time.

When Sagami introduced her to Saionji, Nagiye bowed to him and paid her respects to Otama and Sagami.

The governess added: "Nagiye is from a reliable Kyoto family, she is pretty, and she is already acquainted with the things that I want done for you, Master. When you took us to Kyoto last time and proposed that I should stay there, I asked to have an understudy hired. I could not stay away from you and Little Princess. No, I never thought of it—"

Saionji nodded with his approving eyes on Nagiye. Otama and Sagami watched him.

"Now, now, Master, I can perhaps rest awhile—"

"Yes, Sagami, you should have taken a rest many years ago. Don't you remember that I suggested it time and again, even when Okiku was still here?"

"Oh, Master, your Okiku and Big Princess," she mumbled. "I'd like to see them, see them once more." Her last sentence was barely audible.

A strange silence followed after the light blinked for a second.

The sound of dropping leaves of the paulownia tree in the garden struck Saionji's heart. The moon was already declining in the western sky.

Saionji suddenly noticed that Sagami was slowly falling, her one hand on the mat and the other on her heart. Her face was ashen and her breathing irregular.

"Sagami!" he shouted. Otama and Nagiye stared at her. There was no answer. His eyes fixed on her, Saionji leaped to Sagami's side.

He seized her and shouted again: "Sagami! Sagami!"

His voice trembled. "O-Otama! Quick, the doctor! Doctor, quick! Nagiye, water! Don't stand there, hurry!"

He laid Sagami gently on the mat, calling his governess' name close to her ear: "Sagami! Sagami! Can't you hear me?"

Tears shone in his eyes. He patted Sagami's forehead with his shaking hand.

It seemed to him that Nagiye was gone for hours. A half-filled whiskey bottle stood on his desk. He uncorked it quickly and poured a few drops into Sagami's mouth. It was ineffective—he poured a little more. He watched her face.

Both Otama and Nagiye rushed into the room. "Don't make any noise!" he warned. At that moment, Sagami's chest seemed to expand.

"Water, water!" Snatching the cup, he raised Sagami's head a little on his forearm and poured water into her mouth.

"Oh, Sagami! Can't you hear me!" Her lips quivered. He gave her some more water before he put a cushion under her head and laid the inert body on the mat. He sighed deeply with relief and looked around.

"Shall I prepare a bed, sir?" Nagiye asked.

"Yes, right away—"

"In her room, sir?"

"No, in the guestroom."

When he turned to Otama, the latter said: "The doctor will be here any minute."

"Otama, call Shinko and tell her Sagami has had a heart attack. She is to come immediately." Then he hesitated for a second. "Add that she is to bring her mother, Okiku, along."

The dull eyes revived slowly. "Sagami, can you see me?" he asked hopefully.

Her lips moved but no words came from them. Her face regained a little color. Soon the eyes and mouth were closed again.

Saionji laid Sagami on the soft quilt on the mat in the guest-room. The physician who had come in meanwhile shook his head after the examination. "Marquis, nothing can be done, but a few injections may keep her alive two or three hours—until sunrise, perhaps. No medicine can help. When she wakes up later, you can talk to her. She will pass away like a tired child going to sleep."

Saionji left the room.

"Father! Sagami?"

"Shinko—Okiku! Sagami wanted to see you badly. She talked very gaily until a little while ago—"

"Father, can we see her?"

"Yes. The doctor has given her an injection—"

After they had quietly seated themselves around Sagami's bed, Okiku said: "Prince, Shinko, Sagami is opening her eyes." She clenched her fists before her chest and bent over the sunken face.

"Sagami, do you recognize me? It's me."

Her eyes helplessly fixed on Okiku, Sagami tried to raise her body. She quickly placed her hand back of Sagami's head, which fell gradually back again. The aged woman smiled faintly at Okiku, Shinko and Saionji. She tried to speak.

"Let me talk to her." Saionji moved close to his governess, tenderly pressing her forehead with his palm.

"Sagami, can you hear me?" Her eyes moved. "You are going back to your birthplace, Kyoto, the place you love so much. I'll see to it that everything will be arranged for you. Rest—rest peacefully." Saionji held back his tears until he finished talking.

Okiku, Shinko, Otama and all the servants, who had come in quietly, sobbed when they saw the tears shimmering in Sagami's eyes.

A few seconds later Sagami stared longingly at the alcove.

"What do you want, Sagami?" Saionji asked. She looked at him, then at Shinko, then at the alcove again.

"Father, I know. Our treasured, family *biwa* is there. Before I was married I used to play for her when we were alone."

Okiku brought the instrument to Shinko.

Contentedly, Sagami glanced at her Big Princess. The moon was pale; the dying governess' sight was failing fast. She threw her cold exhausted hands out from under the bedding; Saionji took one into his and Okiku took the other.

When Shinko's plectrum struck the first note of her favorite song, the governess' eyes brightened and then dimmed again. The eyelids half closed and the chin jerked feebly.

The pendulum of a small 'hanging bell' over the veranda struck in the dawn. Its reverberation seemed to wing the passing soul into eternity.

The physician examined Sagami for the last time.

With the murmur of a Buddhist prayer, Saionji and Okiku brought the lifeless hands together on Sagami's chest and clasped them in veneration.

Saionji, Okiku, Shinko and Hachiro, who had just arrived, and then the others each dipped a small brush into the 'last water' and touched the lips of the dead governess.

Tension filled the Premier's office.

"Marquis Saionji, we asked General Uyehara to see that the Army budget be reduced by seven million yen. He insisted that he could not cut more than two million!" The Home Minister, Hara, who was in conference with Premier Saionji and his colleague, Justice Minister Matsuda, spoke rapidly and rubbed his nose with a handkerchief.

He continued: "And now with that 'saving' the War Minister and his supporters propose to create two new divisions. That is not the retrenchment which the Seiyukai Party had long hoped for and which this Saionji Cabinet declared last year. That is an increase. How do they plan to finance the new units in their second, third, fourth year and so on?" Between his words Hara's sharpened lips quivered like a carp's picking at a piece of food. "What is their argument for this outrage, anyway?"

"Well," Matsuda answered, with his thick eyebrows closely knitted, "according to them, the General Staff set the limit at twenty-five divisions so they are pursuing that fixed program—"

"Is the General Staff or the Cabinet running the Government, I'd like to know? If the military disregards the national budget, there'll be chaos and disorder. I can't follow their logic, nor am I able to understand their motives, except—"

"Except that the military hopes to trap my Cabinet by blocking its most vital project," Premier Saionji interrupted.

"Monsieur, do you think Field Marshal Yamagata and ex-Premier Katsura are pulling strings from behind the scenes? The Army is suddenly stubborn. It has been reported that they have an agreement that if you dismiss General Uyehara from the War Office, no General will take the Portfolio. All the active Generals and Lieutenant Generals who are qualified to accept the post have that understanding."

"Huh, I'm not sure about Katsura, but it's possible Yamagata might have a hand in it. The Cabinet is unanimously against any increase in the Army or Navy at this time—" the Premier sighed.

"Chief, let's resort to the final measure!" Hara's lips quivered again. "Will you appeal to the Throne for an Imperial Rescript to restrain the Army from their unreasonable demand for the new divisions and ask that they abide by the Cabinet decision regarding the budgetary reduction? After all, the War Minister is also an administrator in the Cabinet. The senior Sat-cho leaders resorted to that measure time and again, whenever they met opposition. Why don't we do it once?"

"That's right. I agree with you on that. How about it, Monsieur?"

"Huh, I have already sounded out Genro Yamagata."

"What did he say, Chief?" Hara queried. Matsuda thrust his worried face forward.

"Yamagata thought such a step inadvisable because the Emperor has just ascended the throne—"

Hara burst into rage. "How long are we, the Seiyukai Party, commanding an absolute majority in the Lower House, and thousands of its supporters, going to submit ourselves—the whole country—to a few remaining Genros?"

War Minister Uyehara entered the room. As soon as he took a chair, the Premier asked:

"General Uyehara, I'd like once more to appeal to your sense of fairness and statesmanship, not only for our sake, but also for the sake of the Empire, which urgently needs economy and administrative reform. Will you use your supreme influence to convince your colleagues and subordinates of these national needs and ask them to postpone their demands a short while?"

The Premier's mild Kyoto dialect sounded forceful. The General was momentarily taken aback.

"Premier Saionji, I'm sorry, but it is not only our project, we also have the backing of Field Marshal Yamagata and Genro Inouye. Since the Cabinet voted down the proposal for two divisions, I came to ask your reconsideration of the matter—"

"What?" Hara shouted. "Do you mean to say that you, the Army group, expect to run the Government?"

"We abide in the true spirit of the Imperial Army, that is, we get our demands, or—" General Uyehara smiled coldly.

"Or what?" The Premier raised his voice for the first time.

"Or report the matter back to the Field Marshal and I shall resign from the post." He looked around and continued: "Wait and see if you can induce any General to take the War Portfolio. Don't you know that you can't continue the Premiership without an Army Minister?"

"We have means to get one of the officers to sit with us," was Hara's retort.

"Anyway, when I tender my resignation, I'll present my views on the matter to the Throne—"

"You'll not act independently. Your resignation must go through my hands!" The Premier had lost his temper at last.

"Is that so? Aren't we independently appointed by His Majesty, according to the Imperial Constitution? As an Army General I have access to the Palace, too."

He left the room.

After a silence, the Home Minister resumed his argument for the issuance of an Imperial Rescript.

Matsuda joined with Hara. "Monsieur, let's try all possible means to save the situation. Let's show the opposition that we politicians can fight back when we are encroached upon. We gave up the last Cabinet too easily. If we back down this time, the people will lose confidence in our party and in all political parties." Matsuda bit his lip hard. "Let's show the Genros and the Army that we have backbone. We are standing on constitutional ground. Why be afraid? Will you appeal to the Throne to command the Army to furnish the retiring War Minister's successor?"

Premier Saionji raised his hand as if he were signalling to his Ministers, then he dropped it on the table and bent his head. Finally he broke the silence. "I'll resign tomorrow, December 5. The failure of my major policies—that is, administrative reform and retrenchment of government outlays—is now inevitable. I have no desire to prolong the tenure of my Cabinet after its usefulness is over."

"So, you give up once more without a struggle, Monsieur?" Matsuda set his jaw. Hara's lips were purple.

Saionji murmured: "Huh, it seems that my day of parting from you and the Seiyukai Party has come."

When he heard the visitor approaching, Saionji abruptly rested his writing-brush and folded the unfinished paper.

His strained face relaxed at the sight of the younger man, his friend, the neatly dressed Takekoshi.

After their greetings and random chat, the conversation inevitably turned to political affairs. After a while, Saionji said: "You see, last spring, when General Katsura succeeded me, he was opposed by the Lower House, as you know. I, being the Seiyukai President, was commanded by His Majesty to pacify my followers in the Diet who were opposing the Cabinet's measures. The Imperial order was the result of Katsura's request, of course. But I was not able to do so and the Premier resigned." He glanced at his unfinished writing.

"Now, Katsura's supporters blame me for the collapse of the third Katsura Ministry and allege that I was disobedient to the Imperial wishes and all that. I'm disgusted."

"General Katsura could not withstand the rage of the Seiyukai and the 'Safeguarding the Constitution' movement, I suppose," the younger man began. "As a matter of fact, although the General resorted once more to suppressing his opposition by force, he was out within fifty-seven days. Do you remember, Marquis, the bloodshed in September 1905 that Katsura was responsible for, at the conclusion of the Russo-Nipponese War? Five hundred and sixty people were killed and wounded by the police, who themselves suffered over four hundred and seventy casualties, besides the destruction of one hundred and forty police boxes."

"Huh, he is capable and I have been intimate with him for some years, but I did not think he would be so ruthless in securing power or so crafty as to make a rebel out of me."

As Saionji lighted his cigarette from the charcoal fire, Takekoshi said: "The General has the Genros' backing."

"Huh, that's it. After all, the Genros in our politics are something like the grandparents in a conservative family; their words are final. When a man like Katsura is supported by them, he'll try anything. Although the political parties have gained much strength, the Genros' power still persists. So I advised Hara and Matsuda to co-operate with the incumbent Premier Admiral Yamamoto until the tide turns in their favor."

"Marquis, you don't mean to withdraw from active politics, do you?"

Over the pebbles a new automobile rolled into Saionji's yard with a sound like that of small beans exploding in a roasting pan. Genro Yamagata in military uniform alighted from the car. When Saionji and Takekoshi came to the *genkan* to receive him, the Field Marshal saluted.

"Marquis Saionji, I come to pay you my respects before I leave the

Capital for my Odawara villa. Also I want to remind you that from now on, no matter what happens, I want you to be with us, the Genros—it's my personal desire, of course—"

He stood beside his car.

"Will you come in for a minute?" Saionji invited him politely.

"Ah, Marquis, don't bother. Although I'm getting old and sickly, I still have enough strength left to stand for a few minutes. Don't you remember those days, when you were my superior in the Echigo sector in the Restoration civil wars, forty-five years ago? We were young and ambitious—times have changed. I wanted to tell you my plan personally. This way, travel is easier than in those palanquin days—" He indicated his automobile.

"Field Marshal, is the car yours?" Saionji asked.

With great pride, Yamagata replied: "Yes, Marquis, it is. I, too, finally submitted to the way of the times, though whenever my wife urged me to buy a car I stubbornly resisted on the ground that I had three horses and a carriage—and I'm still at ease on horseback, you see."

"How is it that you changed your mind about the matter?"

"I'll tell you, Marquis. When the late Emperor's illness was first reported and I was about to rush to the Palace, one of my young friends asked me to ride with him in his car. Well, I declined and had my carriage drive as fast as possible, but when I arrived, my friend who had started after me had already been there for fifteen minutes. That incident made me change my mind. Immediately after that I placed my order, but it took a long time to get the car actually delivered."

The Field Marshal was in an unusually good humor. "Well, Marquis, I repeat, don't you forget what I said; you'll be with us from now on in deliberating on all important national problems. Soon His Majesty himself will command you to join the Genros. Have a good rest—"

"So far as Yamagata is concerned, Marquis," Takekoshi said after the automobile had disappeared, "you are already considered as one of the Genros or the Elder Statesmen."

Saionji smiled. "Huh, he is stubborn, but when he promises something he usually carries it through."

"Marquis, you are not leaving the Capital, are you?"

"Yes, Takekoshi-san—"

"What are you going to do about the Seiyukai affairs?"

"Huh, Hara and Matsuda will eventually take charge of them—"

"Matsuda-san is popular but old, and Hara-san's ability is admired, but he lacks prestige."

Looking up from the desk to Takekoshi, Saionji said: "You know, I was drafting my resignation as President of the Seiyukai Party when you came in." He became reminiscent. "Succeeding Ito, I've been the Party President six and a half years, and organized two Cabinets—I am leaving for Kyoto, in quest of peace and quietude."

"You, you won't change your mind on your retirement—?"

Calm and collected though he usually was, Saionji could not restrain his emotion.

No words were spoken until Takekoshi remarked: "You have a new housekeeper in the place of the late Sagami, I am informed. Are you going to take your household along with you to Kyoto?"

"Huh, as usual, but Otama wants to remain here. Huh, Sagami was a devoted and dependable woman. For over sixty years, while she was with me, I had no trouble at home—whatever difficulty there was she always managed to iron it out without bothering me. The new servant may become efficient in time. She is young and good-looking—" He looked at his visitor and added: "I have arranged through an agent to hire another girl when I get to Kyoto this time."

"Oh!" Takekoshi smiled in spite of himself.

"Takekoshi-san, Kyoto is the place to rest and yet enjoy many nice things. These days Tokyo is too noisy. Many big buildings are being built, automobiles begin to rush through the narrow streets. Besides, there are too many politicians.

"And you know, still another reason why I want to retire to Kyoto is the fact that the Momoyama Mausoleum of the late Emperor is near there. I like to pay homage there once in a while."

It was at Saionji's Kyoto home in the early spring of 1913.

A young girl with black hair, fair complexion, clear eyes and sensuous features with a soft Kyoto accent, waited on Saionji.

"Yes, my lord." Her eyelids fluttered. When her employer gave her an admiring look, she blushed.

'My lord' had had several glasses of wine.

"Come, come, Ohana, tell me more about yourself and your home. You were born here though? A great number of years ago Zeze, where your people now live, was one of the scenic spots on the southwestern shores of the great Biwa Lake. When I was a young man I used to go through your place on my way to visit the 'Omi-hakkei,' the eight scenic spots of the Lake. Zeze is only six or seven miles from here, is it not?"

"Yes, my lord."

"The 'Omi-hakkei' were the subject of poetry and literature of the courtiers and later the theme for *ukiyoe* painters. Court artists, who yearned for new subjects and inspiration away from this ancient capital, went there. The lake, which is about one hundred and fifty miles in circumference and shaped like the *biwa* instrument, looked like a sea to the people of the time."

"When we were little, we used to think it was an ocean, my lord."

"Huh, I believe it. Some of those eight spots have been forgotten by the public. The evening bells of the Mi-i Temple, the moonlight view on an autumn night at Ishiyama Temple are still spoken of sometimes, but the rest have lost their fame. So many other natural beauties have been discovered elsewhere and are easily accessible by train and good roads. Soon automobiles will make the distances still shorter. To appreciate the 'Omi-hakkei' we have to be in the frame of mind of the people many centuries ago when the old capital had no communication with the Sea of Nippon or the Pacific Ocean, and no popular amusements, like phonographs and cinema theatres.

"Then, you see, those places which are now considered old-fashioned would have inspired you to poetic and artistic expression."

"I see, my lord."

"By the way, Ohana, do you know that according to a legend, that famous book, *Tales of Genji*, was written at the Ishiyama Temple by Murasaki Shikibu in the early eleventh century?"

"I read something about it—"

"You are fond of literature, huh? Good. Who's your favorite writer?"

Hesitating for a moment, she said: "Tayama Katai, my lord, the naturalist. I also like some translations of Zola, Turgenev—"

"Huh, they treat their subjects, particularly sex themes, astonishingly well and without prudery. Another genius of the naturalist school, Kunigita Doppo, was an acquaintance of mine. He died several years ago—I wrote a preface to one of the Nipponese translations of a Zola story. But my preface wasn't published, because of police interference."

"Oh!"

"Ohana, won't you drink a little wine? It's good wine—"

"Oh, no, my lord! I'm sorry, but I can't. I have never tasted any drink, and the housekeeper has—" The girl was frightened.

"Huh, forget Nagiye, she's all right. Whatever I say in my house will not be contradicted by anybody. I'll instruct Nagiye not to—"

Saionji placed a small wineglass into her hands extended fearfully at his insistence.

"Huh, here, just a little bit at first." He poured the wine into her glass.

"I used to drink like a whale but I take only a small portion now. I want you to be my real companion. Oh, don't leave it there. Drain that glass to show your loyalty."

"Well—I, I really don't know if I can keep my head straight after taking this, my lord."

"Come, come! A-h-h, there, you are very brave. You are just as brave as you are pretty and intelligent." The ex-Premier beamed at his new favorite.

He teased her to take a few more glasses. She became talkative and recounted the traditional domestic arts she had learned after graduating from a girls' high school.

Then her tongue and hands lost their agility, her head began to whirl, and her face burned.

"Ohana-san! Ohana-san!" The housekeeper called her.

With a vague gesture, she said: "M-my l-lord, Nagiye-san wants— she wants me there. I—I must go—"

When she tried to get up she stumbled over the long sleeve of her kimono and lost her balance. She fell back on the mat beside her employer with her legs half stretched, like a butterfly struck down by the stick of a mischievous boy. She struggled feebly to adjust the lower part of her kimono around her knees.

Footsteps approached.

The intoxication, the girlish embarrassment and the fear of accusation by her supposed superior, drew the scarlet of the evening glow into her fair complexion.

"Lord, is Ohana-san still there?"

Saionji frowned.

Nagiye came into the room just as the electric lights were switched on by the local station of the electric company. She saw the new servant with her knees exposed, dead drunk, breathing hard and unevenly, her head resting on her master's lap, her dishevelled hair falling on her face.

"Oh! O-Hana—san!" Nagiye tried to control her voice as she glared at the girl. Her face became pale.

Saionji tenderly patted Ohana's cheek. She was still mumbling incoherently, "I—I must—go."

"Lord! Lord, you told me I, I was your—your—" Nagiye screamed with her kimono sleeves pressed against her face.

"O-O-Hana-san!"

To the anguished housekeeper, Saionji said calmly: "Leave Ohana here, I'll take care of her."

"Hara-san, it's nice to see you and your wife here in Kyoto!"

"Marquis Saionji, since I came here with my humble wife to pay homage to the Momoyama Mausoleums I called to thank you for your favor in recommending me to head the Seiyukai Party as your successor, and to report to you about Party affairs."

"No thanks are necessary. It was a natural choice. You have actually led the organization since I resigned the Presidency in February 1913, particularly after the death of our dear mutual friend and co-worker, Matsuda, on March 5 of this year. Your promotion confirmed on June 18 will revive the original fighting spirit. It will also invigorate the movement for true party government in Nippon, I am sure."

"I shall do my best, Marquis."

"I have no doubt of your eventual success. I imagine General Katsura's death last October has made things easier for you. He was only sixty-eight years old, a year older than me. His passing leaves the Choshu group without Premier timber, save General Terauchi."

"Do you think Terauchi will ever head the Government, Marquis?"

"Yes, I do, Hara-san. He was the War Minister many times and our Governor-General in Korea, too. The Choshu Genros will push him forward and he is very capable in handling affairs along conservative lines."

"I have had a prejudice against the military and their Sat-cho backers ever since they caused the downfall of your second Cabinet. This European war in which we are involved because of the Anglo-Nipponese Alliance will again raise the prestige of the men of swords."

"Huh, it is possible. The Army broke my administration, and the Navy, by their refusal to furnish a Navy Minister, squashed the attempt of Viscount Kiyoura, the Premier-designé, last spring. That led to Count Okuma's induction into his second Administration in April, now in power.

"I have no special liking for military men in politics either. But with few exceptions so far, neither the Choshu Generals nor the Satsuma Admirals have missed the highest political honors, after they once attained fame. Usually, a Premier of either Army or Navy origin has good co-operation from the fighting units, whereas we civilian heads of the Government often collide with one or the other, or both groups. The soldiery is too powerful in our political system."

"But at present, Marquis Saionji, there are no more Generals and Admirals of Sat-cho origin on the active list except Tanaka Giichi. There are some outstanding officers, but they don't seem to be big enough even to reach the top rank in the national defense.

"Huh, speaking of the fighting men, what are the latest reports from the European battle front? I was alarmed in the early fall when the German army pushed close to Paris, but the Allies have repulsed the invaders steadily, haven't they? Our capture of the German positions at Kiaochow Bay, China, on November 11 was good news."

"No, Marquis, I have no additional news on the European situation. All I hear is the boom of our industries and commerce ever since we declared war on Germany and Austria on August 23."

"Huh, I am very much concerned about the French whom I love most next to my own countrymen. I recall too well those horrible conditions after the Franco-German War in 1870 when I was in Paris for the first time."

The smooth-faced Hara looked at the smooth-faced Saionji and said in a whisper: "Marquis, I don't know anything about the war, but I know one thing which might interest you. I heard the Okuma Cabinet, or rather Foreign Minister Kato Komei, had instructed our Minister in China to present a group of demands to Yuan Shih-kai, the President of the Chinese Republic."

"What, Hara-san? Why demands on China?" Saionji's eyebrows came close together.

"It's a step to control China at this time, I suppose. It is said if she accepts our twenty-one demands, China will be virtually our protectorate," said Hara.

"Huh, it is true we can't let China fall into the hands of an unfriendly third party, but will such ambitious plans succeed? What do you think?"

"It's beyond me, Marquis." The new President of the Seiyukai Party shook his head.

"Of course, should Germany win the war and storm the East in her victorious momentum, we must be prepared to defend ourselves as best we can. I'm afraid we'll antagonize China by that scheme. Why not a military alliance with her against such an eventuality? But, you see, regarding the war situation, I consult with Genro Yamagata."

"The old Field Marshal ought to know more about it than anybody else in Nippon, Marquis."

"Yamagata said from the beginning that Germany could not win, and of late he added that the Kaiser lost his best chance to win last fall. I hope the Field Marshal is right."

The autumn air brought the fragrance of the chrysanthemums blooming on the Fukiage Terrace.

"It gives me great pleasure, Marquis, to have had a small part in recommending you to be the Chief Delegate to the Peace Conference at Versailles," Yamagata greeted Saionji as they sat in a conference of the Genros in the Imperial Palace. Then he added: "Mutsukata will be in shortly."

"Field Marshal, I shall do my best not to disappoint His Majesty and our people. This is our country's first opportunity to have her envoy sit an equal with those of the World Powers, is it not, Genro Yamagata?"

"Certainly it is. That's why I wanted to have our ranking statesman head our party. There is no other man in Nippon better fitted for the task than yourself. First of all, you have the highest political record. By seniority, you are next only to Matsukata and myself, since Oyama and Inouye followed each other closely in death. Since October 1916, when His Majesty first commanded you to join us Genros, you have shared many burdens. Of late, chiefly you and I have decided upon the major issues—I assume that Premier Hara is glad to see you go. You are his political benefactor." Yamagata's white eyebrows rose gently.

"Huh, after your first visit when you spoke to me on this matter, Premier Hara and Foreign Minister Uchida came and begged me to accept the post. Although I thought it would be better for either Hara or Uchida to take the burden, after much urging from you and the government leaders, I reconsidered the matter. Frankly speaking, I am delighted to go to my 'old home,' where an acquaintance of my student days, Georges Clemenceau, is Premier. He will no doubt be a great figure at the Conference."

The Field Marshal declared: "That's another reason for my supporting you. Some of my followers tried to persuade me to head our delegation, but my health is not too good and I have no personal connection with any international statesmen at the prospective gathering. I know the limit of my ability and above all, I place the country's welfare first. As you know, Marquis Saionji, this is the basis on which I always analyse a problem and draw my conclusions.

"As to the national questions, Premier Hara has been doing well since he took office in September. He will likely defeat the bill to be introduced in the Lower House extending the franchise."

"Huh, Kato, the late Katsura's political successor, originated the measure when heading the opposition to the Cabinet. I was told—"

"That's true, Marquis. But—" the Genro emphasized his words with his waving finger—"but Premier Hara will dissolve the Diet if the bill is presented. The Premier is right. Universal suffrage—ah, it's useless. The masses know nothing about state affairs. They'll be the tools of jabbering politicians, that's all."

The listener smiled.

"By the way, what will the Powers do about the Reds in Russia at the Peace Conference, Marquis? Will they attack them from all sides and wipe them out? Some Nipponese advocate independent decisive action about Vladivostok to safeguard our shores from the Reds. To that end, our Government entered into an agreement with China last May. The two countries will defend themselves against the common evil seeping through the Manchurian and Mongolian borders into the Orient. Since last summer, we have been dispatching our troops at President Wilson's suggestion."

"The problem of the Siberian expedition must be discussed at some future date, Field Marshal."

"Marquis Saionji, not merely discussed—something must immediately and definitely be done about it." The old Genro struck his knee with his fist, and continued: "If the European Powers hesitate to smash the Reds while they are still weak, those radical ideas and propaganda will spread throughout the world."

Saionji assented, adding: "Nippon agreed with America on her proposal that each should send seven thousand men to Vladivostok, but what can the foreign troops do there, Field Marshal, except policing?"

"That's it, Marquis. There is no definite objective, no concentration of enemies. And the territory is vast. It stretches from the coast of the Sea of Nippon to Europe with the Arctic region as the northern limit and the Amur River and the Gobi Desert as the southern boundaries. Seven, even seventy, thousand soldiers would not mean anything in the endless expanse of the Siberian wilderness. The only hope for us is to have an independent state established between Red Russia and Nippon as a bulwark against the Red advance eastward. We must check what they call 'the abolition of private property' idea at all cost. Such an outrageous conception—"

"You know, Field Marshal, I'd like to read the *Bible* of the Communists, the book written by Karl Marx, entitled *Das Kapital*, some time. Many young professors talk about it but no Nipponese translations of the original are available as yet. Since I'm not good at German, I'd like to get hold of the French version."

"What? You want to read that?" The Field Marshal's eyes glared at Saionji.

"Yes, Field Marshal,"—his calmness disarmed Yamagata—"how can I know whether it is as harmful as they say unless I read it? The Marxian dialectic may be too hard for me to comprehend, but I can try." Saionji went on: "Genro, when I was in Paris in the 1870's as a student, I heard something about it. I think Marx had already published the first of the three volumes. His other manuscripts were also published as a fourth volume some years ago."

The Field Marshal folded his arms, murmuring: "I try to prevent its coming into Nippon in any form and you want to study it!"

"It may have some interesting suggestions to aid even us in correcting our mistakes, don't you think so? Before the Meiji Restoration we hated the Westerners and were afraid of them. Then we dropped our anti-foreignism and associated with them. We discovered that white people were also human beings—"

"No, Marquis, you are delving into dangerous thought. Should such a heathen conception possess you—"

"Huh."

"Let me finish this!" The Field Marshal cocked his head and fixed his eyes on Saionji as if he were aiming a spear, in which art he was an expert, and asked: "Do you remember the rice riots in August last year?"

"Yes—"

"A group of housewives in a fishing town in the north instigated those disturbances throughout the country just because the price of rice was beyond their reach. Outrageous. The Government did the right thing to put them down by force, but newspapers and politicians maligned General Terauchi, who had to surrender his Premiership as a result. The actions of the housewives and those of the Russian Reds who killed the rich ruling class and confiscated their possessions are identical.

"Marquis, should such dangerous thoughts take root in our country, riots would be a daily occurrence. Where would we be then? Listen to Matsukata and me. We are more than ten years older and wiser than you. At eighty, one sees things clearly."

Saionji remained cool.

After a while, the Field Marshal smiled apologetically. "I often take things too seriously these days. Don't mind what I say."

"You are always taking the affairs of state seriously."

Both smoked for some time before Yamagata resumed: "I suppose you have made up the prospective members of your party, Marquis."

"Yes, Genro, the Foreign Minister gave me a list of the official members. Makino Shinken is to assist me as my chief lieutenant. Ambassador Chinda at St. James's Court and Ambassador Matsui at Paris will join us, besides legal, army and naval experts and others."

"I see." The Field Marshal nodded.

"But my private party will include my young servant, Ohana, young Prince Konoe Fumimaro in whose future I have great hope, and my daughter Shinko and her husband." Saionji smiled broadly when he mentioned his daughter's name.

"Ah, Marquis, you are fortunate to have your two children; I envy you. Ito used to say the same thing. Our children all died in their infancy except one daughter. I have no complaints about my adopted son. I suppose it is a human weakness to long for one's own offspring." He studied the deep lines on his bronzed hands. "So you are going to take her to Paris, eh?"

"You see, Field Marshal, many years ago, when Shinko was still in school, I encouraged her to study by saying that if she could master the French language I would some day take her to France. She remembered that promise—and I don't want to leave her husband alone at home with their children; they have, or rather I have, three grandsons and three granddaughters."

For some time Saionji proudly talked of his grandchildren.

"Why doesn't Matsukata come?" the Field Marshal murmured.

That brought their conversation back to official business.

"I suppose," Genro Yamagata resumed, "that Nippon can get hold of those former German territories in Asia, namely, the South Sea Islands and Tsingtao, from which our forces swept the Germans away early in the war."

"Huh, as to the South Sea Islands, our possession is a foregone conclusion, because in 1915 the Allies promised them to us as our portion of the spoils should we win the war. And Tsingtao was held by the Kaiser in the same way that the Czar held Liaotung Peninsula at the time of the Russo-Nipponese War, as a result of which we got the Peninsula. But don't you think we'd better return Tsingtao to China for the sake of our future comradeship in the Orient?"

"Ah, Genro Yamagata and Genro Saionji, I am sorry to be late."

Genro Matsukata came in slowly. As he sat down he said: "Accept my humble thanks and also my congratulations for your consent to head our delegation to the Paris Peace Conference." Turning to the Field Marshal, he said, "Thank you, also, Genro Yamagata, for your effort to induce Marquis Saionji to take this great task upon his shoulders." He paused, and then suggested, "Shall we proceed to request His Majesty's audience so that we may make our report to the Throne and have the Marquis' appointment made official?"

The three white-haired men nodded to each other.

VII

❧

THE LAST GENRO

CHAPTER VII

THE LAST GENRO

IT WAS IN THE SPRING OF 1919. TOKYO'S FOREIGN OFFICE clerks and press representatives were working at the Paris headquarters of the Nipponese delegation to the Peace Conference. From time to time they gazed anxiously at each other.

One of the newspapermen, Baba Tsunego, asked a young secretary: "Is there any news? Where are Marquis Saionji and Baron Makino?"

"We are not at liberty to disclose information to you without authorization. You press people are not friendly towards the officials—" Matsuoka Yosuke replied.

"I am not inquiring about things here. Do you understand? We know more about them than you do, anyway. But haven't you received any cable from Tokyo? That's a secret, too, I suppose—"

Matsuoka smiled.

"How about the meeting of the League of Nations Commission on the Covenant? It is to cast its final vote on the question of religious and racial equality. The Nipponese demand that racial equality be included in the Covenant—"

"We have won some demands—"

"What? Do you mean the demand for the transfer of the former German leasehold in Shantung? The South Sea Islands have little economic value and I don't call the Shantung decision by the Commission an acceptance. The Commission merely countered with a proposal that the Chinese and Nipponese settle the question at an independent conference later. You can't tell what the Chinese will be able to do. They have American backing."

"Our leading men who are here have no fighting spirit—" Matsuoka suddenly grumbled.

"Do you think so? But, Matsuoka-kun, be careful. If you want to keep your job, you've got to follow the policy of our bureaucracy. For you, the key to steady advancement is absolute obedience and respect to your superiors, and no errors in your record."

"I know, Baba-san, but you see, I personally feel that our delegation should use a little propaganda to put our demands across."

"We ought to pack up and go home like the Italian delegates if the

Allied leaders are still going to be so cold to us. But, Matsuoka-kun, I bet you won't stay in government work very long. You'll be dismissed—"

"I'll dismiss my Government—ha, ha, ha—"

"You're unfit for the Foreign Office. If you had a job like Marquis Saionji's today, you'd break up the meeting. I'd like to see a little aggressive diplomacy, though I am entirely against the use of armed force—I am sensitive about the moral issues involved in diplomatic or domestic questions. But I am in favor of our delegates' using all possible means to force our proposal—the equal treatment of all races. For the same reason I sympathize with the religious issue sponsored by the Jewish people. After all we Nipponese are involved in that issue as well, since we are largely Buddhists and Shintoists."

"Well, Baba-san, I think you ought to be a college professor or a preacher, not a newspaperman, even though you have a large intelligent audience for your editorials. Were you ever in America?"

"Yes, I was there for four years and wrote for magazines and newspapers after my ten years' work on the *Japan Times* staff, following my graduation from Waseda University. You graduated from an American college, didn't you?"

"The University of Oregon—"

A few more men came into the room. They took seats near Baba and Matsuoka, and mechanically asked: "Any news?"

Baba looked to his left and said: "Prince Konoe, have you seen enough of Paris?" Prince Konoe Fumimaro was a member of Chief Delegate Saionji's private retinue, and also represented a newspaper. He was twenty-eight years old.

"Yes, Baba-san," he answered gently.

Another reporter asked the young Prince: "How long have you known Marquis Saionji?"

"For many years. I attended the Imperial University at Kyoto, where he lived after retiring from the Presidency of the Seiyukai Party. I called on him frequently to get his advice on various matters, just as my father did."

"Your father and Marquis Saionji were close friends, were they not?" Baba asked. "Unlike other former court nobles with the exception of Saionji, your father was active in politics. His political view was definitely nationalistic as against Saionji's cosmopolitanism. He served as the President of the House of Peers for many years and as a member of the Privy Council, but he died rather young, as I remember."

"He died in 1904, when I was a little boy. Yes, my father was a follower of Marquis Saionji. When Saionji went to Vienna as the Nipponese Minister, my father accompanied him as his secretary."

"Prince Konoe, what type of man is the Marquis?" asked Baba.

"He is considerate and unassuming. You know him better as a Party President and Premier, I think. His sense of civic responsibility is keen. The other day his adopted son and I were out with him for a walk in the park. When we saw the lovely purple lilac blossoms, I unconsciously plucked a small twig. He warned me sharply to cultivate the habit of respecting public property. On the other hand, he is appreciative of any favor done him by others. Here he is anxious to meet his old friends and acquaintances again, like the French Premier, Clemenceau; the Foreign Minister, Pichon, and the Governor of Alsace, Milman. Monsieur Milman is one of the three sons of the Marquis' former teacher, back in the 1870's."

"I see—" Baba nodded. "Well, since he knows the French Premier and the Foreign Minister, why doesn't he press our demands at the Conference? That's what I'd like to know."

"Here, here! A cable from Tokyo!"

"Say, don't scream. What's this?"

"The Imperial Diet passed the new law expanding the franchise. By the new statute, the property qualification is reduced from ten to three yen of the direct national taxes. As a result, the number of voters has increased from one million and a half to three million—"

"That's the best news we have had since we came to Paris. I want to go home as soon as I can, and put my energy into the further expansion of the franchise. I'll fight for the people until that property qualification is completely wiped out, so that all male Nipponese can vote." Baba became serious.

"Oh, here is something more, Baba—the public is registering a strong protest against our delegates' failure at Paris to secure all the country's demands."

Baba leaned over to his press colleague. "Is that right?"

The jolly reporter began talking a moment later. "Baba, did you hear that President Wilson of the United States presented Marquis Saionji's woman companion, Ohana, with a very costly necklace—valued as high as ten thousand yen?"

"Yes. Although I have no right to say anything about his private life, Saionji's bringing Ohana on an official mission was a poor move. The press of other countries are making fun of him and consequently of his delegation because of her."

"But the foreigners don't understand the real situation. She is not a mistress in the ordinary sense as they picture her, for he hasn't a wife. Don't they say it's his family tradition not to marry? How old are they?"

"Oh, Saionji must be seventy and Ohana is twenty-four—"

"Say, you are a pretty good judge of people, Baba—what do you think of them? Do you think they are fond of each other?"

"Ha, ha, don't ask me! But my guess is that Saionji is no doubt fond of his family-traditional-wife-mistress. He has a weakness for tender skins—see her luscious complexion and alluring figure. His bringing her over is eloquent proof of his affection. She is pretty and she may reciprocate his affection to some extent—"

"What do you mean? You sound skeptical."

"Somehow, I don't trust her. First of all, the difference in their ages is too great—by that I mean that Ohana cannot be physically satisfied. When curiosity and the glamour of being a great statesman's mistress fade—well—" He shrugged his shoulders. "And then her type—it's hard to explain, but what I mean is that she's not the type—there are danger signs around her flirtatious eyes— But she's efficient and clever all right—"

"Say, Baba," another reporter interrupted, "what do you think of the political future of Marquis Saionji and Baron Makino?"

"Well, the immediate outcome of this Peace Conference, and the effectiveness of the League of Nations that is now being created by the Conference, will certainly change their careers and those of all the other officials present, including young secretaries like Matsuoka here. On the other hand, Saionji is already one of the Genros and he's a graduate politician, but Makino is still a man in the making, in spite of having been in the Cabinet under Saionji. In his favor, he has the influence of his late father, Okubo, and he has the support of the Satsuma clique which his father built up. Although the clannish influence in our politics is fast diminishing because no capable men succeeded the founders, and because of the steady maturity of our political parties, the Satsuma and the Choshu men will attempt to re-establish their grip on the country's affairs. Makino is one of the leading candidates for the Satsuma, and eventually for national leadership."

"That's right."

"But Makino lacks the force and tenacity of a clever and successful politician. At the same time, he is fair-minded and cautious. Once an acquaintance appraised him by saying that he was a man who would sound out the efficiency of a stone bridge with an iron stick, and then would not cross, but would study it some more. He is very careful. And his fair-mindedness is best explained by his association with Saionji, who is noted for that virtue. They are alike in that.

"My bet is, if the League of Nations is active and beneficial to its member nations, including Nippon, and Saionji lives to be the only surviving Genro, this man Makino will be assigned to a very important and steady office."

"What will that be?"

"As Minister of the Imperial Household or the Lord Keeper of Privy Seal, he will be the ideal man—to be an immediate and constant adviser to His Majesty, for instance. Saionji as the Genro and Makino as the Lord Privy Seal will make a good team and serve democracy. It was reported that some time ago old Field Marshal Yamagata asked Saionji if there were anyone who could inform him on the principles of democracy. Saionji recommended Makino, and he took up the job."

Just then, accompanied by his advisers, Baron Makino entered the room.

All stared at him, but they could not determine whether the result of the meeting had been favorable or not. Greeting the newspapermen as usual, he and his subordinates retired to their official suite.

"There they go, seclusion, secrecy, incommunicado with us. At the Conference, they are timid like a mouse before a cat. They can't even protest against dictatorial action like President Wilson's," Baba grumbled.

Baron Makino returned unexpectedly to the reporters and sat down among them. They showered him with questions, especially on the racial-equality clause in the Covenant of the League of Nations.

Slowly Makino began: "Led by the United States, all six major Powers opposed the racial equality clause in the Commission. America thinks that this proposition and her own so-called Japanese immigration question are too closely related. That is, if the League of Nations nullifies racial or color lines, the American refusal to allow Nipponese to enter that country will be considered unfair, and under international pressure she may finally be forced to abandon her attitude towards Orientals—"

"It was rejected there, then?"

"Yes, by six to five votes. Ah, yes, the religious equality proposal met the same fate." In his elongated, intelligent face was determination, though he spoke softly: "As to my own position, I will protest—"

"In the plenary session?" Baba asked.

"Not only there." For the first time the press heard Makino speak decisively and loudly. "But also everywhere else until it is finally accepted. On the merits of our achievements during the World War, we deserve equal treatment with the others. Also, if one of the Allies' most popular slogans, 'A World Safe for Democracy,' is to be carried into serious practice, the subjects of member-nations must be accorded equal and just treatment, without any discrimination against either race or nationality—or religion. If the League of Nations fails in this fundamental principle, she will not be able to adjust difficulties between member nations of different colors and will automatically lose prestige."

He looked at Baba. "I am personally much disappointed in this result. As you know, I'm closely attached to America. I spent my high school days in Philadelphia. The United States is my second home, as France is Marquis Saionji's. I was enthusiastic about doing whatever I could at this Conference because of the splendid American leadership under President Wilson, who advocated the creation of a new peace machine, the League of Nations. Now, I am broken-hearted because it was American opposition which defeated our proposal."

"Ohana, Ohana!" Saionji, elevated to Princehood from Marquis in recognition of his services at the Paris Peace Conference, was in his study at his new home, *Zagyoso*.

This home was located at Okitsu, a small fishing town on the trunk railway line between Kyoto and Tokyo, a little over one hundred miles south of the Capital. The new 'estate' was sixty feet wide and one hundred and fifty feet long. The main house, a tile-roofed, two-story frame structure, had two rooms on the second floor for visitors, and two eight mat-rooms on the ground floor; one of them was Saionji's study, bedroom, dining-room and frequently infirmary, and the other was for the general use of his secretary, his steward, and Ohana. There were also a bathroom and kitchen, and four more small rooms on the same floor for maids and servants. Beside this house, covering about two hundred and eighty square yards, were other small buildings for the stewards, house guards, and for storage.

No fences separated the property on the east and west sides from the fishermen's dwellings. On the north it was shut off from the high-way and the town's main street by a modest teahouse-like wooden gate, and to the south, below a ten-foot stone wall, lay the sandy beach of Suruga Bay.

The main house faced south. At the rear of the buildings was a small grove of evergreen trees and in front, a garden. In one corner of the garden were varieties of black and spotted bamboo bushes, and in another was a little mound with dwarfed pine trees and a miniature gray stone pagoda of thirteen stories. In front of these stood a pair of stone lanterns of the Nara style.

This simple cottage group offered a striking contrast to Genro Yamagata's Odawara Mansion, which was on an old castle site cover-ing over twenty acres. The Field Marshal had different arbors and the houses with their appropriate gardens. Yamagata was an expert gardener and had arranged everything to suit himself.

But Saionji preferred a natural setting. He liked to contemplate the view from his house. To the east were the pine groves on the white sand of Tago-no-ura, rich in legend and celebrated in literature because of its superb outlook. The waters, mirroring Fuji-san and the pines by day and on moonlight nights, had inspired many a poet. Beyond Tago-no-ura was the giant thumb of Izu Peninsula. Then across the bay from the *Zagyoso*, to the south of Okitsu, was a long narrow promontory with Miho Matsubara, another group of legend-ary pine groves. A lighthouse stood at the tip of this horn-shaped piece of land which jutted out into the water to form Kiyomi Inlet on which Shimizu Harbor was located.

The white sails of fishing boats which appeared at dusk and day-break added to the charm of the scene.

A southerly breeze coming in through the garden relieved the heat of summer.

This afternoon, Ohana was reading a popular women's magazine in the adjoining room, with the paper screens on the garden-side pushed aside so she would get the breeze. She was tired, but she had to be awake when Saionji was there. She left several times to drink cold water.

Her resistance gradually waned, and the soft wind, playing in her distorted hair, soothed her. She lay on her side, one arm supporting her head and the other hand holding a magazine; her legs rested one on the other and bent at the knees, were properly covered by the skirt of the thin *yukata*.

Gradually she fell asleep, her arm relaxed, her head sank to the mat. She rolled on her back, her arms inert, and her legs stretched out. The breeze died down in the meantime and the heat and humidity brought out drops of perspiration all over her body. The awkward figure became increasingly unsightly as slumber deepened. Her mouth opened wide in loud snoring, her kimono parted at the breast and knees. Even the flies did not bother her any more.

Unsuspectingly, Saionji stepped in. A frown of disgust creased his brow. "OHANA!" he shouted and stamped on the mat near her head.

She barely stirred. Saionji shouted again. He recalled that at their first meeting she had eventually fallen into a similar pose. Then it had seemed funny and somehow enchanting.

"Oh, oh! My lord, what do you wish?" said she as she sat up on the mat. Still almost asleep she wiped her lips with the back of her hand, then abruptly adjusted the collar of her *yukata*.

Saionji retreated quickly to his study, shutting the paper screen between the rooms with a bang.

Ohana yawned freely before she went to her dressing-room. She came to her master's study and apologized for her unintentional misbehavior. He said nothing. She brought a glass of cold water which he accepted. Although she knew that he was not in a good humor, she said:

"My lord, when are we going to Kyoto or Tokyo or some place cooler than this oven? It may be all right for the winter because it's warmer, but it's most uncomfortable in the summer."

"What do you mean? Why do you ask such a strange question?" he said crossly. "You follow me as I move, I move as I like to. Furthermore, there is hardly any other place in Nippon where the temperature is as even throughout the seasons as in this Okitsu. If you complain about this climate, where do you expect to live?"

"But—but—my lord, this is not certainly the best place. This house itself is among the fishermen's dwellings. On either side the houses and their backyards are unsightly and give unlovely odors of fermenting sea-weed, rotten fish and sewage, mingled with the loud noises of the fisher folk and their gossipy wives. The wind from the ocean is sticky with salt, the roar of the waves bothers me continuously."

He looked at her sternly. Then the memory of Ohana asleep faded and he saw only the grace and the elusive charm that had so long held his senses captive. He sighed.

"But, Ohana, besides the uniform climate of the locale the loveliness of these surroundings excels that of any other resorts on the Nipponese shores of the Pacific. Poets and novelists have admired this scenic beauty with its peaceful waters, pine groves with long stretches of white sandy beach, the autumn moon views from the temple yard above us, and the picturesque shape of Fujisan in the background. To me, it's quiet and most suitable for reading—"

"My lord, the natural beauty you talk about has no glamour—the eccentric literary men may enjoy it and that was all right when there were no popular amusements. You say this place is quiet, but for me it's solitary confinement. I haven't any entertaining companion. The people who come here are old men and they talk of nothing but politics."

"Ohana, I'm amazed at the way you act—you never behaved this way before. What's the matter with you anyway?"

"But, my lord, you are fond of me, aren't you? If you are, why can't you listen to me? You always remind us of reasonableness and all that. Why can't we go to a really cool place in the summer, and why can't I have a little time of my own to amuse myself, and why can't I see people of my own liking, too?"

"Come, come, don't get excited, Ohana. We can go to a cooler summer resort without much difficulty, and you can have a little of your own time, too. Huh, if you wish, we can arrange that you leave for half a year or so. I'll miss you, though."

He involuntarily put his hand out to her shapely one. "Must you go? Your youth means so much to me—you don't know—but then it isn't fair to keep you bound to an old man."

A triumphant smile touched Ohana's lips.

Under the soft autumn sun, Prince Saionji was strolling with Take-koshi in the garden of the *Seifuso*, his Kyoto home. Ohana followed them at some distance.

"Takekoshi-san, don't you think these our traditional autumnal herbs are truly part of us? The glaring imported flowers seen in many modern gardens don't appeal to me, somehow."

"Certainly, Prince, the seasonal flowers chosen and liked by our ancestors seem to suit our life better than the showy ones. By the way, Prince Saionji, don't you think Premier Hara has been carrying on his political campaigns too strenuously? Under his command, the Seiyukai Party Cabinet has crushed all opposition since September 1918. Some people are afraid of him, and even hate him. I fear they may harm him."

"He moves fast and acts decisively, and as my successor to the party leadership he shows ability."

"Can you suggest some—"

"Huh, my days of active leadership ended when I retired from the Presidency of the Seiyukai Party in 1913. As a Genro, I must be passive and impartial to all the factions. The senior Genros used to make and unmake the Cabinets, of course, but my feeling about the Genros is that they should act purely in an advisory capacity to His Majesty, who may wish for their views at a critical time. In the choice of the successor to the retiring Premier we may still be useful. But in that capacity, too, his chances to be of service will decrease because the political parties are becoming so strong. If Premier Hara, the Seiyukai Party President, should resign, the leader of the opposition party will be entitled to the honors. In that way, the succession to the chief executiveship becomes almost automatic and the Elder Statesmen's recommendation will be a mere matter of form."

"I see. So you are determined to pattern our politics after those of Great Britain?"

"Furthermore, I believe that while His Majesty's trusted Premier is in the office, neither the Genro nor anyone else has any business to interfere. I shall be glad to listen to the Premier or other Ministers for information on the nation's affairs but I will never tell them what to do. I hope that the day will soon come when I am not needed. After all, the Genros form an extra-constitutional body. The Imperial Constitution effective since 1889 includes no such office as you know. We must give full play to that document for which many leaders fought and which was finally granted by the Great Sovereign, Emperor Meiji.—Anyway, Takekoshi-san, let's leave politics alone."

When they came near a bush of the roses of Sharon, Saionji stopped and sighed deeply. The change in his humor puzzled Takekoshi and Ohana.

Saionji murmured sadly: "This was my late daughter's favorite flower, especially those light purple ones. Shinko used to grieve because of their hasty fading."

"Literary men often liken the abrupt ending of a glorious life to the fading of the rose of Sharon, don't they, Prince?"

His half-frosted eyebrows relaxed as he said: "Shinko was such a lovely child, intelligent and very considerate of me. I took her to Paris a few years ago because I not only wanted her to see Europe, but I also knew she was worried about my health." He held a faded flower in his left hand and seemed to talk to it.

"You see, Takekoshi-san, it's already over a year since she died, but I can't believe she's gone. My adopted son and grandchildren are broken-hearted, and I, too— She was only thirty-seven years old."

The flower had broken off in his hand. He sat down on a rock, his companion sat next to him. Ohana stood, looking bored.

"She was a charming person ever since her days in the cradle."

"Huh, her death was so sudden, and to think that I was too late to see her! I rushed to her bedside from Okitsu, but she spoke to me no more—"

He grasped the withered flower tightly in his hand. His gentle brown eyes watered. In a low and shaky voice he went on: "She died of influenza during the epidemic— She was pregnant then. I couldn't believe in her passing until I saw her laid speechless—dead. I was grief-stricken. In my agony, I almost broke the treasured *biwa* in the alcove near her bed. She, too, was fond of that instrument. But when I realized it was our ancestral heirloom that never could be replaced, I put it back after having torn a few strings.

"My sole consolation was the fact that until her last minute she was surrounded by her beloved husband and children—and—and her mother, Okiku. She asked for me with her head resting in Okiku's arms."

Like autumn dew on leaves in the soft breeze, Saionji's tears fell on the hand that held the flower.

"I had never tasted such a bitter human experience."

"I can well sympathize with your feeling towards her, Prince Saionji."

"Thanks, Takekoshi-san, for your kind words. Huh, somehow my family has been ill-fated in the last few years. You remember that my adopted son, Hachiro, was attacked by a group of ruffians not long after Shinko's death. Fortunately, the injury was not serious—"

"Yes, I remember, sir."

"Hachiro was merely one of the court officials who were assigned to accompany the Crown Prince to Europe. The attackers, who had misconstrued the purpose of that tour, demanded that he should persuade the court to stop the trip. Despite that attempt, the plan was carried out and Hachiro fulfilled his part well."

"Speaking of outrages, Prince, was not Yasuda Zenjiro's end tragic? He was fatally stabbed in his Oiso Mansion."

"True, Takekoshi-san, it was too bad that he was slain. I think it was not because he accumulated such a huge fortune that he made enemies, but because of the ruthless way he went about making it."

"That's my understanding, sir. The late Yasuda had been abused by the liberal groups as a miser and exploiter. Political assassinations are not rare, but the cause of the Yasuda murder was different."

"Huh, times have changed, I suppose. Before the adoption of the Imperial Constitution, dictatorial statesmen were always the target for assassins, but that method seems out of date now. In addition, there are no great politicians left—maybe Premier Hara is one of the most powerful—"

"Of late, Premier Hara's opposition to our participation in the Naval Limitation Conference at Washington, now in session—"

"He will not mind any opposition on that question, but those extreme nationalists who oppose any sort of international co-operation are difficult to handle. They don't understand the trend of the times—"

Takekoshi smiled at the last words, one of Saionji's favorite phrases.

"Huh, huh—" Saionji laughed softly. "The general trend is towards international co-operation instead of rivalry or isolation. The League of Nations is the reflection of that tendency and this Washington Conference is also the outcome of the same movement. I am strongly for world brotherhood in the true sense of the term."

Saionji rose, followed by Takekoshi and Ohana. They walked towards the house.

As they passed by the pond, a pair of cranes resting at the edge of the water shrieked.

"Huh, huh, that's strange."

The shrieking continued after they had reached the veranda of the guest room.

"Prince Saionji, don't they say the bird shrieks when it senses some unhappy event?"

"Huh, I have had enough bad luck, Takekoshi-san."

They grinned at each other.

"My lord, may I serve you some refreshment?" asked Ohana.

"Huh, yes, Ohana. What would you like, Takekoshi-san?"

"I prefer tea—"

Ohana went into the house.

"Telegram, sir!" A messenger boy on a bicycle stopped at the gate.

"Huh, what? From the Minister of the Imperial Household? What? Listen to this! Hara, Premier Hara was assassinated this morning at the Tokyo Station. A Genros' meeting is called to recommend his successor! Why, I can't believe it—"

They stared at each other for a moment.

"Prince Saionji, here comes an automobile."

The President of the Lower House of the Diet, Oku Shigesaburo, alighted from the car.

"Prince Saionji, I am here to convey sad news to you," began the Parliamentary leader.

"Huh?"

"I was instructed over the telephone by the Seiyukai Headquarters, and also by the Chief Secretary of the Cabinet, to inform you of the assassination of the Premier and to get your suggestion as to the conduct of the Seiyukai Party and also the Cabinet."

"Huh—!" Saionji groaned. "It's a pity!" After a moment of silence he added: "I believe the Cabinet Ministers have tendered their resignations, but until the Premier's successor is chosen, someone must act as Premier *pro tem*. The Foreign Minister, Uchida, will be best. As to the selection of the next *Soridaijin*, I must consult with Genros Yamagata and Matsukata. And the leadership of the Seiyukai Party— That is a big task—except for the late Hara, the secondary leaders are all alike."

He paused for a while and said: "I shall take an express train for the Capital early tomorrow morning and get there in the evening. Then I shall see you and the other leaders of the Party to discuss matters."

The clear but melancholy sounds of the many Buddhist temple bells echoed against the mountain ranges surrounding the city.

It was early summer at Saionji's Okitsu home.

"Sonoko!"

"Yes, Father!"

"Won't you come with me? I am going to take a little walk along the beach. It's such a lovely day. Although I am expecting a visitor, I'll have some free time this morning. Soon you will leave for the woman's college. You must stay at the Tokyo home most of the time."

"Yes, Father. I'll miss you very much. I would like to help Ohana and Nagiye air their belongings and ours, but I'll be glad to come with you."

Saionji looked at his daughter admiringly: "Huh, is that the outfit you'll wear at college?"

"Yes, and do you know, Father, this is one of those practical dresses my big sister brought back for me from Paris when she went there with you!"

"Huh, Shinko was fond of you, wasn't she?" His voice dropped momentarily, but when he saw Sonoko's charming pose he became cheerful. "Huh, when your college starts, Sonoko, I'll miss you, too. Ah, let's go!"

As they strolled near the surf below the house through a flock of plovers, Saionji asked his daughter: "Shall we take a boat-ride across this Kiyomi Inlet to the Miho pine groves? The water is calm and blue. There is no wind, but when we get on the boat, there'll be a soft breeze."

"That'll be wonderful, Father!"

Saionji had his narrow-brimmed hunting cap on his snow-white head. His daughter was hatless and wore her long black hair combed back. They sat side by side in the sampan. At the stern, the boatman's single *ro*, the elbow-shaped oar, made sounds like an old clock. At each stroke, the boat and its passengers tilted rhythmically to one side and then to the other, but the boat cut straight through the ripples.

Sonoko's hair hanging down her back began to fly.

"Oh, Father, what a wonderful smell! That orange blossom on the hillside—" Sonoko expanded her chest, Saionji breathed deeply.

The boat glided along.

"You know, Sonoko, since you'll be away from me soon and be staying among strangers—" Saionji began.

"Father, why so serious? Are you afraid of my mingling with people? I have been away from you most of the time in the past, while I attended the Girls' Middle School." His daughter was cheerful, her ringing voice and laughter travelled far over the water.

"Oh, no, Sonoko! On the contrary. I needn't say this to you, for I know you and I trust you but—just this piece of advice. Open your eyes—"

"What do you mean, Father? You haven't said anything like that before. I can't understand what you mean by 'open your eyes'!"

"When you see or hear things, think about them. Do not take anything for granted. This applies to your new friends, young girls and young men."

"Father!" She blushed, her fair complexion changed to scarlet on her cheeks and neck. She murmured: "I wouldn't think of looking for young men friends."

Tenderly patting her shoulder, he said: "My child, you must."

Sonoko looked directly at him.

"Why? Father!"

"In the end no one but you yourself can help you choose your lifemate. Make friends with as many young gentlemen as you can, without interfering with your school work, and get to know them. Don't be misled by family title or wealth. They won't make your married life happy; often they work against it. If a young man possesses a fair amount of education, good health and a disposition that you will admire for the rest of your life, even if he comes from an ordinary family, he may make a happy home for you. I will bless any man of your own choice as my son-in-law."

"But, Father, Shinko's marriage was not arranged that way, was it?"

"No. It was much in the country's tradition. I was worried for some time, but it turned out ideally, for your brother-in-law is a good man. They were fond of each other. But as for you, I must leave everything to you as far as your future mate is concerned—for times have changed."

In the meantime at Saionji's home, Ohana and the housekeeper, Nagiye, were removing the aired kimonos and dresses from the bamboo poles hanging on the veranda, some in the sun, and the others in the shade.

They had finished putting away Saionji's and Sonoko's garments.

"Now—we'll take care of our own clothes," said Ohana to Nagiye. They sat on the mat to fold their garments.

"It's easy for you, isn't it, Nagiye-san, since you have so few clothes? My, you must have a lot of moth-balls—what a smell! You haven't seen my European dresses before, have you? See, this is what they call an evening dress. That is a gown. I wore them and many others in Paris. Did I show you the necklace President Wilson presented to me?"

"I haven't seen these dresses or your necklace, but I've heard of them many times. I know them by heart even to the last detail."

Nagiye continued: "You must have felt like a queen when you had them on and mingled with the ladies of the great men from all over the world. I hope, Ohana-san, you keep on using them."

"What do you mean? Do you think I'd throw them away?"

"Well, if your secret desire comes true—"

"What are you driving at? I barely know that young bank clerk. But don't you say too much. You are a left-over from the old days when that Sagami brought you in, I was told. Anyway, you yourself used to be very intimate with Nishi—more than friendly. But when you got old you—"

"Ohana-san, stop that nonsense! You—whispering love at rendezvous on moonlight nights to a man almost young enough to be your son."

"Ha, it's spring—" Ohana was still calm. She sneered at the housekeeper. "It's the season. The weather rejuvenates even hardened veins, I suppose. After all, Nishi was originally your lover, wasn't he? If he is young enough to be my son, he is young enough to be your grandson. I heard all sorts of things about you from him. How far you went and where you stayed with him, how often, oh, oh!" Ohana snickered.

Nagiye blushed; her mouth twisting in anger and eyes glaring at Ohana, she grabbed a broom and jumped up.

"Stop, stop! Stop, you thief, you love thief! You stole our lord from me. You stole Nishi from me! But don't you forget. Now I am merely a housekeeper again, but you, you are still our lord's favorite. Should I disclose your secret love affair to him, you'd be thrown out of here."

"You liar! If you don't stop that, I'll close your mouth for you," Ohana shouted.

"Is that so? You may shut my mouth but you can't erase your sins and the facts uncovered by other people."

"What do you mean?" Ohana was shaking.

"Would you like to know?" The housekeeper stuck her chin forward and tossed her head before she resumed. "Everybody in the town knows your affair with Nishi but how about your frequent visits to your doctor friend in Kyoto?"

"The doctor is just another friend."

"Then there must be a misunderstanding on the part of reporters—"

"What—what, reporters!"

"Yes, they even discovered you and your doctor friend stopping at numerous hotels as man and wife. They're going to publish their version of your secret life in their newspapers. But you keep your face clean at the lord's side like a frog in the rain. Our lord is broad-minded, but I wonder whether he will be patient with someone like you for ever and ever."

"Keep quiet! Pack your things and get ready to leave this house! You jabbering, jealous creature!"

Saionji returned from his short boat ride with his daughter.

"My lord, Takekoshi-sama is waiting for you."

"Takekoshi-san, glad to see you. At last you honor me by visiting my hut."

"Prince, it was my great desire to come—"

"I know, you have been busy. How do you like my place?"

"Oh, Prince Saionji, it far exceeds your description. It's refreshing and lovely. What is the name of your new home, Prince?"

"Huh, the 'Zagyoso'—"

"It sounds very poetic. I suppose there is some classic reference?"

"Huh, it's an allusion to something in Chinese history and to my position in state affairs together with the nature of this locale. The name was suggested by the former Minister of the Imperial House-hold, Viscount Watanabe."

"How fitting!"

"Do you know, Takekoshi-san, that in the adjoining yards I often see the fisherwomen's washing, including the women's red loin-cloths."

"Haw, haw—Prince Saionji!"

"Don't you think this place a great improvement over what I had some years ago at Oiso, before I acquired my Oiso cottage? Do you remember that rented shack?"

"Yes, I do very well—I'll never forget it!"

"Maybe because when the Crown Prince proposed to call on me there, you hid yourself in the chambermaid's room. Later I told the incident to Genro Ito. He was exceedingly amused, knowing you and the circumstances.

"That reminds me that his widow sold the *Sorokaku* with the Four Sages' Arbor for one hundred and twenty thousand yen."

"Is that so?"

"By the way, what is the public attitude towards the new Cabinet under the Premier, Admiral Kato Tomosaburo?"

"The people are seemingly satisfied with the Admiral. His achievement at the Washington Naval Limitation Conference has proved his statesmanship. Under him, retrenchment in both the Navy and Army

Departments will likely be carried out. I suppose that was your motive for choosing him for the post at this time."

"Do you know, Takekoshi-san," the host smiled, "I talk politics with hardly anybody now, except you and young Prince Konoe, my protégé. It has long been my experience that I can talk to you without any reservation. You never let things out. In the earlier days many people considered you as a member of my household. Your judgment is fair and unbiased. My responsibility in national problems seems to be increasing because of Genro Yamagata's death last February and because of Genro Matsukata's confinement to bed. I'd like to know more, but except for the Cabinet Ministers, I meet fewer people all the time. I want you to keep me informed as you did before!"

"Well, Prince Saionji, that's a great compliment and honor!"

"Huh, it's not a compliment, it's a fact—"

"Well, do you think, Prince Saionji, that Field Marshal Yamagata's death has made military curtailment relatively easier?"

"No doubt!"

"Will a Choshu man fill that soldier-statesman's shoes, Prince?"

"Huh, there may be one or two in the making but there will never be another Yamagata. He was anxious to bring the former War Minister in the late Hara's Cabinet into the limelight as his probable successor. General Tanaka Giichi has shown excellent ability as an army executive, but I don't know whether he will be able to handle the general state affairs as well as he did the defense units, for politics is not as simple as the fixed military administration. Some time ago, the late Yamagata confided to me his wishes regarding General Tanaka. I suggested jokingly that his army protégé better throw off the uniform and join a party if he wanted to become a political leader. The Choshu stock of statesmen is exhausted, at least temporarily. That was one of Ito's constant worries, do you remember? But the Satsuma group has a few men. What do you think of the new Lord Keeper of the Privy Seal, Viscount Makino? He is supposed to come here today, too."

"Prince, I think it is a natural and wise advancement. He is one of the most balanced and liberal leaders today, and will fill the post ably."

"I'm glad you think so. These are difficult times with the young Crown Prince made Regent on account of the Emperor's ill-health. Makino is the most cautious of all the Sat-cho men. That disposition he inherited from his great father, Okubo, who was almost stupid in comprehending new ideas and schemes. When, however, Okubo did understand and once began to work he was sure to bring the plans to a successful conclusion, with his courage, skill and patience. He was an interesting contrast to my sponsor, Kido. The latter was courageous, intelligent and liberal but lacked Okubo's patience and political skill. They were an ideal team."

"Prince, you seem to think the Satsuma contingent has a premier-timber man. Do you believe Viscount Admiral Yamamoto, the former Premier, will come back?"

"Possibly, Takekoshi-san."

"Then, Prince, what will become of the political parties, the Seiyukai, for instance, should you still be inclined to give a non-party man a chance to head the Cabinet?"

"It has no aggressive leader like the late Hara who can carry on a party Cabinet unshaken. President Takahashi is a good man but he is no politician. He is a gentleman financier. That's why the Seiyukai Party has disintegrated. After I made him Premier, as successor to Hara, he resigned within seven months."

"So do you think that if the political factions lose the confidence of the people, a Sat-cho leader may return to take the Premiership—?"

"Some time ago I was sure the two-party system in our politics had come of age but that was largely because of that dynamic figure, Hara. After his passing neither his successor nor his opposition has been dominant enough."

"Oh, Prince, I have heard that you bought an estate at Gotemba at the foot of Fujisan. Is that right?"

"Yes, but it's another small place—a renovated old farmhouse with only a few rooms. It is located about half a mile west of the railway station and about forty miles from here and seventy miles from Tokyo. I love that vast open plain around the great mountain. I'll spend every summer there. It's cooler there than it is here, and this place is becoming too popular with visitors—"

"You are certainly fond of nature."

"How strange that the wisteria vine has blossoms at this time. Oh, there is a snake, there comes another one and another! May we go back to the house?"

Saionji and Ohana were resting in the Gotemba garden. Ohana had caught his kimono sleeve.

"Huh, don't get excited. They won't harm you. Huh, look, a gopher is coming up. These beasts seem agitated, don't they? It's almost noon, isn't it? Let us go around the bamboo grove."

"Look in this direction, towards Tokyo and Yokohama! Look at that black cloud."

"Huh, something is wrong somewhere— Listen to that booming sound from the earth, Ohana!"

"Oh, my lord, look, look at the house! The building is swaying to the right and left and oh, that smokestack and that telegraph pole are crashing down! My lord, let's run to the house! I'm afraid—I can't walk straight!"

"Ohana! Ohana! Stop, don't go! Come, come into the bamboo grove—it's an earthquake."

Saionji seized Ohana's elbow. They held fast to the long bamboo stems.

"That underground roar is getting louder, my lord!"

"That must be the advance sign of another great heave— Here it comes. Look at the tips of the bamboo! Without the slightest wind they're shaking as if they were in a big storm."

"Let's go out, my lord! I'm afraid!"

"No, no! Don't be foolish, Ohana. You must not! In an earthquake the bamboo groves are safest because their strong underground root-stocks are meshed deep and wide. So the ground here will not crack and nothing heavier than light bamboo branches will fall. For many generations there wasn't any earthquake around your home town; that's why you don't know anything about it."

"Oh! There, my lord, again the buildings and everything are shaking, the ground, too. The servants came out of the house; they are running this way."

"Huh, that's fine! We'll stay here this afternoon— Say, cook, did you extinguish the fire in the kitchen?"

The two maids and the cook began to prepare a picnic, while Saionji and Ohana surveyed the results of the earthquake.

"My lord, look at the train standing there. That came in when the earthquake began."

"Huh, maybe the railbed is damaged. The first few shocks were very severe. I hope it did not cover a wide area— Oh, Ohana, there goes a messenger boy to the house; call him!"

"Sir, this is an intercepted message. The postmaster instructed me to tell you that he was not sure it was the right thing to do, but you might be interested to hear this news. I also am to report to you there is no official mail for you from Tokyo as there usually is."

"Huh!"

"At the first shock all telegraph communication between Tokyo and Yokohama was stopped. This message was supposed to have been dispatched by the Kanagawa Prefectural authorities on board the S.S. *Korea-maru*, the only ship still afloat undamaged in the harbor."

Saionji read the message: "Today at noon a great earthquake took place. Following the shocks, fires broke out and the city became a mass of conflagrations. There is no way of knowing how many tens of thousands of people are dead and injured. Communication and transportation completely paralyzed. Tidal waves swept the coast. No water, no food available. Immediate assistance urgently requested!"

"Boy!"

"Sir."

"Tell the postmaster to keep sending me any message that he can get hold of from and to Tokyo and Yokohama about this disaster. I'll be responsible for his doing so."

"Oh, my lord, how about the Surugadai home and the Okitsu home? Are they destroyed? Can you find out—?"

"Ohana, stop!"

"But, oh, my lord, all my good clothes and—"

"His Majesty and the Imperial Family may be in the center of the stricken area," Saionji murmured after a deep sigh.

Baron Sumitomo, with his young son, Atsushi, called on Prince Saionji at the latter's Kyoto home on a summer afternoon.

"Takamaro,"—Saionji still addressed his brother by the old name—"how old is your son?"

"He is fifteen years old and is in middle school."

As they talked, they looked at the young boy and Haruko, one of Saionji's granddaughters, playing together in the garden.

"Huh, he looks like an intelligent and handsome boy—very much like yourself, Takamaro."

"Ha, ha, Brother, thanks for your compliments—Atsushi is intelligent all right. We think he takes after you."

"Huh."

"He is fond of literature and history. He is always writing poems."

"Huh, he may be revealing what you and I are supposed to have inherited from our long line of Fujiwara ancestors. It's interesting,

is it not, Takamaro? We, by heritage, are not fitted for anything else—
Huh, you are different. You disproved our old saying: 'The melon-
vine produces no egg-plants.' Think, the courtier-ancestors see one of
their descendants become a great financier and industrialist of international fame, but your son and I revert to them, ha, ha!"

"I think you and my son will get along better together than you
and I!"

They looked at each other and laughed again.

"Well, Brother, I—" Sumitomo wanted to say something important.

"Huh, Atsushi and Haruko seem very friendly, don't they?"

"How old is Haruko, Brother? She will be a lovely lady; she is
almost an exact replica of the late Shinko."

"Huh—Shinko was a charming girl. Haruko is my favorite because
she resembles her mother so much. Shinko used to say that Haruko
was musically inclined, and wanted to give her piano lessons—but
Shinko has gone. Since her mother died, although Haruko is only
eleven years old, she helps her young brothers and sisters at home.
This time I brought her over from Tokyo."

"Brother, these days the Cabinets change often, don't they?"

"Huh, Admiral Yamamoto lasted four months and Viscount Kiyoura
Keigo five months. I hope Premier Viscount Kato Komei holds out
longer than his immediate predecessors. He is supported by the
Seiyukai in addition to his own Kenseikai Party. A Premier without
definite party following is like a fish out of water; he can't last long."

"Brother, have you considered the rebuilding of your Surugadai
home, which was destroyed by the earthquake-fire? Remember, I
spoke to you about it some time ago?" he asked at last.

"Huh, I don't think I need to cause you any more expense. My
part in politics is getting dimmer and dimmer, as you know. And I
have my Okitsu home and Gotemba cottage besides this one—though
they are all modest."

"Well, you can use my Tokyo home, too, but I thought you would
like to have your old living-quarters rebuilt. If you prefer, we can
construct a modern Western style building on the same site—

"The 1923 disaster was dreadful. I imagine you lost things that you
can't replace."

"That's right, Takamaro. Among them were several personal gifts
of the late Emperor Meiji. By the way, the great sympathy expressed
by foreign countries, particularly by the United States, was amazing,

was it not? She immediately sent us money, food-stuffs and medical supplies in large quantities."

"By the way, Brother, what caused the sudden revival of anti-Nipponese sentiment on the Pacific Coast? I get reports from the men of my branch banks there."

"Huh, it's very unfortunate. The movement seems to be spreading like wildfire throughout America. According to the Government's information, the Washington Congress now in session is about to pass a law directed against the Orientals, totally excluding us. That would be a terrible insult, and hinder the advancement of our mutual friendship."

The lines on Saionji's forehead deepened.

"Although whatever the United States does is her own affair, I am much disappointed in that country, you know, from the standpoint of progress in real international harmony. Her President, the late Woodrow Wilson, who died several months ago, initiated the League of Nations and her Congress refused to ratify the Versailles treaties in order to stay out of the League."

"Yes—"

"I don't see how the Americans with their honesty of purpose expect to win over other nations to advancement towards world fraternity. They continue to be active in that direction even after rejecting this fundamental framework, the League of Nations."

"Well, I believe you have some personal, sentimental attachment for the Geneva institution."

"Huh, I feel that way, Takamaro, and then this serious injury to our national pride by enacting the exclusion law—I can't understand why the American Congress is uneasy about the Nipponese: there are only one hundred and thirty thousand or one hundred and forty thousand of our immigrants there. In addition, after that 'Gentlemen's Agreement' was entered into, our people ceased going to America, anyway."

They sighed.

"Going back to the housing proposition, how would this be, Brother? If you are not interested in the new models, take one of these houses over to Tokyo. Probably you'd feel much at home in these familiar structures if I had one of them moved to Surugadai for you."

"Huh, that's another story. But don't go to any extra expense on my account. I appreciate your offer just the same."

"I'm glad you accepted it." Sumitomo wiped his moustached face with his handkerchief, and appeared to have more suggestions.

"Huh, it's hot, isn't it, Takamaro?"

"Yes, Brother—" He looked at Saionji for a moment and then remarked, "I don't know whether it's the proper thing to tell you or not, but—"

"Huh, what is it?"

"But—you know here in Kyoto and in Osaka people talk so much about Ohana's love affair with a doctor—I think it's unbecoming on her part—"

"Huh, I know about it. I read about it in the newspapers—"

"Oh! You know about it, Brother? What are you going to do with her?"

"Huh, we can't blame Ohana very much," Saionji mumbled and went on, "Not only the physician here, but she also is having an affair with a young bank clerk in one of your Tokyo branch banks, I think."

"Oh, Brother!"

"Don't be alarmed, neither your employee nor Ohana is to be blamed entirely—I'll leave the matter to my steward."

"I see—I thought you didn't know it."

"My lord!" Ohana and a younger woman were bowing. "The new housekeeper came today. May I present her to you and to Lord Sumitomo—Aya—who takes Nagiye's place."

"Huh—" Saionji and his brother looked at the new servant and then studied Ohana.

Aya bowed low a few more times.

"Huh, that's fine!"

Just then the steward came in. "My lord, a message from Tokyo that Prince Genro Matsukata passed away."

"Huh!" With a clouded face he turned to Sumitomo and said: "Genro Matsukata is gone—now I am the only Genro."

"Fortunately you are very healthy, much more so than myself."

"Huh, what is the matter? You sound discouraged."

"Brother, I don't know why, but every time I hear of death or tragedy I feel that I am falling into a dark, bottomless pit." Sumitomo held his hand to his forehead.

Saionji's gray eyebrows knitted in sympathy. "Huh, I'm all right, have no particular illness, but I'm getting weaker, too. But you must regain your spirit, Takamaro. I've never seen you so downcast. I think mine is due to my advanced age, but you are still young."

"I'm sixty years old, Brother."

"Huh, it's from now on that you'll reap the benefits of your accumulated experiences and matured judgment."

"Yes, Brother, but I have done enough. Owing to your kind advice about thirty years ago, I stay away from politics; I have concentrated on my business. The World War put me in the top rank in heavy industries. Whether you know it or not, in some fields I occupy a supreme position, even ahead of both the Mitsui and Mitsubishi Houses. However, the Mitsui supersedes me in coal mining and the Mitsubishi in shipbuilding—and they have immense trading monopolies which I don't have."

"Huh!"

"Soon I'll be the largest individual income tax-payer in the country. So I'm satisfied, Brother."

"You've attained your life objective, huh? It's gratifying!"

"You, too, Brother. There were many noted statesmen among our Tokudaiji ancestors and also among your adopted forefathers, the Saionjis, but none exceeded your rank and service in the country. You are now the last of the Genros."

They looked at each other and smiled.

"Huh, now you can enjoy the fruits of your past efforts, but in one sense my responsibility is increasing. On the other hand, although my mind is still sound, sometimes even just listening to boastful politicians and government officials seems too much for me. But as I must continue to advise His Majesty on vital national affairs, I must, as you know, be fully informed, so that I may not make mistakes in advising the Emperor or do injustice to any man or group of men whom my recommendation would eventually affect through His Majesty's decision."

"That's another thing I was going to talk to you about. It must be tiresome for you to meet these self-centered politicians, yet you can't dispense with their opinions and reports and still be loyal to your duty as a Genro— How would this be?"

"Huh, another scheme?" Saionji's smile as he interrupted seemed to be reflected in Sumitomo's mind—his pale face brightened.

"If a plan something like this could be worked out to your advantage, Brother Saionji." His face was radiant again. "You get some young man, trustworthy and capable, to be your representative and informant. He will receive various reports and information from the officials for you so that you will be spared their untimely yet indispensable visits."

"Huh, although I had never given the thought expression, that was my reason for having Takekoshi-san report to me. He has all the qualifications. He has understood me thoroughly since back in the early 1890's. He was my personal councillor when I first entered the Cabinet as Minister of Education. But he is occupied as an appointive member of the House of Peers, and he is writing a book on the country's economic development and other things. He is still willing to do me favors, but like yourself, he is about your age, too."

Sumitomo nodded.

"See, it is hard to find a man fit for the job. I think that young Prince Konoe likes me, and I can trust him. But he is also a member of the Upper House, so my request may hinder his work. Another problem these days is the material compensation for such service—Takekoshi-san's was purely gratuitous. We can't ask for service without compensation."

"That's right, Brother Saionji. Well, you do the choosing, of course. Brother, may I suggest this?"

"Huh?"

"When you do find your man, may I pay him, pay him in some way? I'll give him a position without duties in one of my firms in Tokyo so that he can devote all his time as your emissary and secretary."

"Huh—Takamaro. You've forced me to accept another of your offers."

The brothers smiled at each other once more.

The laughter of Saionji's granddaughter and Sumitomo's son came to them from the garden.

"Ohana, we'll walk up to the Seikenji temple grounds this morning where we can see the sunrise and the neighboring views better. Late cherry and early peach trees are blossoming together."

"Well, my lord—"

"Huh, what is the matter? Why are you so slow these days? Come, come."

"You are impatient, my lord."

As they walked up the pine-wooded slope from Saionji's *Zagyoso*, Ohana often asked to rest. She looked pale and was breathing hard.

They were resting on the stump of a pine tree by the side of the path. She said: "My lord, is there anything at Seikenji besides the panorama of neighboring fishing villages, the blossoms and the ocean? —We know them so well."

"Huh, nothing now, but in the great past the temple itself was a show-place on the Tokaido Highway. Even now, many travellers who are going to Tokyo or to the ancient capital and the National Shrine at Ise often get off at Okitsu station to worship there. The original Seikenji was supposed to have been erected about 680 beside the toll-gate, called *Kiyomi-ga-seki*. The first priest was invited from China.

"Then each dictator of the country like Ashikaga donated monas-teries and other edifices, and designated the temple as one of the ten great Buddhist sanctuaries. Even the Tokugawa Shoguns gave build-ings, with the result that once there were over fifteen magnificent structures grouped about the present site."

"I see, my lord."

"Let us go on to the temple yard." They followed the leaf-covered winding path.

"Why is it, my lord, that the town is called Okitsu instead of Kiyomi, like the old tollgate?"

"Huh, nobody seems to know why and when. Huh, here we are. Let's go to the side of the bell-tower. Look at the crimson sky over the tip of Izu Peninsula! The sun will come out soon."

They sat on one of the foundation stones of the building which commanded an extensive view.

"Huh, we have been in Okitsu for some years but we never saw this inspiring scene before. Isn't it lovely? The Izu Peninsula on the east and the shore line leading up to Omayezaki Point on the west— they are like a pair of arms embracing this vast Suruga Bay. We now sit at the head of the distorted triangle. The fishing villages lie under the sleepy morning haze as if they were in a dreamland. See the pale smoke rising from the thatched roofs of the fishermen's huts. And directly below are the Miho pine groves. When we watch the pines from our beach, the stretch of the evergreens appears to divide the water and the sky. Now we can overlook it directly below us."

"My lord—the last time I was at my home—I read descriptions of Kiyomi Inlet and this neighborhood."

"Huh, that's fine! Whose works did you read, Ohana?"

"Oh, some by Takayama Chogyu and some by Anesaki Chofu, my lord."

"Huh, did you like their writings, Ohana? Takayama's is a bit too sentimental—but he's popular."

"My lord, I was deeply impressed, and even more now than when I read them. It seems that his excellent but melancholy tone harmonizes more and more with my life."

"Huh, he died young, but Dr. Anesaki still produces exquisite prose— Oh, here, Ohana! You, you are reeling. Are you ill?"

She was pale; Saionji supported her shoulders.

"Well—my lord, I—I was dizzy—"

"Say, Ohana, what is the matter with you? You are breathing so hard—I noticed the other day, but I thought it was my mistake—you really do breathe hard, from your shoulders!"

Staring at Ohana for a moment he said: "Say, Ohana, you—you are not going to have—"

"A baby—yes, my lord." Covering her face with the handkerchief, she sobbed.

He was radiant: "You mean—we—you and I—"

She shook her head violently.

A lump filled his throat, then his temples hammered.

The sound of wooden clogs came near. He turned around and saw a priest. His head was shaven close, resembling a pale watermelon against the morning light. He wore a simple black clerical garb over his white linen kimono, and one hand against his breast held a rosary. His clear voice chanted a prayer as he walked straight to the bell-tower.

The priest bowed slightly to Saionji and Ohana. His hands now held together, he faced the sun rising over the ocean, and closed his eyes as he offered a silent prayer.

He stretched out his hand to the rope attached to the horizontal bar of hemp-palm. One, two, three—the priest's lean, strong arm moved in perfect rhythm as the bar beat the bell. Every stroke produced a subdued boom. The lingering reverberation reached the people along the shore and the fishing boats near and far on the sea.

After he had finished ringing the correct number of times, the priest meditated anew.

Then with a genial smile he advanced a few steps towards Saionji and made low bows. Saionji and Ohana returned the courtesy.

"It is a lovely spring morn, sir!" He bowed again. "Please forgive my rude greetings and my informal manner. If I am not mistaken, you are Genro Prince Saionji, whose advice even His Majesty, the

Emperor, seeks frequently. I am humble Priest Furukawa Taiko, the master of this Seikenji. It is my great privilege to greet you, Prince Saionji." He bowed once more.

"I am Saionji Kimmochi, now residing among the fishermen's dwellings at the foot of your famous sanctuary. This is my companion, Ohana. We shall be greatly honored if you will permit us to number ourselves among your acquaintances. Since it is my recent custom to take a walk before sunrise every morning, we strolled up to your enclosure at this early hour."

"Prince, at night or in the daytime, now or beyond, the world of spiritual meditation knows no boundaries. The Seikenji welcomes you and everybody at all times."

The priest and Saionji smiled at each other and bowed.

"Prince, would it be too rude to ask you and your lady to take morning tea with me?"

"We shall with pleasure, Priest!"

The autumn sun shone over the Yoyogi Cemetery in the northwestern section of Tokyo.

Saionji was walking among the gravestones and *sotoba*, the wooden posts indicating the newly buried. Here and there thread-like streams of smoke from joss sticks rose straight into the morning air.

"Huh, it's nice of you, Sonoko and Shoichi, to visit Shinko's grave with me. It's almost the seventh anniversary of her death. I know you are anxious to go to your new home, but how glad Shinko's soul will be to see you two together here."

He often looked back at the couple following him. Sonoko carried with her a bundle of fragrant chopstick-shaped incense wrapped in colored paper. Her husband had a few roses of Sharon in one hand and a pail of water in the other.

Saionji continued as they proceeded. "Shinko loved you dearly and you liked her, didn't you? She liked to take care of you as if you were her own child—when you were born she was already seventeen years old. I think you can remember those days, but—you don't remember Sagami, my old governess, do you?"

"No, not very well, Father. I remember that I used to cry and cry whenever I was with some old lady. I know now what she looked like from hearing her description."

"Huh, your mother, Otama, and the governess got along none too well. Sagami insisted that she should bring you up without interference from anybody, even from your own mother—Sagami acted the same way with Shinko when she was a baby. Despite that fact, the governess made no attempt to take you away when Shinko played with you, so Shinko and your mother were very friendly, and Okiku and your mother likewise became good friends."

"Ah, here it is. Oh, look at this, Father, someone has already attended to the grave. The incense is still burning. I wonder who came over this morning. Didn't you say that Brother-in-law was busy with his court duties, Father? He probably came before he left for the Palace."

"Huh, Hachiro must be very busy but— Oh, maybe he or the grandchildren came over. Well, let me light the joss sticks, I have matches."

Sonoko held the incense almost horizontally and her father put the match to its tip.

In the meantime, Shoichi put the flowers into the pair of bamboo vases placed in front of the grave.

"Now, Sonoko, let me have the incense." Saionji put a few pieces into a small pot between the flower-vases.

"May I have the water-pail?" He poured water on the gravestone and into the vases, and knelt down and prayed.

Sonoko and her husband knelt beside him.

Saionji heard a noise near-by, but he did not turn. There was childish whispering again. Before they had time to look they heard: "Grandpa, Aunt and Uncle! We're here first!"

His youngest granddaughter appeared from behind a large tombstone several yards away.

"Oh! Miyoko, who is with you?"

"Grandma! See, Grandpa, here she is!"

"Okiku! You were here ahead of us, huh?"

"Prince!" The gray-haired Okiku was much more excited than her grandchild at the sight of Saionji, but she controlled herself.

"Okiku, I want you to meet Sonoko's husband, Takashima Shoichi. He is an engineer by profession—"

They bowed to each other. When they resumed their standing pose, tears were trickling down Okiku's wrinkled face, and her thoughts travelled back to the time when her own daughter, now lying in the grave before her, was married.

She forced herself to offer compliments to Sonoko. "How lovely you look, Princess Sonoko—I, I con—" The rest was lost in tears and sobbing. Sonoko was also unable to speak. Saionji and his son-in-law maintained their dignity, but in Saionji's eyes moisture reflected the sun.

"Grandpa and Aunt Sonoko! All come to Miyoko's house, will you? We are lonesome, Father is in the office and—"

Miyoko timidly pulled at Saionji's kimono sleeve as she looked up at his face. Her innocent gesture caused the women fresh tears. He silently nodded to her.

"Prince Saionji, I am happy to see you in good health," Prince Konoe greeted his host at the *Zagyoso*.

"Thanks, but these days I catch cold frequently. It's nice to see you. You always look fresh and fit." He looked at Konoe's closely trimmed moustache, and continued: "Huh, I must thank you for your efforts in making the arrangement with Baron Harada Kumao. I am fortunate to have him as my constant emissary and private secretary. Baron Harada is like yourself—young, intelligent and reliable."

"Prince Saionji, I'm glad you think so. He is my close friend. Do you remember years ago when Harada-kun and I were still attending Kyoto Imperial University, we used to visit you at your Kyoto home?"

"Yes, I remember very well, Konoe-san. He was a few years ahead of you, wasn't he?"

"He was a junior when I came to the university, Prince Saionji. After graduation he entered the Bank of Nippon and was sent to England. In 1924, he was a private secretary to the Premier."

"Huh, how do you like your position in the House of Peers?"

"I can't comment on anything yet, because I haven't had enough experience there, sir. But in the light of contemporary democratic tendencies and practices, I feel that the Upper House may need some modification to make any progress."

"I am glad to know that you have some ideas regarding a better House of Peers. Keep on exploring. You have bigger jobs ahead of you. Like your father you'll be promoted to the Presidency of the Upper House soon and something more. The trend of the times is towards progress. Universal manhood suffrage that finally became a law in 1925 soon will be tested. It may cause many changes. Are you keeping up with the now popular study of Socialism and Communism?"

"Not very seriously, Prince Saionji, but since my major subject was political economy and the university has been one of the chief centers of radical learning, I read a little and have some understanding, sir."

"Huh, did Baron Harada tell you that I decided to study Communism?"

"No, sir."

"Huh, I have read the first volume of *Das Kapital*—the French translation."

"You have great ambition, Prince Saionji!"

"Huh, I must know what the Communists are talking about, why the authorities are afraid of them, and what merits, if any, the Marxian dialectic has— We may be able to benefit by some of it."

Konoe looked doubtful. Saionji changed the subject.

"How do you keep yourself fit?"

"I play golf. I used to play baseball."

"Huh, these days people take up all sorts of Western sports. Golf, baseball, tennis, hiking are popular." They conversed lightly for a while before Prince Konoe said, "I must bid you good-bye. I just wanted to see you for a few minutes."

"Huh, don't go! I like to talk with you. Contact with a young man like you always gives me new and fresh ideas. Huh, I'll see you in Tokyo when the weather gets warm. I must call on the new Emperor and the Imperial Family to tender congratulations on the coronation and thanks for the Collar of the Grand Cordon of the Chrysanthemum, which they granted me in commemoration of the great occasion. When I come to the Capital, I also would like to celebrate with you, Count Makino and others, the tenth anniversary of the Versailles Peace Conference."

"That would be interesting, Prince Saionji."

"I would really like you to keep me company. I invited Koizumi Sanshin today, but he hasn't arrived as yet. I have become well acquainted with him. He is an interesting man."

"Wasn't he the one who spent his entire fortune for the 'Safeguarding the Constitution' movement some years ago?"

"Huh, that's the man. When I made Viscount Kiyoura the Premier, Koizumi was one of those who was responsible for throwing Kiyoura out because the induction of a man like the Viscount, without direct political party affiliation was unconstitutional, as they interpreted it. And they succeeded. Koizumi sold his Tokyo estate and gave almost a quarter of a million yen to the cause, I was told from various sources."

"But now you are friends?"

"Huh, we are, Konoe-san. Anyway, as you know, some time ago I made some rules to keep out tricky politicians and annoying newspapermen because too many of them not only disturbed my peace but also used my name to their selfish advantage, thereby giving the public a false picture of my attitude towards important questions. And I get the usual government information through Baron Harada. As a result, the number of visitors has been radically reduced. But sometimes I am lonesome for company, though I enjoy reading books, magazines and newspapers."

"I know that because your influence is so great, your conduct is carefully watched. Even your entry into the Capital often gives rise to fantastic political gossip. I'm sure that you are amply justified in barring sycophants, Prince Saionji."

"Huh, I've got to be careful. After interviews with me, even a responsible Cabinet member sometimes gives to the newspapers as my own, greatly exaggerated, practically imaginary statements. Usually I listen to the political visitor's reports and ask a few monosyllabic questions, and only rarely do I express myself in a sentence or two.— By the way, Konoe-san, did you hear any more about the public reaction towards the Kellogg-Briand Non-Intervention Pact? Premier General Tanaka had a difficult time in getting it ratified by the Privy Council. The Premier as an army leader was a capable man, but as the Emperor's chief civil executive he hasn't lived up to our expectations. Even his original supporters are disappointed in him."

"The opening phrase of the Pact 'In the names of the peoples' caused much discussion. Did they understand that we Nipponese always begin 'In the name of the Emperor'?"

"Huh, that point was cleared early by the State Department at Washington, the co-author of this memorable peace treaty. Despite that, Premier Tanaka is still like an exhausted bull in knee-deep mud. Nor has the General handled our policies towards China satisfactorily. His big talk and high-handed method of dealing with the Chinese authorities antagonized them rather than gained their friendship. Baron Shidehara Kijuro, three-time Foreign Minister from June 1924 to April 1927, brought much better results by his conciliatory policies. Under Shidehara's influence China and Nippon began to work hand in hand, but Tanaka put an end to that. He contends that because of the Shidehara policy the Chinese became contemptuous towards us. America and England punished the natives at Nanking last year by bombarding them, he says. I still think Shidehara is right."

Prince Konoe sat back on the matted floor. "Since the political parties gained strength, you have attempted to keep aloof from national affairs. But in reality the country needs the Genro more and more in order to guide the leaders into the proper channels of constitutional practices."

Saionji saw that Konoe looked tired. "Konoe-san, do I bore you?" He smiled.

The somewhat confused young prince answered quickly: "Oh, no, Prince Saionji!"

"I suddenly recalled what I used to think of those senior Genros, particularly Genro Ito. Terribly boring when he started to tell me his past achievements, sitting there on the tiger skin, stroking his goat whiskers, and puffing imported cigars."

The Seikenji's bell announced the sunset of the short winter day, the Miho pine groves beyond Kiyomi Inlet slowly dimmed against the wall of darkness, and the lights on scattered fishing boats were growing brighter when Prince Konoe finally left the *Zagyoso* for his home in Tokyo.

"Aya, bring me a hatchet, saw and knife."

"Yes, my lord," answered the woman who had come as the housekeeper to succeed Nagiye. After the dismissal of Ohana from the Saionji household she was Saionji's constant companion.

When Aya returned, he was in one corner in his garden where the grove of black bamboo grew.

"My lord, what are you going to do with these?"

"Huh, I am going to make a new bamboo stick—I always make my own. You don't see me carrying a cane with decorations, do you? I used to prance around with canes of costly gold and silver design when I was young, but those days are gone. And those short ones aren't a real help. To get the real use of it you must have a long one, preferably light and durable—"

"My lord, may I call the steward to do the cutting?"

"Oh, no, Aya. I'll make it myself; I love to make things. I used to do a lot of engraving but my hands aren't steady enough now for delicate manipulations. I also made a lot of flower-pots. See, there are still some of those orchids which the steward takes care of now—I originally planted them and watered them.

"Let me see which one to cut. Huh, that one there. It's straight and long enough."

Genro Saionji severed the bamboo close to the ground and smoothed off its branches from the trunk. He cut out a piece measuring a little over five feet.

Rounding off the rough edges and the projecting joints, he carried it back to the sunny veranda, like a hunter with a prize and sat down with it.

"Huh, now I'm going to polish this. You see, it is the season when all plants have stopped growing and are ready for the next spring. That's the best time to cut them for use."

"My lord, do you carry canes of your own make every place you go?"

He stopped long enough to look at Aya's inquisitive face, and as he resumed polishing he said: "Every place I go and with any attire I wear, on my daily walks or to the Imperial Palace or in kimono or ordinary Western suit or full-dress suit."

"Even to the Imperial Palace, my lord?"

"Huh, I'll soon be accorded a message of special Imperial grace permitting me to use my stick in Court, too. See, it's an old court practice to allow the aged servants of state to carry their canes if they wish. In the past, there was some difference as to the time at which this grace was given, some Sovereigns issued permission when one became forty years old and others withheld permission until one was sixty or seventy—or at present eighty."

"I see, my lord."

"Huh, nobody will stop me from carrying a bamboo cane of my own make, Aya. Some time ago, when I paid homage to the Momoyama Mausoleums in a silk hat, frock-coat and my home-made bamboo stick, passers-by turned around and stared at me."

Aya held her kimono sleeve over her mouth to hide her smile.

"Oh, my lord, a newspaperman is coming!"

"Huh, chase him away!"

A few moments later his secretary, Baron Harada, came into the garden. "Prince Saionji—"

"Huh, Harada-san. See, don't you think this new cane is well made? I just finished it."

He stood up and tested its strength.

"Certainly, Prince Saionji!"

"Say, it's such a lovely day. Won't you come along with us for a short walk? All the hillside orange orchards look very pretty, they say. The fruits are already deep yellowish red among the heavy green leaves. I'd like to use this new cane right away." Saionji smiled at it. "By the way, what made you come over today?"

"Nothing in particular, sir. I was requested by the Premier to inform you on routine government affairs."

"Huh, you can tell me that later. Come, come with us! Aya, ready!"

"Prince Saionji, I'd like to, but—"

"Huh, that's all right, the Premier's ordinary reports can wait. Whether I hear them or not he is responsible for them, and my knowledge of them doesn't affect routine affairs, anyhow."

"My lord, the orange orchard may be a little too far for you."

"Then tell the chauffeur to bring the automobile immediately!"

"Yes, my lord!"

Genro Saionji's car bearing the registration number S-101, 'S' for Shizuoka Prefecture in which the Okitsu fishing town was located, rolled slowly along the streets.

In the rear seat, Aya sat on one side, and on the other was the secretary with Prince Saionji in the middle.

Aya had little of Ohana's charm, and she was already past the prime of youth. But sometimes her face lit with the attractiveness of her yesteryears, and her dove-like brown eyes, which harmonized with her well-balanced nose and full mouth, indicated dependability and loyalty.

She always dressed her hair in the old style and wore a kimono of traditional striped pattern over her slender figure.

The Baron, at the height of his manhood, in Western clothes with a felt hat to match, was well groomed.

Saionji wore his shabby hunting-cap, a brown kimono, a muffler of similar color, white *tabi* and light sandals.

As the S-101 car passed by, the fishermen's wives and children, who had spread thin rush-mats on the ground in the sunny spots near their huts, were mending their belongings and gossiping. They whispered to each other.

"This must be a really nice day. Look, Saionji-sama is going for a ride. Like a cat, he always comes out of the house when the weather is good," said an honest-looking woman.

"That Aya-san is with him as usual. Do you think it's any fun for a woman to be with an old man like the Prince?" a talkative fisherman's wife asked her companions.

After the laughter subsided, the honest-looking one said: "That has been the main topic of our chatterings for how many years—ever since that flippant Ohana-san was dismissed following that scandal."

"Ha, I would have fallen for that young scamp, her lover, too, had I met him, do you know? He was so handsome and really a lady-killer," said the talkative one.

"You are always ready to fall for a young man!" an elderly woman hissed through her protruding upper teeth.

The talkative woman continued: "Wasn't that exciting though? My, the rumors were so thick they made me shadow the bank clerk and Ohana-san whenever they were in their love-nest in the fishing village yonder. Later they didn't mind other people seeing them at all. Their hiding place was a tiny inn near the water's edge. They used to stroll along the surf near the house, arm in arm, in the moonlight. My, he was handsome under the moon!"

"You gave us a lot of news about them, didn't you? But you didn't know she had another sweetheart in Kyoto," the ugly one sneered, but the talkative woman kept on and on, repeating what she had told countless times in the course of the past years. As usual, she went into the most intimate detail about the secret meetings of Ohana and her lover.

"At that time, you ridiculed me and hooted at me, but what happened? She even had a baby by him, and still Saionji-sama took her back, but he had to let her go after all." She jerked up her pockmarked face at the group. Then she added: "She deserved it. I'm glad that Saionji-sama did treat her that way. And then she died when her daughter was four years old, and her daughter stayed on with Ohana-san's brother who had adopted her at birth."

"And didn't they say that the Prince was much excited when he found out Ohana-san was pregnant? He wanted to have a son— the poor man, at that age, but the baby wasn't his!"

"I told you then the baby wouldn't be his, but—" the talkative one insisted.

"Didn't the newspapers say that nobody or no message from the Prince came to her on her death-bed?" An unidentified one elaborated on the problem which had for a long time divided the fishermen's wives into two opposing camps on the moral issue involved.

"But, listen, why should we argue so much, everyone almost spitting at the other, about somebody else's affair? Ohana-san is dead, her lovers are not here, and Saionji-sama is such a big man he knows what he is doing. Why should we worry about him? Don't they say that even *O-Tenshi-sama* listens to him whenever something terrible happens? All we should worry about is—"

The honest-looking woman was interrupted by the talkative wife: "Whether our Emperor listens to him or not, I don't know, but we know this much, don't we? When something happens we find out right away, because those big men from Tokyo hurry over here to see Saionji-sama. Some of them look as worried as if they had a terrible stomach-ache after eating rotten, raw fish. And after that, Saionji-sama always goes to Tokyo."

"All we should worry about is that our men come home from fishing safely, and how to buy more things for our money so that our husbands and children won't go hungry." The kindly one squared her jaw.

They looked towards the ocean, and the talkative one, suddenly dismal, said: "That's true. Things go up higher and higher and so much taxes for everything and more taxes—" and slapping the cheek of her little son who was fighting the neighbor's child at her side, she added: "Say, why don't Saionji-sama do something about these high prices?"

"Say, don't shout like that, he may hear you. See, his car is coming closer—he is smiling at us—and he has nothing to do with it, has he?"

The neighbors responded to Saionji's friendly gesture, waving their rough hands at him, the children stopped their mischief in the street long enough to let his car pass; even the cat lying comfortably on the dirty porch heard the automobile horn and awoke from his slumber to greet the Genro, stretching first upward, then backward and forward, then opening its whiskered mouth as far as it could. Now a cloud of dust hid the car from sight.

In the S-101 Saionji was conversing on various matters with his secretary. When the car approached the yellow-spotted green orchards, Baron Harada informed him: "You see, Prince Saionji, in these years the local orange production is very large, next to Wakayama Prefecture. It amounts to four million yen, and most of it will be exported to North and South America."

"Huh, it may rank next to our tea production. Don't they say Shizuoka Prefecture produces over thirteen million yen of tea each year? Say, chauffeur, stop on this hillside somewhere. It's a pretty view over the orange groves and the whole district—but be careful not to block the traffic. The road is narrow, isn't it?"

They drove into the entrance of an orchard.

"Huh, let's rest in the sun."

As they left the car, the secretary remarked: "Aya-san, you can eat all the oranges you want to, free. They don't charge you anything—but if you want to take them home, it's a different story."

"Oh, no, no, Harada-san, don't you dare take anything for nothing. Find the guard, we'll buy some. It's the fruit of the farmer's toil. They are kind-hearted and allow you to eat, but we mustn't take advantage of it. It's no easy task to produce anything."

Looking at his palm, Saionji mumbled: "I got a blister this afternoon when I made this cane."

The secretary, Aya, and the chauffeur grinned.

"Baron, you are the one to do the errand. If anybody sees a member of my household, he won't take money for the fruit. You go over and talk to the guard and buy some."

Soon Harada returned to them with a basketful of oranges. He was accompanied by the aged farmer who gave Saionji the gift of another basketful. He took pride in showing 'Saionji-sama' his orchard. Saionji, carrying his long bamboo cane, walked around side by side with the farmer.

"Huh, on the way home we'll stop at the agricultural experimental station, chauffeur."

"Yes, my lord!"

Soon they were in the government farmyard. The director of the place took them through the green-houses and to the flower and vegetable lots. He told them to pick any flower they liked. Saionji was pleased and with his bamboo he directed his secretary and Aya to make up a small bouquet of his favorites.

"Oh, my lord!" Aya spoke suddenly as if she had touched a snake. "There, there is that newspaperman!"

"Prince Saionji, may I have an interview and a picture?"

"No!" Saionji swung his stick.

"Why did you come unannounced?" the Baron demanded.

"Because you never give us interviews any more, and the editor is always after me." The young reporter pleaded directly with the Genro. "You see, Prince, if I can't get your picture or a story about you, I lose my job—"

Quickly turning to him, Saionji said: "Huh, I see. Well, Baron Harada, wait a minute! Now, what do you want of me?"

"An interview and your picture."

"I won't say anything about politics, as you know, because if I do, the whole nation will shake, but my picture—you've got your camera, haven't you? Do you think my old farmer-like attire is all right? If so, hurry!"

At the unexpected reply, the reporter hastily snapped one. "Thank you very much, Prince Saionji!"

"Is one enough? Take one more; it might be convenient for you to have another."

After the second shot the reporter again asked for an interview, but was refused. "Why don't you give us some news, Prince Saionji? We can meet any condition you make."

"Huh, one vital reason is this: If I give you reporters interviews, hundreds of other people will ask the same privilege, those politicians, you know. At heart I am fond of newspapermen—I was a newspaperman myself about fifty years ago—but I can't do it. I hate cheap politicians— Don't you put this in the papers, ha, ha, ha!"

With his household Prince Saionji was once more at his *Seifuso* home in Kyoto to pass the fall season.

After his early walk and breakfast, Saionji meditated in his study for some time, and then called:

"Aya, come over and prepare ink."

"Yes, my lord."

The housekeeper spent nearly an hour rubbing a cake of Chinese ink against the shallow part of the rectangular inkstand after dipping it time and again into the water at the deeper end.

"Now, bring a large writing-brush and that piece of silk cloth I bought the other day, and also a piece of clean linen to spread under it."

When everything was ready he said: "Help me pin these down on the mat, the linen first, and then the silk. Huh, there! Until I call you again you may retire."

The soft morning sun shone into his room through the paper screens. After another period of deep meditation, he picked up the brush in his right hand, dipped it gently into the ink and slid close to the silk piece spread over the mat. His eyes measured the space. He held his breath for a moment, and tried to steady his shaking hand before he put his brush on the silk. After the first stroke was drawn, his brush worked smoothly and boldly. Five large Chinese characters appeared.

Resting his brush on the inkstand he smiled at his fine writing. He lighted a Pall Mall, his favorite imported cigarette, and watched the white smoke.

"My lord, Koizumi-sama is here to see you!"

The visitor, clad like an old tea-master with the characteristic hood and short coat over his kimono, was ushered in. They exchanged friendly greetings as the 'tea-master' took a seat.

"It's splendid script! What are you going to do with it, Prince Saionji?" Koizumi inquired eagerly.

"Huh, some time ago, the priest of the Seikenji asked me to donate my writing to the temple. Since he is my intimate friend these days, I consented. I felt inspired this morning, so I just finished."

"Priest Furukawa is to be congratulated on having your script. I believe he intends to keep it among the temple's treasures."

Koizumi looked around the room curiously and asked: "Prince Saionji, I am here in your Kyoto home for the first time. I have heard of your library. How many volumes do you keep here?"

"Huh, maybe twenty thousand or more."

"Twenty thousand! I see many Chinese classics."

"Huh, Chinese, Nipponese and French. These days my eyes get tired easily when I look at small print—many French and Nipponese books are printed in small type—for that reason I spend much time with the Chinese which are generally larger."

"But you don't use eyeglasses, do you?"

"Fortunately my eyes and ears—my health generally is sound except that I suffer from chronic diabetes. That is not serious either, since I am careful to exclude all sugar from my diet. You know my hands shake a trifle, but I think this is because of my advanced age."

"Oh."

"I gave up my carving. Besides my almost constant reading, I play card-games of different kinds that I learned when I was in France over half a century ago."

He pointed at the bird cage hanging on the veranda. "Look at that, Koizumi-san, I take care of the nightingale I bought some time back. I clean the cage and give him food and prepare the food, too."

"You are very active."

"Huh, I may live as long or longer than Genros Yamagata and Mat-sukata, who got to be eighty-four and eighty-nine.

"Speaking of long life, around my neighborhood in Okitsu I found five men and women among the fisher-folk over eighty years old. They received commemoration gifts from the Emperor last year at the time of the coronation. I invited them to my house the other day and we had a celebration of our own. In our reckoning I was also eighty then. I intend to do it every year as long as any of the old neighbors is left. Don't you think that's a good record for the district?"

"Yes, Prince Saionji."

There was a short silence. Then the visitor said: "The late Premier General Tanaka died suddenly—"

"Huh, he was still a young man."

"He was sixty-nine years old. He was a good soldier but a mediocre statesman."

"Were you disappointed in him, Koizumi-san?"

The 'tea-master' shook his head and replied: "The General was convinced that 'might is right.' When the Chinese were dissatisfied with his dealings in their country, he swung his sabre. When the liberal groups criticized his policies, he tightened up the Peace Preservation Law to cut their supporters, and suppressed the masses and liberal intellectuals, so that the re-election of the liberal Representatives, now eight members, will be difficult if not totally impossible. And on the other hand, he spent nearly ten million yen for the last general elections to influence the vote."

"Huh, the entry of the liberals and young men into active politics is the only hope for rejuvenating our political parties, but if they plug that fountainhead that way, I am afraid it will be suicide."

"Moreover, the high cost of elections almost prohibits the candidacy of the leaders of the masses, Prince Saionji. Some critics charge that the election is bought and sold through brokers. Whoever, no matter how, can offer the most money is almost sure to win. When the Diet members are elected they concentrate first on getting their expenses paid regardless of the source. They say some Representatives accept money consideration for their legislative votes, for their official allowance is a trifle in comparison with the cost of their parliamentary seat."

"Huh, so that any big money-man, if he so desires, can influence both the election and the national legislation? Those Sat-cho leaders, like Okubo and Ito who gave little freedom to the people, were de-voted to the betterment of state affairs. In their eyes there was nothing but Nippon. Our present-day politicians have given the people the franchise—and buy it back for their own gain. Anyway, Koizumi-san, General Tanaka was hard to talk with. As I came to know him, I also thought his knowledge was limited."

"Ah, Prince, as you know, these days the leading party men are well informed in their own lines. The former President of the Seiyukai Party, Premier Takahashi Korekiyo, knows more about finance in practice and theory than anybody in the country; the former Premier Wakatsuki Reijiro is also a financial expert and scholar in parliamentary government, and the present Premier and Minseito Party President, Hamaguchi Yuko, is an authority on state finance. They read constantly to learn 'the trend of the times.' Some time ago, Takahashi sighed deeply over his inability to obtain a large type English-Nipponese dictionary so that he wouldn't need a magnifying glass. He read many foreign publications in English, too. But—" Koizumi shook his head sadly and he went on: "But General Tanaka's favorite reading matter was magazines and books of fantastic stories and feudal heroism."

"Huh, once I hinted that the people would be benefited if the government leaders could reconstruct their thinking by getting them to read and study new ideas."

"Yes, Prince Saionji, he told me that! He was puzzled by your remark, he said. And another time he confided your suggestion to me 'to be lenient with the liberals and to adopt good points advanced by them instead of booting and persecuting them.' The General said 'all the liberals are irreconcilable Reds, because they criticize *my* policies.'"

"Huh, he had a high opinion of himself, didn't he? At any rate, his death was sudden."

"I thought it was lucky for him that he died, for if the wild rumors of his close relationship to alleged scandals had been exposed, he would have really been in a bad position. Although his intentions were honorable, he was not of the calibre to head the Government, which is, at least on the surface, moving towards more democratic practices."

"Huh."

"Prince Saionji, do you think our delegation headed by former Premier Wakatsuki at the London Naval Limitation Conference will fail?"

"Huh, what do you think? My belief is that Wakatsuki will endeavor to make it a success. But a group in the Imperial Navy is raising a strong protest against any sort of an agreement at London. Although the Admirals say that America and England increasingly encroach upon our navy strength by means of treaties, I feel that the Government must avoid any unlimited naval building race at this time and make economic readjustments at home. The farmers, fishermen, and working classes are badly situated, I'm told."

"Well, Prince Saionji, today I have a request to make—"

"What is it, Koizumi-san?"

"Well, I'd like to have your own story of your life—"

"Huh, I'm sorry but I don't do that."

"That's why I'd like to have it. Such records from your own lips will be invaluable some day as a part of the country's authentic history. Only a glimpse of your experience can be seen in your own narrative, that tiny book published thirty or forty years ago."

"I dislike so-called biography, exaggerating the man, his achievements and so forth. Some time ago, Takekoshi-san wanted to do the same. I objected to it but added, however, that I would not mind if he wrote his impressions on my hobbies, interests, and character. A clever description on these points is interesting to read. After all, you may not be able to find anything new about my past."

"Well, Prince Saionji, although I'd rather like to undertake that, I'll bring some questions. How is that? You see, Takekoshi-san is a scholar and credited with several books, but he is academic. I am told that both Kimura Ki-kun and Shirayanagi Shuko-kun are preparing your biographies, but they don't know you."

"So, in other words, you want to be both a biographer and my friend. Is that it?"

"Well, Prince Saionji—" The 'tea-master' scratched his head.

"Huh, you know how to get your way, don't you? But not that."

"Well, I'll visit you whenever you are not busy and take notes on your past political activities."

"Huh, that would be too dry. However, if you insist. Once in a while I like to have intelligent company, too. By the way, why do you use your three-monkey penname, 'San-shin'?"

"That's very simple, sir. I was born at the hour of monkey, in the monkey month and in the monkey year, according to our zodiacal system."

"Huh, I imagine that's why you are full of 'monkey-shines.' You were successful in business, in politics, and also in literature, and what else—?"

"Doctor, will Father pull through?"

The physician who had felt Saionji's pulse looked through his eyeglasses into Sonoko's heavy eyes as he tucked the patient's hand back under the blanket.

He mumbled to himself, biting his moustache: "If he can only hold out for the next few days, his chances will improve. He is old and this high fever—"

He continued in a low voice: "Have you informed the relatives—?"

"Well—yes, but, Doctor? Is it so serious?"

"Serious? Oh, yes! Don't be alarmed, but it's better if the relatives be notified."

"Then, Doctor, he is not recovering? What am I going to do?"

"There is a chance, of course." Shaking his head he added, "The patient is getting every possible medical care, you see. But still my advice is to take the safer course, that is, to let the relatives know about it."

"The safer course is to inform the relatives!! Yes, yes, Doctor, I understand—" Sonoko held her upper lip between her white teeth, tears filled her eyes.

Saionji continued to sleep. The physician left the room. Sonoko sat tensely on the mat a few feet away from her father. Although trained nurses and doctors watched by turns, she would not leave his side.

Exhausted towards evening, she retired for a short while. She had a long-distance telephone conversation with her husband which relaxed her somewhat.

While the steward and Aya took care of the hundreds of messages and dozens of callers, Sonoko returned to sit silently within the reach of her father's hand. Her eyes were often closed but any motion or sound on the part of the patient brought her sight back quickly and clearly, as when the brilliant autumn moon emerges from masses of white floating clouds.

Pushing strands of hair back to the sidelock, Sonoko studied her father's profile. He had aged rapidly in the last few weeks. His hair was usually closely cropped, but in the absence of the barber's care it was left growing. Now it appeared very sparse, and the snow-white had lost its luster. The eyebrows were still of the same shape, but had lost the grayish tinge and become opaque. A moustache and beard had grown on his smooth-skinned face.

His eyes in the long ovals formed by the high arch of the eyebrows and the curve of the wide sacs below now seemed very large.

The flesh over his cheekbones and in the heavy jowls was sunken. The lower lip dropped over the now pointed jaw and the cords of his neck had become thick. The triangular-shaped ear-lobe was shrivelled. Only his aristocratic nose remained unchanged. The lines on his forehead were deeper and the skin wrinkled like silk crepe had lost the radiance of his younger days, when even in his portraits, it seemed as if it would thrill touching finger-tips.

Saionji's head began to roll, his ashen mouth moved helplessly, giving out the warm medicine-scented breath, and his eyelashes quivered. The head became steady. Slowly, like those of a sleepy child, his brown eyes became fixed on his daughter's face.

"Sono—Sonoko—"

"Yes, yes, Father!" His eyes closed again. With chopsticks she picked a piece of cotton, dipped it into ice water, and gently wiped the cracked lips.

"Sonoko, don't you worry—I'm all right," he whispered.

She leaned over his face, and held her breath to listen to her father's voice between the quick and tired breathing. She heard the sound of socks, *tabi*, on the mat, and the hiss of the nurse's starched uniform. From behind her ear came: "Please, don't agitate the patient!"

Sonoko did not look up; she only nodded.

"Huh, I can't see you, Sonoko. Where are you?"

"You don't open your eyes, Father."

"What happened to those carpenters? They don't bang their hammers, they don't use their planes on the lumber for the new annex. Why did they stop? I'm not ill—I'm all right. Don't you worry, my child."

She was glad to hear his voice.

"Huh, the carpenters are still at work—huh, I smell the fragrance of fresh pine, cryptomeria and cypress. Huh, the annex is almost completed—wish they wouldn't bother to paint the room. I love the plain surface of the wood—"

He talked in a delirium. The annex construction had been called off before his condition became critical, the lumber had been piled away.

"Oh, oh, Okiku! How did it happen? What? Did you pray at the Tsurugaoka Hachiman Shrine for my recovery? How sweet of you! Oh, Okiku, don't go, stay with me—"

His feeble fingers came out from under the cover. Sonoko held them. After a while he began again: "Tell—tell the secretary to find out if the Naval General Staff and the Cabinet have come to an understanding regarding the ratification of the London Naval Treaty—"

The steward thrust his head out from the next room and gestured to Sonoko to say yes.

"Oh, yes, yes, Father. They did, it was reported."

"Huh, now I can rest at ease, can't I, Sonoko? Is Aya there? Tell her to get my things ready. I must take my morning walk soon—"

He dropped off to sleep again.

Sonoko heard fragments of the greetings in the next room.

"Sonoko, who's there? It sounds like an Imperial Messenger."

"I don't know, Father."

The steward came in softly, walking as if he were afraid to touch the matted floor. He held a package of wine bottles, with Imperial crests of chrysanthemum and a bouquet of flowers.

Saionji kept his eyes closed.

Suddenly he asked: "Steward, is that you coming in—who was there?"

"My lord, it's the Imperial Messenger inquiring about your condition and here are the presents from His Majesty and Her Highness."

"Sonoko, help me get up and bring me my clothes. I must dress and receive the gifts."

"Oh, Father, you can't get up—"

"My lord, your condition is not—"

The nurse who was in the next room came in as fast as she could. She shook her head violently at Sonoko and the steward.

"Father, you'd better not. It's the doctor's orders, the nurse says so—"

"Huh, am I so ill? And—my doctor orders me to stay in bed. Sonoko, get me my *haori* and put it over my quilt, and, Steward, place the Imperial gifts on this side so I can see them without moving."

"Yes, Father. Your *haori* is on you."

"Huh, I consider myself fully dressed."

Saionji tried to open his eyes wider. They were covered with a thin veil of white matter.

Tears rolled to the pillow. "I can't see the gifts." He sighed, and then said with a faint smile: "But I can see the noble countenances of the Imperial Personages, His Majesty, Emperor Hirohito, and Her Highness, Empress Nagako.

"Steward, forward this message to the Court, with my heart-felt thanks for the gifts: 'His Majesty's feeble old servant lies helpless in the humble hut on the lonely seashore, but the old man's mind is always with the Emperor in time of peace or emergency.'"

"Yes, my lord."

"Huh, Sonoko, just before I heard the conversations in the next room, I was dreaming. No, don't stop me—I'm all right. Somehow, I was admitted in Audience to the three past Emperors, beginning with Emperor Komei under whom I served as a boy-chamberlain at the age of three, then Emperor Meiji whom I served for forty-five years from the days of the Meiji Restoration Wars to his last burial rites in 1912, and Emperor Taisho. The Emperors ordered me to be especially loyal to Emperor Hirohito. The present Emperor is like his immediate ancestors, particularly like his grandfather, Emperor Meiji, possessing the high qualities and divinity inherent in the throne from time immemorial. His reign will be enlightened and peaceful.

"Steward, is there lilac in the bouquet? I smell it, huh, how fragrant!" The patient was visibly affected by the gifts.

"Yes, my lord. Purple lilac and early white tree peony, sir."

"Oh, how thoughtful of Her Highness! They must be from her own flower garden in the Fukiage Imperial Terrace, one of the most beautiful gardens I ever saw, with all domestic and foreign varieties of flowers included there. About this time last year, the Empress and the lovely Princesses allowed me to accompany them into the Fukiage Gardens.

"Sonoko, this lilac fragrance brings back to me all my memories of those student days in France. Then your father was about your age. Those scarlet field poppies were scattered over the great expanse of plains and the lilac bloomed in the small farmyards in the French countryside— Now Her Highness—"

His words were lost, his head sank deeper into the soft pillow, a contented smile rested on his weather-beaten face.

After two years' absence, Prince Saionji was back at his Surugadai home in Tokyo. It was late spring.

"Aya, is Konoe-san here yet? I won't meet any officials today."

"My lord, both Prince Konoe and Baron Harada are on their way here. Your car is ready too!"

"Huh, that's good! Isn't it tonight that Haruko plays in the amateur music concert?"

"It is, my lord."

"Call up a florist and find out what kind of flowers are available. I want to have a bouquet prepared for her."

"My lord, do you expect to attend the concert?"

"Huh, I'd like to, but if I appear people make such a fuss. Any excitement may affect my granddaughter's debut. I'd better stay at home. I want you to distribute the tickets I bought to the servants so you all can go."

"My lord, the gentlemen are here."

"Huh, give me that brown felt hat, Aya. Huh, I'm ready, Konoe-san."

"Prince Saionji, we'll be your guide today on your sight-seeing tour through the new Tokyo streets. Three years ago you drove around."

"Huh, at that time the reconstruction was just beginning and the view was very bad. The other day I paid a visit to the Meiji Shrine. The memorial buildings and stadium on the Shrine grounds looked magnificent. Which way are you going to take me today?"

"Well, first we go around the Imperial Palace grounds; we'll start our tour from Nagatacho, then to Hibiya Park, to Kanda bridge and Asakusa bridge. The route will pass through one of the sections destroyed by the earthquake and fire in 1923 where most of the property damage and human casualties occurred."

Saionji's Cadillac with its S-101 wound through the busy streets. The three occupants exchanged memories of the historic disaster.

"Huh, that was really tragic. How many people lost their lives?"

"Over one hundred and thirty-two thousand, sir." Baron Harada continued: "And the injured numbered over one hundred thousand. And nearly six hundred and twenty thousand houses were burned or swept away by the tidal waves. The total damage was estimated at over two billion yen."

"Huh, we are in the Miyakesaka district— It's our starting point, huh? Some government buildings around here were reported badly damaged, but they look quite normal now."

"In this neighborhood the only building which escaped any serious harm was the Imperial Hotel beyond Hibiya Park, they say, sir."

"Huh, wasn't that building designed by an American architect?"

"Frank L. Wright, I believe," Prince Konoe said.

They rode on along the outer moats of the Palace grounds, passing in front of the Army Department, the Headquarters of the Army General Staff, and Metropolitan Police Headquarters. Then came the Sakurada Gate on their left beyond the moat. Before the Department of Justice, Saionji bowed through the car window as he saw the bronze statue of Matsuda Masahisa, his friend since his Paris days, and one of the distinguished leaders in that Department. Further on their right was Hibiya Park. A house formerly located near the other side of the park had been his Tokyo home after Saionji was relieved from his diplomatic post in the early 1890's, when Shinko was still a little girl.

"Huh, this is a very busy corner. Hundreds of bicycles, motorcycles and many automobiles. Huh, look at the busses with girl conductors in green uniforms. What a change! What a change, Konoe-san. There isn't a single jinrikisha in sight. You know, when I returned from France in 1880, jinrikishas and horse-carriages were popular. In the Ginza there were a few odd-looking, two-story, red brick houses which were regarded as the finest model structures. That building on our right is the Imperial Theatre. By the way, Konoe-san, you had a trying experience during the earthquake, didn't you?"

"Yes, Prince Saionji. My wife and children were at our Karuisawa summer home. I was worried about their safety when I saw the indescribable scenes of the dead and injured and the raging fires. Mostly on foot, then by the freight car, I travelled from the Capital to Karuisawa, over ninety miles. They were unharmed, but I was exhausted."

"Huh."

"That trip put me under the doctor's care for a year and a half."

A few minutes later Saionji removed his hat, turned his head to the left, and bowed to the Imperial Palace beyond the Nijubashi at the end of a wide thoroughfare.

"At the time of the Meiji Restoration this was the vast field where the new Government encouraged cultivation of tea and mulberry fields when the *daimyo* mansions were vacated by the feudal lords. General Omura—you know of him from history books—urged me to buy a mansion with a lot for five hundred yen, that would easily have been worth five hundred thousand yen now. I told him if I had that much money, I would like to stay in a geisha house until it was gone. These buildings around here are magnificent in contrast with those old storehouses. Since I stay away from the Capital most of the time, I'm like an old farmer visiting Tokyo for the first time. I have to ask you everything. How tall and large are these skyscrapers, Konoe-san?"

"Some are ten stories high and the largest building now is the Marunouchi Building—or the Maru-biru, for short—eight stories, with a floor space of over eighteen thousand *tsubo,* equivalent to fifteen acres, I'm told, Prince Saionji. And that structure was designed by the Mitsubishi experts."

"Huh, immediately after the devastation in 1923, it was doubted if we could ever rebuild the city, but at least these main arteries are even more beautiful than they were before, with their wide streets and better traffic facilities. And didn't you say many new parks have been made?"

"Yes, the late Mayor Goto, upon the advice of Professor Charles A. Beard of America, made the original plans for the reconstruction on this ambitious scale."

"Huh, at that time people merely ridiculed him, didn't they? But the scheme so far has worked out quite all right. Now we come to another group of government buildings. Those buildings I know, these two are the Departments of Home Affairs and the Treasury, and the Department of Education, where I began my Cabinet Ministership almost forty years ago under Genro Ito."

"Prince Saionji, we'll soon come to Kanda bridge. From there we intend to drive on to the Asakusa bridge. Is it too much for you?"

"No, no, Konoe-san, go on. This is very interesting and instructive. It is only a few minutes' ride from Asakusa bridge to Ryogoku bridge, isn't it? I'd like to go that way."

Like a fine thread unrolling from a huge spool, a long, long series of events drifted through Saionji's mind.

He recalled the walk with Okiku in her youthful geisha clothes in 1869, when she trotted timidly beside him while the onlookers stared. She had turned him from his geisha-house life to serious study. While he was away in France, she had been faithful to him. He saw himself back in the homeland, full of new ideas, and then possessed of a desire to make the star geisha his own. As the car passed along the highway, he saw Shinko again as a child, Shinko growing to womanhood while her mother waged a losing fight for his affection. He felt once again the loneliness in the Surugadai house when he discovered that Okiku was gone. Then he had the round-faced Otama, and Okiku's memory faded into the routine of politics and new interests.

Okiku appeared again in his thoughts, holding Shinko in her arms when Shinko shut her shining eyes for the last time; he saw Okiku at Shinko's grave with flowers and water. Many young faces and spirits had been about him in his life, and yet today the memory of his first walk toward Ryogoku bridge brought with it Okiku's occasional flashes of mischief and her devotion. He sighed. Was he lonely for the sight of a wrinkled old face, like his own, and of the woman who had been trained in the feudal tradition?

Saionji was looking at his small garden.

Several pots of orchids stood on a board against the wooden fence. In front of the orchid shelf were two short rows of iris. When his eyes caught the purple swallow-shaped flowers, he murmured to himself: "Huh, those are Okiku's favorites."

A contented smile softened his face. Under the warm late-spring sun, the nightingale in the cage near by began to twitter.

Shortly after the household left for the concert, he heard an automobile slide into the yard. He heard Baron Harada's voice and footsteps. Before his secretary announced the visitor, Saionji said: "Thanks for your mission!"

"Sir, I'll be back later." Harada retreated, leaving his charge.

A serene old woman with gray hair, in a plain kimono, sat down on the mat and bowed low. "Prince, I'm so—" The rest of her words were lost in another bow and a soft choking sound.

"Oh, Okiku, I'm glad you came!" he said excitedly.

His affectionate greetings brought a joyous tear to her eyes. For a moment they stared at each other, then Okiku composed herself. "Prince, I'm very sorry for this," she said, putting her handkerchief to her eyes, "but it seems so unreal to me to be here. Although I never doubted your affection all these years and I still think of you morning and night, I could not believe my ears today when Baron Harada brought me your message to come to see you this evening."

"Okiku, you are just as sweet as you ever were. I regret deeply that I made you leave me over twenty-five years ago."

"Oh, Prince, don't say that, gone is gone—gone our beloved daughter, Shinko. How glad would she be if she could see us together once more."

"Okiku—!" This time Saionji was overcome with emotion.

After a long silence, he said: "I have wanted to see you badly for some time. Of late, I have retired from politics—"

That remark rekindled Okiku's old spirit. "Oh, Prince, every time I hear of political changes or that you've been called by His Majesty, I'm overcome with joy and feel great pride in you, though I'm far away! And I worry and dream about you. You, at this advanced age, carrying such a heavy load on your back, walking uphill toward the limitless height."

"Huh, your hero-worship still persists, huh? You and Sagami were my original supporters. Anyway, these days two big political parties, the Seiyukai and the Minseito, take turns in organizing the Cabinets, so that my recommendation to the Emperor about the retiring Premier's successor is a mere formality."

"Oh."

"And of late, with Sagami and Shinko gone, though Sonoko and my grandchildren are close to me, I missed you, particularly when I took ill. I did not tell anybody, but I miss your faith and trust in me, Okiku."

"Well, Prince, that's rather strange for you, isn't it?" She looked at him.

"Huh, as I said, the loss of relatives and intimate friends and also—"

"Also what, Prince?"

"O—Ohana's betrayal!" His soft brown eyes were fixed in space for a while.

"You were very fond of her—?" she said with a faint smile in her eyes.

"Huh, I was! She abused my affection and trust. See, you to whom I have done injustice are still loyal to me, while Ohana carried on her love affairs behind my back. She disgraced me."

"Prince, her beauty blinded your keen sense of judgment, perhaps?"

"Ha, ha, Okiku, I think you are right about that—after all, charm is only skin deep, isn't it?"

"You mean, beauty is. You were quick to turn away when that was gone." Okiku's sarcasm recalled vividly the early days of their romance, when her quick tongue had fascinated him.

Time vanished and Saionji and Okiku relived their years together.

"Okiku, if you want to, you can come back and live in this house, or if I go back to Okitsu you can come there, too."

She beamed at the offer, yet asked: "Do you want me to?"

"Yes!"

"No—Prince, though I appreciate your offer, I prefer to live alone as I have done since I left you. But I'd like to visit you whenever you're back, so that we may have tea together. My returning would disturb your now long-accustomed household habits. But your kind words make my heart young again and will keep me ever faithful and make me think of you more often, if possible. Furthermore, this house is entirely strange to me. You've rebuilt it, and it isn't like the place where once I waited and waited through days and nights for you to return."

"Huh, the old house burned down at the time of the earthquake and fire some time ago, and my late brother, Sumitomo, brought this for me from Kyoto. Do you remember the place where you and I spent one summer?"

"Yes, I do, Prince. Wasn't the death of your younger brother a shock? He was still young and he was such a gentleman. When I heard of his passing, I was very sad, almost as if you were gone."

"Think, he was only sixty-two years old. Well, Okiku, that reminds me of some good news. Do you remember my nephew, my brother's son, Atsushi, who inherited the Sumitomo fortune and his father's name, Kichizayemon? Through Prince Konoe he proposed to marry our granddaughter, Shinko's daughter Haruko. What do you think of it?"

"Oh, Prince, isn't it wonderful news! We actually'll live to see our granddaughter's marriage. Oh, long, long ago when you got appendicitis in France, I feared you would not even see our daughter's wedding."

"Huh, Okiku, you say you don't see anything here that recalls the past, aren't you forgetting one thing?—or maybe you didn't notice it. You used to take care of it yourself, even the first spring we were here. Year after year, it was kept alive by the caretaker whether I was here or not. Come!"

Putting on her light wooden clogs, Okiku followed him to the garden.

The moon hung over them.

Saionji led her by the hand.

"Oh, Prince! How wonderful that these rows of iris are still alive! I remember that I planted and watered them. Oh, there, there your orchids are still blooming and with such fragrance!"

"Huh, you remember them, don't you? And now if you don't want to come here to live with me, you must at least visit me—often, very often—"

They smiled at each other, still holding hands.

The moonlight shone on the two serene figures with the snow-white hair.

"Prince Saionji, where are we going, do you think? Everything seems so confused to me these days. In view of our undeclared war in Manchuria and Shanghai, and all the signs of national disintegration, the quarrels between the civilian authorities and the military leaders and between the organized political parties and the reactionary groups are most distressing—"

'Tea-master' Koizumi was with Prince Saionji at the latter's Okitsu home.

Saionji said slowly: "Huh, it is hard to imagine what the future will bring. As you say, our defiant attitude towards all international agreements regarding the present conflict is dangerous, and the lack of co-operation between the Cabinet and the Army General Staff, which both have denied, is a grave matter. Moreover, the paralyzed state of the Seiyukai and Minseito Parties is pitiful. Not only that but the discontent and poverty of the great majority cannot be ignored. For years the Cabinet Ministers offered me various excuses whenever I questioned them. What do you think are the chief causes for the present unrest?"

"Prince Saionji, the real causes and their effects can only be determined by future historians, but we can roughly trace a few major developments, though they seem to be all interrelated."

The 'tea-master' lightly wiped his high-cheekboned face.

"Huh, that's an interesting approach."

He resumed: "Can't we say that one cause for unrest is the reaction against everything that has preceded here and perhaps in the world—in the last ten or fifteen years, and the other is the chasm between rich and poor?"

"Huh—"

"The internationalism or cosmopolitanism that carried us for some years led us into naval and military retrenchment, for instance. The Washington Naval Limitation Treaty, the Nine Power Treaty protecting Chinese territorial integrity, the Kellogg-Briand Non-intervention Pact, the London Naval Treaty and the reduction in the Imperial Army had their opponents. In spite of that the measures were carried. The prevailing troubles with China may to a certain degree have originated in a reaction against our friendly diplomacy towards the continent."

"Yes—" And Saionji himself went on: "And the same tendency was clear in our domestic politics. Since the establishment of the Imperial Diet in 1890, the franchise spread until universal manhood suffrage was legalized in 1925 and became effective in the national elections in 1928. The people hoped for great things from the vote and expected to take part in the management of national affairs. But as you said some time ago, they soon discovered that the parties did not represent the masses, but only the economic upper class. The average man was first disappointed, then he became desperate and agitated against the political parties and the moneyed few."

Saionji looked into Koizumi's eager face. "I detest outrages and political assassinations, but these terroristic acts become more understandable from an analysis like this. Of course, political murders were frequent in the early reign of Meiji, but attacks on wealthy people have been rare, as in the case of Finance Minister Inouye Junnosuke of the Minseito Cabinet, and Baron Dan Takuma. The Baron, for example, personally was likable, but he became the target of mass hatred because he was the Mitsui's leading figure."

"That's quite true, Prince Saionji."

"This proletarian hatred of accumulated wealth is related to the second factor, the disparity in riches among people. Many decades ago when Genro Ito was still active in politics, I warned him often that his governmental policies tended to create a politico-economic class. I was afraid that some day that new class might divide the people and the Imperial Family as it has already done: the voice of the people is not effectively heard in the Imperial Diet today. The Diet is after all meant to be one of His Majesty's means of getting into close touch with his subjects. But actually it is directly and indirectly obliged to protect the wealthy.

"Anyway, Koizumi-san, you and I know full well that the condition of the masses is bad beyond description, the growing number of farm disputes and strikes, for instance, and the luxurious and easy life of the upper strata is leading them and their families into moral decadence unworthy of the privileged class in a society. But I can't agree with these extremists."

"Don't you think, Prince Saionji, that in our history there are several parallels to the present state where the oppressed masses and the discontented military men—call them reactionaries or Fascists—worked hand in hand against the authorities?"

"Huh, almost every fall of ruling clans was brought about by that combination—particularly the sword-wielding class has had a habit of making friends with the farming elements, and the farmers have looked to the soldiers as their closest friends. I believe that same spirit prevails between them today. The mass support for the Manchurian expedition shows that. Besides, right now, because of the conscription system, our national defense units are the sons and brothers of the farmers and fishermen, and the officers are from the middle and lower economic groups."

"Then it is natural, is it not, Prince Saionji, that some army officers back drastic measures for rural reconstruction and against the rich?"

"Huh, their purpose is good but I disapprove of their method of solving the problem. Don't they agitate for the Manchurian conquest as a solution of the domestic economic ills? They also advocate the establishment of a military dictatorship, like our old 'Shogunate' which we destroyed. Any war with another nation unites the country but always increases the people's burden. We have the Imperial Constitution with its forty years' history. Under no circumstances can I side with people who advocate shelving or crippling that great political instrument. I am personally very much attached to it. Not only did I have a small part in its editing under the leadership of Genro Ito, but also it was one of the monumental works of Great Emperor Meiji, to whom I literally pledged my body and soul. I must guard the Imperial Constitution at all cost."

Saionji said this firmly. To quiet him Koizumi remarked jokingly: "Some reactionary young men would mark you on their black list if you expressed your opinion in public at this time, for they are enthusiastic about dictatorship and drastic economic reform based on the principles of State Socialism. It's no longer idle talk."

"Huh, if the reactionaries want to carry their ideas into effect here, they can take my gray head first—"

"Are you so determined, Prince Saionji?"

Saionji grinned in assurance. "I am!" Then he softened his tone and continued: "I'll cling to the document like a hungry tick clings to an animal even when its abdomen is nipped away, you know, ha, ha! I feel as if the cold wave of reaction were beating on my weakened back. The police told me a fanatic they caught some time ago intended to attack me. But, when the country decided to withdraw from the

League of Nations as a result of the moral censorship of that body on our stand against China, I could not help feeling some personal concern."

"You took part in creating the League many years ago, but the Geneva diplomats were not just in that instance. They could not understand the intricate conditions in the Orient. They don't have any sympathy with our fundamental position and need. Since every 'white' country on the other side of the Pacific Ocean with her vast natural resources closed her doors to our peaceful expansion, the Asiatic mainland is the only outlet for our fast growing national energy. The Big Powers must either let down their barriers against us or let us find breathing space beyond the Nippon Sea. It seems quite evident now, as our military men contend, that every international agreement made since the World War, including the League of Nations, has been worked out to check our expansion and to protect their status with the least expense in the name of peace. If there is a real statesman in the West, why doesn't he propose solving this fundamental problem? A child crying because of hunger will never be stopped by soothing talk, scolding or spanking; he must be fed."

"That's our argument. Although I'm aware that the Chinese politicians misconstrued our liberal policies towards her—I thought by such measures we could show our neighbor our true amity and lead her to the state of real mutual existence in the Orient.—At any rate we need more territory for nearly seventy million Nipponese which more than doubled in my lifetime. I still don't want to see our name taken from the League roll. And it is ironical that the man who is nominated as the Nipponese delegate to deliver our farewell message, Matsuoka, the former vice-president of the South Manchurian Railway Company, was one of the young secretaries attached to the official group under me thirteen years ago at the Paris Peace Conference.

"Our reactionaries who clamor for secession from the League seem to think that Count Makino and I are their chief obstacles because of our former activities. You too seem to think that I fail to recognize the new forces and factors. That is not so. Theoretically I even sympathize with them. The other day War Minister General Araki Sadao told me about the country's conditions, but I thought he was prejudiced. He overshadows conciliatory senior Generals."

The 'tea-master' suddenly noticed the southern sky. "Look, Prince Saionji, at that black cloud! That's a disturbing sign, a black whirling cloud with white streaks in that direction at this time of the day—"

"Huh, what do you mean? What is the matter? Huh—you are superstitious about natural phenomena? Don't you think that's a thundercloud? It's already late spring and it's very hot today. There may be a shower this afternoon."

"Well, Prince Saionji, since I studied a great deal about that famous rebel, Yui-no-Shosetsu, who was said to have depended upon signs in the sun, moon, stars and the like for prophesying political developments, I sometimes believe in them, too."

"Huh, what does it signify in your astrological signs?"

Saionji was joking, but the 'tea-master' was in earnest. "That portends a rebellion!"

"Huh, don't you think we'd better drop political subjects and prophecies and go on with the dictation we began the other day? Somehow you sidetracked me. I guess that's how you inspire and often instigate even an old man's actions."

"Well, I don't know, Prince Saionji, but often I feel something is burning in my system. That makes me throw myself into whatever confronts me."

They finally set to work and kept at it for about two hours before Koizumi left for his hotel.

Half an hour later, he hurried back to Saionji's house; he saw that two uniformed policemen had arrived from the local government seat, Shizuoka, to guard the *Zagyoso*. After a long explanation he was allowed to enter the gate. Another carload of officers came in the meantime.

"Prince Saionji, Prince Saionji!" Koizumi was excited. "I heard a rumor in the town that a *coup d'état* took place in Tokyo. Premier Inukai was assassinated in his official residence and several public buildings and Count Makino's home were bombed. Is that true? Do you have any information? Where are you, Prince Saionji?"

He rushed into the room. The Genro was quietly playing solitaire and answering the machine-gun-like questions in characteristic monosyllables: "Huh, huh, yes, yes!" Then he added: "Right after you left I had some code messages from Tokyo authorities. I deciphered them all. Your information is correct."

"Then, Prince Saionji, don't you think you should go to the Capital? Are you waiting for the Imperial Messenger from Tokyo?"

"Huh—"

"What are you doing?"

"Huh," the Genro grinned, "I am testing my fortune by the cards."

Koizumi watched impatiently. Saionji kept on for a long while and at last threw the cards on the mat. Looking at the 'tea-master,' he said with a deep sigh: "I have no luck in that, but I am going to Tokyo. I have no regret as to my age—I lived long enough—even if I, too, were to be shot on line of duty."

Then grim determination flushed his face and he repeated: "I'll go to the Capital regardless of physical danger. I must not remain here idle, I must be close to His Majesty. That's my duty as the only Genro —Koizumi-san, nobody can take the Cabinet by force."

He threw his shoulders back and called: "Steward, Aya, everybody get ready! Aya, take the nightingale along! And also my bamboo cane."

"Prince Saionji, today I am here to inquire about your health before you return to your Okitsu home from this Gotemba," said Koizumi.

"Huh, stay longer and chat with me. I haven't had any company for many months except Prince Konoe and our Ambassador to the United States, Saito Hiroshi. Konoe came back from America where he acted as a goodwill ambassador. Huh, your political eyes are as keen as your astrological ones."

Saionji recalled the 'tea-master's' correct cloud prophecy over two years back when the May 15, 1932, *coup d'état* took place.

"Ah, Prince Saionji," Koizumi countered, "you laughed at me when I said that, but a few hours after I saw you at your cards."

"Huh, I don't deny that. What do you think of the new Cabinet under Admiral Okada Keisuke who succeeded Admiral Saito Makoto?"

"Before I express my opinion I'd like to know why you recommended those non-party men for the Premiership, while the major political parties were left holding the bag time and again—and they were old, too. Premier Saito was seventy-six—"

"What is your guess as to my display of uniforms?"

"My guess is that you are trying to tide over this stormy social and political season until we have fair winds again. You covered a boil with ointment, for you are afraid of drastic operations. It may be all right for the time being, but I am afraid the boil will burst."

"Huh, you turn out to be a sharp critic."

"But it's my candid opinion, Prince Saionji—"

"That's my worry, too. You will agree with me that the larger political parties have neither true command over the people nor are there real leaders, unafraid and purposeful, like the late Hara type among them—that's how the reactionaries became powerful to start with. For instance, if I had recommended another Seiyukai leader as the Premier to succeed the slain Inukai, just because the Party held the majority in the Diet, I am afraid another *coup* against the Cabinet would have followed."

"Yes—"

"On the other hand, if I had paved the way for a fiery military-Fascist leader, I should have been afraid that his Administration would throw the Imperial Constitution to the winds. Where would we have landed then? So, as you said, I wanted to have a man able to keep the military-Fascist contingent in check and the party government somewhat intact. I found Admiral Saito. He didn't like the job very well in the beginning. Although he proved his ability during his Korean Governor-Generalship many years ago, he was too old, what do we say, 'an old steed is slower than a donkey'?"

"Is it true that the old Satsuma clan adherents supported him strongly?"

"Huh, they liked the Admiral who was the protégé of former Premier Admiral Yamamoto of Satsuma, but their support was overestimated. By no means could either the Satsuma or the Choshu or even their combined forces control the country's politics single-handed today. They don't have the men."

"People talk about the possibility that the President of the House of Peers, Prince Konoe, may take up the Premiership."

Saionji smiled and shifted his position on the mat.

The 'tea-master' continued: "The rumor goes that since you are fond of him, you'll put him into the office, but they'd like to know when."

"Do they talk about him? Huh, I like him very much indeed, as you know, but several things make me hesitate to force him. He is popular among the Peers, I think, but he has no political party of his own. He has no experience as an active administrative head, especially in the Cabinet."

"You consider previous ministerial experience an indispensable qualification?"

"Yes, I do, Koizumi-san. And I am afraid he is too young for the highest post. We have the habit of respecting seniority in society. He is forty-two or three. And—"

"And you don't want to have a black mark chalked up against your protégé at that early age resulting from possible failure of his Cabinet leadership in the current parade of Premiers."

"No. And there is another reason. His wife is devoted to him and she doesn't want to have her husband dragged into the stormy seas of active politics where everything could and has happened—assassination and so on."

"I can sympathize with Konoe-fujin, Prince."

"Huh, I do too. On the other hand if he remains as the President of the Upper House, his position is secure and he already commands prestige and dignity worthy of the successor to that great Konoe house of the Imperial scion, in a direct line from the founder of the Fujiwara clan."

"I see, Prince Saionji. Then what is your solution?"

"To me the solution still lies in the proper working of representative government based on the Imperial Constitution—next time I'll recommend a non-military man to head the Cabinet, then gradually return the leadership back to party men."

"Who are dead."

"Huh, that's it. They are, for some reason, semi-paralyzed. They can jabber, as Field Marshal Yamagata used to say, very noisily but they can't do anything. All they can do is take bribes. I was willing to give them the benefit of the doubt, but even during the Diet session the Cabinet Ministers one after another were forced out of office by the alleged charge of bribe-taking. I'm disgusted but what can I do? That Foreign Minister Koki Hirota, who they say represents that Toyama patriot group, may make a good Premier at this time."

"They, the last Cabinet and this, seem to keep everything in the *status quo*, don't they?"

"What do you mean, Koizumi-san?"

"Well, they don't do much to readjust the agricultural troubles and so on—they have done a little, but it's like a drop of water on a glowing stone."

"Huh, perhaps they misunderstood my suggestions when I said to keep things intact. The peculiar part of it is that the Finance Minister, Takahashi and other Ministers through various propaganda organs, make speeches to the destitute farmers—it doesn't cost much. I can't see how the poor people can recover their over-mortgaged properties, or how they can even fill their stomachs. I think the military men are right in insisting that hungry men must be fed first."

"Well, Prince, Takahashi, former Premier Saito and Premier Okada are all good men. If they had the resources, I'm sure they would like to help the country people, but—"

"Huh, but they can't, because they don't have any resources.— Where is their statesmanship, then, Koizumi-san? If the Minister's job is to dish out something already there, anybody can do that, even a three-year-old child can do it."

"That's true—"

"Huh, we have a depression in statesmanship, too. Huh, those builders of the new Nippon, like Kido and Okubo, were remarkable—later Ito and Yamagata tried to follow in their footsteps—they also created something out of practically nothing. They had shortcomings too; they drank with the geisha girls, were dead drunk often. It was the only way, they used to tell me, to rest their minds from the country's troubles. For them the nation's well-being was their life aim, first and last."

"The politicians of today follow their example in one respect, Prince Saionji."

"Huh, they drink a lot—with geisha girls, you mean?"

In his Okitsu home, Saionji was reading a large-print Chinese book. He sat at his low desk on the carpeted floor, a thick cushion under him. He enjoyed the good light and the electric heating-system in the single-room annex which had been completed not long ago. It was now his study. The old study he used as his bedroom.

"Aya, will you open the curtains?"

She pushed them aside and remarked: "My lord, it's still snowing heavily."

"I know it. I like the view." He rose with difficulty, his hand on one painful knee.

"My neuralgia, Aya." He limped to the window. "Huh, it's lovely, isn't it? The silvery snow covers everything, good or bad. Look at the thatched and tiled roofs of the neighbors' houses—they all look like paper buildings. Their usually smelly back yards are purified with the heavy snow blanket. I wonder how deep it is—how many days has it been snowing?"

"Maybe two weeks, my lord."

"Huh, the papers say it's the heaviest fall in the last fifty-four years in eastern Nippon. In Tokyo communication and traffic were blocked. Some nights ago the theatres were suddenly turned into temporary hotels for their audiences because there was no way to get home. The actors, actresses, stage hands and the patrons spent the night lying in groups all over the house."

"We can imagine, my lord, how bad it is in the Capital, since here in Okitsu, which is supposed to be much warmer, we have so much—"

"Huh, beyond Kiyomi Inlet the Miho pine groves look odd without their deep green. Our garden is pretty. Look at the dwarfed pines, each tier of branches forms a sort of silver-foiled staircase. And the midget stone pagoda and the stone lanterns are coated with the glittering silver."

"Yes, my lord."

"Huh, Aya, did you provide the guard with plenty of charcoal? I imagine his house beside the gate is very cold. Tell the cook to furnish him with some hot dishes for his supper, and rice wine. Huh, the branches of the pine trees on the hillside are breaking under the weight of piling snow. Listen to that!

"Aya, look there, those husky little fellows, the fishermen's children! They have started snow-balling, bare-foot and hatless. Huh, a stray snow-ball struck the window, my, my. Aya, leave them alone!

"Oh, more snow, huh? Such large pieces—the wind, too, is increasing."

"It's time for your afternoon nap, my lord."

"Huh, you are taking my temperature, as usual."

"But, my lord, this is part of your doctor's orders—"

"I know, I know—"

Before he retired for his two-hour sleep he told the housekeeper: "Aya, I want to have Renoir's picture on the wall changed to that other French painting that I showed you the other day."

"But—this one was your favorite, my lord—"

"Yes, I still like Renoir's for it makes me think of warm and sunny southern France, but its coloring is too strong for me, though ever since I was a young man he's been my favorite French artist. Huh, I am growing really old, maybe. I was eighty-six last October—"

Sometime before ten o'clock at night, Saionji was in his old study. Leaning against the charcoal brazier, he looked through his stamp album. There was no sound except the turning of the pages and the soft and almost rhythmic whispering of the falling snow outside.

He yawned, and then: "Aya!"

"Yes, my lord!"

"Is my coffee ready? Make it a bit stronger than usual."

"My lord, your coffee is always strong and it's against the doctor's advice."

"Huh, I know it—I take sleeping powders, too. I know the strong coffee counteracts the doses, which I need badly to keep me asleep for several hours. What a contradiction, says everybody. In spite of that warning I keep taking coffee and sleeping medicine and I'm pretty healthy, am I not?"

"Well, my lord," Aye smiled a little, "regular sleeping hours and a proper amount of exercise by taking walks, and your luke-warm evening bath at five o'clock, all of which are arranged for you by experts in whom you have great confidence."

"Huh, I trust the doctors and scientists all right—"

"And, my lord, you exclude sugar from everything you take to keep your diabetes from getting worse, so now you shouldn't—"

"Huh, I know what you are driving at—but I won't give up my strong bed-time coffee."

After Aya left in feeble protest, Saionji put the stamp album on the mat. Then while he was sipping from the steaming cup, he said: "Don't you think, Aya, I am otherwise a pretty good patient? Under your shining eyes I don't break the rules. For my breakfast, I take oatmeal, a glass of milk, a piece of bread and a little potato; for my lunch I take a European plate, a vegetable soup, a piece of bread and a tiny cup each of white French wine and champagne; and for my supper, I have our own dishes and sake. The only change from time to time is seasonal fruits."

"Quite true, my lord."

Soon it was ten o'clock. With the master in his bed, the Saionji household went into a death-like silence, but the large snowflakes kept hissing on the white crust below.

At midnight he became half-awake. The snow was falling beyond the paper screen and wooden sliding door. He heard the sound clearly as if the flakes were hitting the lobe of his ear. Then it seemed to move away from him inch by inch. Soon he was asleep.

He awoke again. Pine branches were breaking near his house, and the piling snow tumbled from them. He heard the subdued whistle from the small steamer entering Shimizu harbor a few miles away, and the continuous lashing of the waves below.

He felt pains of neuralgia in his leg. He rolled back and forth. Half-awake he held his breath: the bamboo in his garden breaking under the weight of the snow sounded like pistol shots.

It was a little after five o'clock when he groaned in a nightmare in which he saw many heads side by side with bloody decapitated bodies lying in the knee-deep silvery heap, crimson—the scene somewhat resembling that of the famous classical drama, *Chushingura*, when the Okaho *ronin* invaded the enemy's mansion to avenge their master. He was vague about the place and time. He was dazed and stumbled about in the drifts with his long bamboo stick. His weak legs caught, he was about to call for help. Just then from the dark shadow someone fired at him. He shouted for help.

"My lord, my lord, an urgent official code message!"

"Hu—u-uh, Aya. What is it?"

"My lord, this is the second official message from Tokyo!"

"Huh, I had such a terrible nightmare. Oh, someone is knocking at the door, maybe another messenger. Let me have the codes."

When the housekeeper returned to his room Saionji was sitting up in his bed, reading them. His lean hands were trembling

"What, what is it, my lord? Something has happened?

"Oh, it's terri—terrible, Aya! Give me that one, quick! And my kimono—" His lips quivered.

He stared at the page: "Aya, how terrible, think, soldiers murdered Finance Minister Takahashi; the Lord Keeper of the Privy Seal, Admiral Saito; and the Director of Military Education, General Watanabe in their homes. The fate of several other high government officials including Premier Admiral Okada is unknown!"

"Bang!!" Both Saionji and his housekeeper jumped to their feet. That was another bamboo in the garden breaking down. Outside it was still pitch-dark.

"Huh, still another message— Here, the rebellious battalion of the Tokyo Army Division occupies the center of the Capital around the Metropolitan Police Headquarters! It is suspected by the authorities that certain rebel companies are heading by automobile for Count Makino's country home where he is now.

"What? They are coming after me, over here, here too! They are mad, what have I to do—they are mad, Aya!"

"Oh, my lord, my lord! *What are we going to do?*"

"Aya, get me my *obi*. Don't get excited. If they should actually come, there is no way of escaping in this snowstorm. Besides I have had neuralgia pains since last night. We can't defend ourselves. The best way is—"

"What, my lord?"

"You go upstairs and stay there—" Saionji sat down with the messages in his lap. "I stay here—I submit myself to their pistol-muzzle and die like a man, if they don't listen to my reasoning. But to be shot down by rebels—I who hoped to die for His Majesty!"

Aya was speechless and walked back and forth in the room.

Saionji shouted: "Aya! Go upstairs and stay there, and have everybody else stay where he is until they leave the house! Don't make any move, they may hurt you!"

The dazed Aya was about to leave for the second floor when Saionji said to himself: "Listen to that, an automobile stopped in front of the house, they're coming— Oh, Okiku—Okiku—"

Aya stood petrified; Saionji quickly tightened his ribbon-like sash over his kimono.

"Oh, my lord, they're banging on the door! They'll break in in no time!"

"Sh-h-h! Listen!"

After a few knockings, a whispering came between the front doors: "My lord, Prince Saionji!"

"Oh, that's the house guard!" Aya said, trembling, and thus made the rest of his whispering unintelligible. But then another voice followed: "Sir, Prince Saionji, we are from police headquarters to guard you and you must come with us. Your house is not safe any more. Please get ready immediately."

When Saionji himself unlocked the door he saw the house detective and about thirty policemen and gendarmes standing on the snow-covered ground.

Saionji's wrought-up emotions subsided: his neuralgia returned. When Aya was putting more clothes on him, he slowly sank down to the mat.

"Oh, my lord, your leg?"

His eyes shut and with tightly held jaws: "I'd—I'd better not go."

The worried steward who just came in spoke to the police officers. "Prince Saionji is in no condition to go out in this weather. I wish you would do your best to protect the house."

The guards agreed with him.

In another automobile the Governor of the Prefecture and the Prefectural Police Director arrived. Seeing Saionji's state, they had no better suggestion. It was daybreak.

The steward advised that they take Saionji to his own cottage a few blocks away, as a precautionary measure. The stretcher was prepared: at the same time S-101 and two official cars with armed police at the front and rear made ready to rush out of the gate at a moment's notice.

Saionji was on the stretcher, warmly wrapped.

"Telegram, sir!" The messenger boy delivered it to the steward.

The Prefect and the Police Director looked on as he read.

"They are coming, heading this way, men!" shouted the Police Director.

The whistling from a small motorboat below *Zagyoso* interrupted his instructions.

The steward read the telegram to Saionji: "Several young men in khaki attire are speeding toward you in a large automobile—"

The Prefect asked quietly, "Prince, which route do you prefer? We can do two things: Take you by car with the armed guards to the Shizuoka Prefectural seat, or that motorboat will carry you from here to the coast-guard boat—then we'll take you to the coast of Izu Peninsula."

"Take me whichever way you think best. I'm helpless, I can't even walk. Why should they frighten me like this—!"

"Well, then," the official continued, "I'm very sorry, but will you get into your machine? The Police Director and I with the guards will lead in the first car, you with the chief detective and his followers in yours follow us, and the second police automobile will be the rear guard."

With the steward and Aya assisting on both sides, Saionji raised himself on the stretcher and attempted to climb into the S-101. His face twitched at every move.

Suddenly he looked up. "Aya—my bamboo cane!"

With it in his hand, he leaned back in the car and closed his eyes.

The Police Director gave final instructions to the police and the motorcorps remaining at the Saionji estate before he jumped into the first machine.

As the automobile caravan sped out from the gate towards the west on the national highway, the Seikenji's bell above the *Zagyoso* proclaimed the sunless dawn.

They drove fast because some cars which were trailing the Saionji escort could not be identified. The snow was falling heavier than before and the visibility was poor.

When the S-101 reached Police Headquarters of Shizuoka Prefecture, the best-protected spot, the party held a conference.

The Police Chief said: "This place may be attacked, if the rebellion should come here. Soldiers are besieging the Metropolitan Police Headquarters building in Tokyo. And I still suspect those machines which came after us on the highways this morning. Will you get back to your car, Prince Saionji, so we can look for another hiding place?"

The motor caravan was speeding through the narrow city streets.

"Steward, where are we going?"

"I have no idea, my lord. We can't see anything in this snowstorm, but they are following us again."

"What, Steward?"

"My lord, look back through the rear window. There, there, we can't see the machines, but their headlights—there's another one!"

"Huh, no wonder they speed up. I wish they'd drive faster— But I don't see how we can elude them. They are not closing in on us, are they, Steward?"

"Yes! No, no, my lord, no—"

The Saionji party halted once more, but there was neither enough protection nor was the heating sufficient for the ailing Genro. As they left this second refuge, the cars reappeared in the distance.

Through the main streets and by-ways, the S-101 and its escorts staged a game of long hide-and-seek. Saionji's white eyebrows knitted, his face was pale, and his hands clenched tightly. Aya was on one side and the steward on the other. Frequently they looked back through the hazy window.

The car stopped, the three Saionji party members were almost thrown to the floor of his automobile.

Aya screamed.

The Police Director, standing beside the S-101, said: "Prince Saionji, at last we've come to the official residence of the Prefect. We'll protect you here tonight. No matter where we went someone followed us. Now we've shut the iron gate and I've already ordered armed guards around the mansion."

His eyes and his gold teeth flashed in the dim automobile light.

"By turns I'll have the cars ready for any time, sir."

The heavy arming of the official residence continued until three o'clock on the following afternoon when six automobiles dashed out of the yard as if the motored unit were charging against an enemy line. One car which was of the same make as Saionji's S-101 was among the six, its shades drawn and the number changed.

The motorcar troop proceeded to Saionji's home at Okitsu. The road was heavily guarded for a mile on each side. Around his house a cordon of eighty police and gendarmes was posted so that not even an ant could slip through to harm the Last Genro of the Empire.

Saionji's return was prompted by the report of a favorable development at the Capital. Under the enforcement of a martial law and the beginning of peaceful negotiations between the rebellious young military officers and the high command of the Imperial Army, Tokyo had somewhat recovered from its first terror in the military uprisings the morning before.

Other new items also reached Saionji: the car-load of uniformed young men reported racing towards the *Zagyoso* had been peddlers of a certain patent medicine, a sales system which is popular; at least five police officers guarding the residences of victims died in line of duty; wives of slain dignitaries attempting to protect their husbands from the invaders' bullets were badly wounded; a few rebel leaders committed suicide upon realizing their misconduct; Premier Admiral Okada, who had been thought a victim, was found alive and owed his life to the sacrifice made by his brother-in-law, but his Cabinet had resigned; Count Makino and his family, whose country home was attacked and set on fire by the soldiers, narrowly escaped injury, saved by loyal house detectives who died defending them; and the cars following the Saionji motor caravan had been those of newspaper reporters.

Despite the report of the hopeful developments in Tokyo, the *Zagyoso* and its surroundings remained a war zone. The armed guards were there; the machines were still kept in readiness for a quick escape, and the coast guard boat off the shore was steamed up and manned to weigh anchor at any time.

The snow had stopped, but the grayish sky was low and cold.

When Saionji returned to his Okitsu home, it was a little late for his afternoon nap. He immediately retired.

"Aya, who arrived just now? What's the noise outside that woke me up?" he asked a few moments later from his bedroom.

"My lord, the Imperial Messenger—"

"Aya, I'll get up."

"My lord, you haven't rested enough and your neuralgia—"

"This is no time to idle here! No more menacing condition ever faced the nation." He spoke in determination. "Many high dignitaries of the Emperor were murdered like cattle, the country is fear-stricken with this military mutiny, and, to top it all, His Majesty and the Imperial Family must be suffering the greatest anxiety. When the Emperor calls, all my personal fears vanish."

"My lord, are you going to the Capital?" Aya, who was now helping him dress, timidly asked him.

The anxious steward, too, interfered: "The trip to Tokyo at this time would be like walking into a tiger's den—"

"Did you forget, Steward, almost exactly sixty-eight years ago I led the loyal troops with the Emperor's Banner of Golden Brocade and the Imperial Sword, into the enemy territories? Let them sever my gray head from its shadowy frame, should one more murder reawake the true spirit of national unity and insure the safety of His Majesty! I shall die smiling under the glaring swords of the rebellious soldiers or in the rain of their bullets. I repeat, Steward, I am ready to die for His Majesty!"

"Yes, my lord!"

"Aya, that *haori*, I must receive the messenger first. Steward, get ready for the trip!"

A little later the S-101 was racing to the station between the unbroken lines of police.

After the long fall of snow over Tokyo, the heavy sky still prevented the late winter sun from shining on the metropolis. Most of the Capital had outwardly resumed normal activities but the section of the Imperial Palace, government-building quarters, Nippon's 'Wall Street,' and the Tokyo Station which is the heart of the country's land transportation were still under martial law.

Tokyo's five million people, as a matter of fact the entire country, had spent another uneasy night, as after a severe earthquake. Even the gayest of all the metropolitan streets, the Ginza, a few blocks away from the line of the military cordon, awoke with a sinking heart. No news had come through; there was no telling what the next wind might bring. Fear lamed everyone.

Then the soldiers near the Tokyo station and along the wide streets between the station and the Sakashita Gate to the Palace grounds began to make way, holding the civilians strictly to the sidewalks and suspending motor traffic.

Crowds gathered on the thoroughfares whispering and speculating, their faces pale with apprehension.

Within the station several platforms were cleared of passengers and filled with police.

A special train slowly came to a halt. The commanding officer of the gendarmes, with his men who had been assigned as bodyguards, alighted and lined up close to the exit of the car.

The last of the Genros, Prince Saionji Kimmochi, assisted by his steward and Aya, descended to the platform. He wore his silk hat over his snow-white head, his morning-coat under the brownish overcoat, black shoes and carried his long bamboo cane.

Leaning on the cane, he shook his right leg a few times before he proceeded to the automobile dispatched by the Department of the Imperial Household. Under his eyes the half-rings had deepened and looked like the frames of horn-rimmed spectacles. The space between his eyes and arched eyebrows was wide; the pale jowls sagged and the full lips were closed. His palsied hand gripped the black bamboo. His footsteps on the pavement threw echoes against the wall.

As he entered the automobile, the morning sun broke through the clouds over the Imperial Palace and a military observation plane with its silvery wings circled in the sky.

For the first time since he had heard the alarm of the military uprisings, a broad smile lit his face. After a contented sigh he mumbled to himself as he took a seat in the automobile: "The green of the old pines and the blue of the moat-water on the Palace Grounds never change, and as long as the sun shines over the '*O-uchi-yama*' His Majesty and Nippon will be safe.

"Steward, give me matches. I want to light my cigarette before the motor starts."

Saionji, protected by an escort of cars and rows of bayonets, rode towards the crowds.

"Oh, there!" An office worker in European clothes shouted and waved his hand high in the air. All stood on tiptoe and turned their heads in the direction of the sirens and horns.

"The Genro! The Genro! Prince Saionji! Here he comes!" The whispering travelled from mouth to mouth. Then silence prevailed. The sound of the automobile tires against the road surface, *shu, shu, shu,* could be plainly heard.

"Ah, we thought he was hindering the country's progress towards democratic political practices, but isn't it lucky that we have him now? Now he is a political safety-valve and the guiding torch of ninety million people at this darkest moment of the nation's history," a student said softly.

The car approached the corner. A voice shrieked: "SAIONJI!"

"Saionji!" "The Genro!" "Prince Saionji!" "Saionji, *Banzai! Banzai!*"

"My lord, your steward has been informed by the Imperial Household official that your lordship's quarters are provided in the Department building from which you may reach the Palace through the long corridor."

"Huh, that's unusual treatment. I originally intended to go to my Surugadai home or to the Tokyo mansion of my late brother Sumitomo, where protection against violence would be easy."

Leaving the frenzied crowds behind, the Saionji car entered the Sakashita Gate of the Palace Terrace. The Genro threw away his cigarette and spoke with emotion: "It was thirty years ago, during the reign of the present Emperor's grandfather, that I rode through this gate in a jinrikisha to receive the first insignia of His Majesty's Premier. Nippon was already rising then, like this passage to the higher grounds." He frowned for a second. "I hope—I hope that the Empire is still on that upward march to which our most beloved Ruler, Emperor Meiji, gave the momentum."

GLOSSARY

ABE ISOH (1865-   ): President of Shakai Taishuto (Socialist Mass Party) since 1932; Sociology Professor at Waseda University.

AN CHUNG-KEN (1878-1910): A Korean; fatally wounded Prince Ito Hirobumi at Harbin, Manchuria, in Oct. 1909; executed.

ANESAKI MASAHARU (CHOFU) (1873-   ): Dr. Lit.; Emeritus Professor at Tokyo Imperial University, Author.

AOKI SHUZO, Viscount (1844-1914): Diplomat, first Ambassador to the United States.

ARAKI SADAO, Baron General (1877-   ): War Minister (Dec. 1932-Jan. 1934).

AYA: Saionji's housekeeper, succeeded Nagiye.

BABA TSUNEGO (1875-   ): Author, Political Critic, correspondent at Paris Peace Conference.

BAKIN (see TAKIZAWA BAKIN).

BASHO (see MATSUO BASHO).

BOTO ICHIRO: Saionji's assumed name used at Nakamura-ro.

CHINDA SUTEMI, Count (1856-1929): Diplomat, attended Paris Peace Conference.

DAN TAKUMA, Baron (1858-1932): General Director of the Mitsui Financial House; assassinated by a reactionary young man.

DANJURO (see ICHIKAWA DANJURO).

ENOMOTO BUYO, Viscount (1836-1908): Statesman and Diplomat; first Western-trained Nipponese Admiral under Tokugawa Shogunate and the last convert to the new Government.

FUJIWARA: The largest and most powerful and one of the oldest clans in the court circles, intermarried with the members of the Imperial families, Fujiwara-no-Kamatari, one of the early ancestors already held a high political post in the 7th century; Konoe, Saionji and Tokudaiji and many other former *kuge* (court noble) families are Fujiwara descendants.

FUKUZAWA YUKICHI (1834-1901): Journalist, Author, Educator; the founder of Keio University.

FURUKAWA TAIKO: Priest of Seikenji at Okitsu.

GOTO SHIMPEI, Viscount (1857-1929): President of the South Manchurian Railway Co., Cabinet Minister many times, Mayor of Tokyo.

GOTO SHOJIRO, Count (1838-1897): One of the leaders of the 1868 Restoration; Liberal Statesman; Councillor of State; Cabinet Minister.

HACHIRO (see SAIONJI HACHIRO).

HAMAGUCHI YUKO (1870-1931): 28th Premier (July 1929-April 1931); Finance Minister; Minseito Party President; fatally wounded by a reactionary.

HARA KEI (1856-1921): 19th Premier (Sept. 1918-Nov. 1921); Cabinet Minister many times, Seiyukai Party President; assassinated Nov. 1921.

HARADA KUMAO, Baron (1888-   ): Saionji's private secretary and official spokesman.

HARUKO (*see* SAIONJI HARUKO).

HASEBA JUNKO (1854-1914): Education Minister in Saionji's 2nd Cabinet; Seiyukai Party leader; President of Lower House.

HAYASHI TADASU, Count (1850-1913): Ambassador to Great Britain; Foreign Minister in Saionji's 1st Cabinet.

HIROHITO, EMPEROR (1901-   ): 124th Sovereign, eldest son of Emperor Taisho and grandson of Emperor Meiji; Regent, 1921-26; ascended throne, Dec. 1926.

HIROTA KOKI (1878-   ): 33rd Premier (March 1936-Jan. 1937); Foreign Minister in Konoe Cabinet (June 1937-   ).

HOSHI TORU (1850-1901): Trained in England; Minister to the United States; Seiyukai Party leader and Cabinet Minister.

IBA SOTARO (1851-1903): Assassin of Hoshi Toru; school principal.

IBARA SAIKAKU (1642-1693): One of the great masters of *hokku* and the greatest novelist in early Tokugawa era.

ICHIKAWA DANJURO, 9th (1837-1903): Most celebrated '*kabuki*' actor in modern Nippon; performed in the presence of Emperor Meiji and other high dignitaries in 1887, thereby raising the social standard of theatrical people from the 'river-beach beggar' to that of artists.

ICHIKAWA SADANJI, 4th (1829-1904): Together with Danjuro 9th and Kikugoro 5th presented the 1887 memorable 'audience' performance.

IKEDA SEIHIN (1867-   ): Managing Director of Mitsui Financial House; President of Bank of Nippon.

INOUYE JUNNOSUKE (1869-1932): Finance Minister; President of the Bank of Nippon; assassinated.

INOUYE KAORU, Marquis Genro, Choshu (1835-1915): Saionji's senior friend; Finance and other Cabinet Portfolios; Komyoji Saburo's sponsor.

INOUYE KOWASHI, Viscount (1844-1895): Education Minister in Ito's 3rd Cabinet; succeeded by Prince Saionji.

INUKAI KI (1855-1932): 30th Premier (Dec. 1931-May 1932); Continuously elected to Diet since 1890; many Cabinet posts; President of the Seiyukai Party and Premier; assassinated (May 15, 1932, *coup d'état*).

ISHIMOTO SHINROKU, Lieutenant General Baron (1854-1912): War Minister in Saionji's 2nd Cabinet.

ITAGAKI TAISUKE, Count (1837-1919): One of the leaders of the 1868 Restoration; Founder of the first political party in the 1870's and later President of the Jiyuto Party; Councillor of State; Cabinet posts.

ITO HIROBUMI, Prince Genro, Choshu (1841-1909): Four times Premier (Dec. 1885-March 1888, Aug. 1892-Sept. 1896, Jan.-May 1898, Oct. 1900-May 1901); Kido Koin's follower and Saionji's later sponsor; Founder and President of the Seiyukai Party; Resident-General of Korea; President of Privy Council 4 times; Framer of the Imperial Constitution; assassinated by An Chung-ken at Harbin, Manchuria; many times in America and Europe.

IWAKURA TOMOMI, Prince (1825-1883): Court noble; before Restoration served in Imperial Court, Kyoto, with Saionji and Sanjyo; regarded as one of four builders of modern Nippon—Kido Koin, Okubo Toshimitsu, Saigo Takamori; Chief Envoy to America and Europe, 1871-1873, with Kido, Okubo, Ito; Minister of Right.

IWASAKI YANOSUKE, Baron (1851-1908): Director of Mitsubishi Financial House which his elder brother, Yataro, founded; President of Bank of Nippon.

IWASAKI YATARO (1834-1885): Founder of Mitsubishi Financial House.

IYEYASU (see TOKUGAWA IYEYASU).

KAKIMOTO-NO-HITOMARO (687-707): Celebrated Poet of Imperial Court during Nara period under three Sovereigns.

KANEKO KENTARO, Count (1853-   ): Special Envoy to the United States during the Russo-Nipponese War; Cabinet Minister; Privy Councillor; President of Meiji Restoration History Editing Office.

KANG YU-WEI (1858-1927): Chinese Scholar and Statesman.

KANO FAMILY: Beginning with Kano Masanobu (1454-1550), gradually divided into many branches, for four hundred years maintained famous Kano School in Nipponese painting.

KATO KOMEI, Viscount (1860-1926): 24th and 25th Premier (June 1924-July 1925, Aug. 1925-Jan. 1926); Son-in-law of Iwasaki Yataro, Foreign Minister in Saionji's 1st Cabinet, organized and later became President of the Rikken Doshikai Party; Premier.

KATO TOMOSABURO, Fleet-Admiral Viscount (1861-1924): 21st Premier (June 1922-Aug. 1923); Delegate to Washington Naval Limitation Conference.

KATSU AWA (1823-1899): Negotiator of Tokugawa Shogun to surrender Edo (Tokyo) to Imperial Military Command, Spring, 1868; later joined Imperial Government and occupied important posts; first Nipponese captain of steamship.

KATSURA TARO, Field Marshal Prince, Choshu (1847-1913): 11th, 13th, and 15th Premier (June 1910-Jan. 1906, July 1908-Aug. 1911, Dec. 1912-Feb. 1913); first War Ministership in Ito's 3rd Cabinet; organized the Rikken Doshikai Party which became Kenseikai Party under Kato Komei after Katsura's death, and finally became present Minseito Party; studied in Germany.

KIDO KOIN (1833-1877), Choshu: One of the four builders of new Nippon; led Choshu clan against Tokugawa Shogunate; Councillor of State; responsible for many progressive measures including the proclamation of the 'Imperial Oath of Five Articles,' the abolition of feudal political system, proposal for the adoption of a monarchical constitution (1873); planned 'colonization' of Korea in 1869 with Omura Masujiro but in 1873 opposed Korean expedition advocated by Saigo Takamori and other Councillors upon his return from Western trip with Iwakura Tomomi, Okubo Toshimitsu, Ito Hirobumi, etc.

KIMURA KI (1894-   ): Author and Journalist.

KIYOURA KEIGO, Count (1850-   ): 23rd Premier; President of the Privy Council; Premier.

KOICHI (see SAIONJI KOICHI).

KOIZUMI SANSHIN (SAKUTARO) (1872-1937): Author, Businessman, elected to Diet seven times.

KOMEI EMPEROR (1831-1866): 121st Sovereign; enthroned 1843; the father of Emperor Meiji.

KOMURA JUTARO, Marquis (1855-1911): Minister to China during Sino-Nipponese War; Foreign Minister and Chief Delegate to Portsmouth Russo-Nipponese Peace Conference, 1905.

KOMYOJI SABURO (1849-1893): Son of a Buddhist priest and follower of Inouye Kaoru; Secretary to the Nipponese Legation at Paris; associate justice of the Supreme Court; elected first Diet; Saionji's best friend during his Paris sojourn.

KONOE FUMIMARO, Prince (1891-   ): 37th Premier (June 1937-   ); Goodwill Envoy to the U. S., 1934; President of House of Peers; Saionji's protégé.

KORIN (*see* OGATA KORIN).

KUNIGITA DOPPO (1871-1908): War Correspondent during Sino-Nipponese War and novelist of naturalist school; edited and published *Toan Zuihitsu* which is Saionji's only published autobiography.

KURODA KIYOTAKA, Lieutenant General Count, Satsuma (1840-1900): 2nd Premier (April 1888-Dec. 1889); Chief aide to Commander Saionji in Echigo sector during the 1868 Restoration wars; Minister of Colonial Affairs; President of Privy Council.

KUROPATOKIN, A. N. (1848-1925): Russian General and Commander of Czar's army in Manchuria during Russo-Nipponese War, 1904-1905.

LI HUNG-CHANG (1823-1901): Chinese Diplomat and Statesman; Chief Delegate to Shimonoseki Peace Conference, 1895, at the conclusion of Sino-Nipponese War.

MAKINO SHINKEN, Count (1861-   ): Son of Okubo Toshimitsu; Governor of Fukui Prefecture; Minister to Austria; Education Minister in Saionji's 1st and 2nd Cabinets; Foreign Minister in Yamamoto Cabinet; Delegate to Paris Peace Conference with Saionji; Minister of Imperial Household; Lord Keeper of Privy Seal; many attempts on his life.

MASAMUNE (*see* OKAZAKI MASAMUNE).

MATSUDA MASAHISA, Baron (1845-1914): Associated in *Oriental Liberal Newspaper*, and joined Saionji in Ito Hirobumi's Seiyukai Party organization; elected to the Diet; Cabinet Posts and Minister of Justice in Saionji's 1st and 2nd Cabinets; Saionji's friend since Parisian days; President of Lower House.

MATSUI KEISHIRO, Baron (1868-   ): Ambassador to Great Britain and Delegate to Paris Peace Conference; Foreign Minister.

MATSUKATA MASAYOSHI, Prince Genro, Satsuma (1835-1924): 4th and 6th Premier (May 1891-Aug. 1892, Sept. 1896-Jan. 1898); led Satsuma group after Okubo's death; Finance Minister many times; Lord Keeper of Privy Seal; together with Yamagata and Saionji personal adviser to Emperor since World War days.

MATSUO BASHO (1644-1694): Greatest Master of *hokku* or *haikai*, a poem of seventeen syllables.

MATSUOKA YOSUKE (1880-   ): Secretary to the Nipponese Delegation at Paris Peace Conference; entered South Manchurian Railway Co., later its director; elected to the Diet; Chief Delegate to League of Nations Assembly, 1932; President of South Manchurian Railway Co.; graduate of Oregon University.

MATSUZAWA KYUSAKU (1854-1886): Publisher of the *Oriental Liberal Newspaper*.

MEIJI EMPEROR (MUTSUHITO) (1852-1912): 122nd Sovereign; Son of Emperor Komei; Enthroned 1867.

MENDES, MME: Collaborated with Saionji in translating and publishing Nipponese play and poems into French.

MITSUBISHI: 2nd largest financial organization owned by the Iwasaki family.

MITSUI: Name of the family which is the largest financial house.

MITSUKOSHI: One of the largest department stores.

MIYO: One of Saionji's housemaids.

MIYOKO: (see Saionji Miyoko).

MORI ARINORI, Viscount (1847-1889): Studied in England and America; 1st Minister to the U. S.; Education Minister; assassinated.

MORI MOTONORI, Prince (1839-1896): Former Lord of Choshu; Father of Saionji Hachiro.

MOTONO ICHIRO, Viscount (1862-1918): Minister to France; Foreign Minister.

MURASAKI-SHIKIBU (pen-name) (978-1015): Author of *Tales of Genji* and many other novels; the daughter of Fujiwara Tamenobu; no real name known.

MUTSU MUNEMITSU, Marquis (1844-1897): Most celebrated Diplomat; Minister to the U. S.; Agricultural and Commerce Minister; Foreign Minister in Ito Hirobumi's 2nd Cabinet; with Ito represented Nippon at Shimonoseki Peace Conference at the conclusion of Sino-Nipponese War.

NAGIYE (full name: OYAMA NAGIYE): Saionji's housekeeper.

NAKAE CHOMIN (1847-1901): Author and Journalist; associated with Saionji in *Oriental Liberal Newspaper;* translated Rousseau's *Social Contrat* into Nipponese; elected to the Diet.

NOGI KITEN, General Count (1849-1912), Choshu: Commander of Port Arthur siege and of the Third Army at Mukden during the Russo-Nipponese War.

OGATA KORIN (1658-1716): Celebrated Artist, studied Kano and Tosa Schools, succeeded in creating his own school of pure Nipponese style of painting.

OHANA (full name: OKUMURA OHANA, 1895-1929): Saionji's third mistress who accompanied him to Paris Peace Conference.

OKADA KEISUKE, Admiral (1868-   ): 32nd Premier (July 1934-Feb. 1936); Navy Minister; Premier; attempt on his life by Feb. 26, 1936, in military mutiny.

OKAZAKI MASAMUNE (1264-1344): Celebrated swordsmith; his masterpieces commonly called 'Masamune.'

OKIKU: Saionji's sweetheart and first 'wife' and Shinko's mother; former geisha TAMA; real name: KOBAYASHI KIKU.

OKU SHIGESABURO (1862-1924): Elected to the Diet eight times; President of Lower House.

OKUBO TOSHIMITSU, Satsuma (1832-1878): One of the four builders of new Nippon and father of Makino Shinken; Councillor of State; ablest statesman in the Meiji reconstruction period; assassinated.

OKUMA SHIGENOBU, Marquis (1838-1922): 8th and 17th Premier (June-Oct. 1898, April 1914-Oct. 1916); leading statesman of non-Sat-cho origin; after the death of Kido Koin and Okubo Toshimitsu he was the senior Councillor of State; the founder of Waseda University; organized the Rikken Kaishinto Party and advocated an English pattern for the political system; honors of Genro accorded but never exercised.

OMURA MASUJIRO, Choshu (1824-1869): Military strategist; during Restoration wars and immediately afterward closely associated with Saigo Takamori in all military campaigns and planning modern military system for the country; supported Kido Koin's Korean colonization scheme.

ONOE KIKUGORO, 5th (1844-1903): One of the two greatest *kabuki* actors.

OSHIMA YOSHIMASA, General Viscount (1849-1926), Choshu: Commander of the Mixed Brigade first landed on Korean soil in Sino-Nipponese War, 1894-1895.

OTA DOKAN (1432-1486): Warrior and Poet; Builder of original Edo Castle (now Tokyo Imperial Palace).

OTAKE: Name of a chambermaid of the Nakamura-ro.

OTAMA (real name: NAKANISHI FUSA): Former geisha, Saionji's second 'wife' and Sonoko's mother.

OTORI KEISUKE (1832-1911): Tokugawa Shogun's army leader; later appointed to various posts; Minister to Korean Court at the beginning of Sino-Nipponese War.

OYAMA IWAO, Field Marshal Prince, Genro, Satsuma (1842-1914): Commanded Nipponese Armies in Manchuria during the Russo-Nipponese War; singularly devoted to military affairs; Lord Keeper of Privy Seal.

OZAKI YUKIO (1859-   ): Elected to the Diet ever since its first Session in 1890; Minister of Education, Minister of Justice, Mayor of Tokyo.

ROKA (*see* TOKUTOMI ROKA).

SADANJI (*see* ICHIKAWA SADANJI).

SAGAMI: Saionji's governess.

SAIGO JUDO, Fleet-Admiral, Marquis (1843-1897), Satsuma: Saigo Takamori's younger brother; held Navy and other Cabinet Portfolios.

SAIGO TAKAMORI, Satsuma (1827-1877): Greatest military leader in modern Nippon; one of the four builders of new Nippon; broke away from the Government in 1873 on the question of Korean expedition; unsuccessfully rebelled against the Government in 1877; committed *harakiri*.

SAIONJI HACHIRO (1881-   ): Saionji's adopted son and heir (Shinko's husband, father of Koichi, Haruko, Miyoko, etc.); Commissioner to Department of Imperial Household; accompanied the Crown Prince (present Emperor) to Europe.

SAIONJI HARUKO (1913-   ): Saionji's granddaughter; married to Baron Sumitomo Kichizayemon (Sumitomo Atsushi), Saionji's nephew.

SAIONJI KIMMOCHI, Prince Genro (1849-   ): 12th and 14th Premier (Jan. 1906-July 1908, Aug. 1911-Dec. 1913); Son of Tokudaiji Kinzumi, younger brother of Sanenori and elder brother of Takamaro (later Sumitomo Kichizayemon); father of Shinko and Sonoko; adopted by Saionji family; served Emperor Komei as Boy-Chamberlain and Middle-General of Right Imperial Guard;

Commander-General of Tamba Expedition and later Echigo sector assisted by Yamagata and Kuroda, followed Omura and Kido during Restoration wars; organized and edited *Oriental Liberal Newspaper;* joined Ito Hirobumi (Sat-cho group) and went to Germany with Ito; Minister to Austria, Germany and Belgium; Privy Councillor; specially dispatched to Korea; Education Minister in Ito's 2nd and 3rd Cabinets and Acting Foreign Minister; President of Privy Council and Premier *ad interim* by Ito's request; Seiyukai Party organizing committee under Ito's leadership; Seiyukai President, succeeding Ito; Premier; Genro since 1916; Chief Delegate to Paris Peace Conference.

SAIONJI KOICHI (1906-   ): Saionji's grandson.

SAIONJI MIYOKO (1915-   ): Saionji's 3rd granddaughter.

SAIONJI SHINKO (1887-1920): Saionji's 1st daughter by Okiku; married to Hachiro and had three sons and three daughters; accompanied Saionji to Peace Conference.

SAIONJI SONOKO (1904-   ): Saionji's 2nd daughter, by Otama; married to Kawashima Shoichi.

SAITO HIROSHI (1886-   ): Ambassador to the U. S. since 1934.

SAITO MAKOTO, Admiral Viscount (1858-1936): 31st Premier (May 1932-July 1934); Navy Minister in Saionji's 1st Cabinet and held the post until 1914; twice Governor-General of Korea; Premier; Lord Keeper of Privy Seal; one of the victims of Feb. 1936 military mutiny in Tokyo.

SAKAI YUZABURO (-1900): A young Socialist; follower of Saionji; died in Paris.

SAKATANI YOSHIRO, Baron (1863-   ): Financier; Finance Minister in Saionji's 1st cabinet; member of House of Peers; Mayor of Tokyo.

SANJYO SANEMI, Prince (1837-1891): Premier (before the installation of Cabinet System). Son of Sanetsumu.

SANJYO SANETSUMU (1802-1859): Court noble; held high posts including Premiership (of old order) under three Sovereigns.

SHIBUSAWA EIICHI, Viscount (1840-1932): 'Dean of Nipponese Financial World' and Philanthropist; Sakatani Yoshiro's father-in-law.

SHIDEHARA KIJURO, Baron (1873-   ): Member of House of Peers; Foreign Minister in 5 Cabinets; noted for his conciliatory policies toward China; son-in-law of Iwasaki Yataro.

SHINAGAWA YAJIRO, Viscount, Choshu (1843-1900): Minister of Home Affairs in Matsukata's 1st Cabinet and charged with brutality committed during general elections.

SHINKO (*see* SAIONJI SHINKO).

SHIRAYANAGI SHUKO (1884-   ): Author and Journalist.

SONOKO (*see* SAIONJI SONOKO).

SUMITOMO ATSUSHI (1909-   ): Succeeded his father Kichizayemon as the head of Sumitomo Financial House, married Saionji Haruko, Saionji's granddaughter.

SUMITOMO KICHIZAYEMON, Baron (1864-1926): Formerly Tokudaiji Takamaro, son of Tokudaiji Kinzumi, younger brother of Sanenori and Saionji Kimmochi, adopted by Sumitomo family; increased family fortune to the third largest in the country; succeeded by his son, Atsushi, now called Kichizayemon.

SUYEMATSU KENCHO, Viscount (1855-1920): Cabinet Minister, Seiyukai organizing committee, author; married Ito Hirobumi's adopted daughter.

TAISHO EMPEROR, YOSHIHITO (1879-1926): 123rd Sovereign; son of Emperor Meiji and father of present Emperor Hirohito; enthroned in 1912, appointed Crown Prince Hirohito Regent in 1921.

TAIKO (*see* FURUKAWA TAIKO).

TAKAHASHI KOREKIYO (1854-1936): 20th Premier (Nov. 1921-June 1922); Financial Commissioner to England and America during Russo-Nipponese War; Finance Minister many times; Seiyukai President succeeding Hara Kei; one of the victims of Feb., 1936, military mutiny in Tokyo.

TAKAMARO (*see* TOKUDAIJI TAKAMARO; SUMITOMO KICHIZAYEMON).

TAKASHIMA SHOICHI (1900-   ): Saionji's son-in-law (Sonoko's husband).

TAKAYAMA CHOGYO (RINJIRO) (1871-1902): Author and literary critic.

TAKEKOSHI YOSABURO (1865-   ): Personal Councillor to Saionji as Education Minister in Ito's Cabinets; author, newspaper and magazine editor; elected to the Diet five times; member of House of Peers.

TAKIZAWA BAKIN (1767-1848): Foremost novelist in Tokugawa period; best known among his two hundred and sixty books is *Hakkenden* or *Story of the Eight Dogs*.

TANAKA GIICHI, General Baron, Choshu (1863-1929): 27th Premier (April 1927-June 1929); first War Ministership in Hara Kei's Cabinet; President of Seiyukai Party succeeding Takahashi Korekiyo; Premier.

TAYAMA KATAI (1871-1930): Foremost novelist in naturalist school.

TERAUCHI JUICHI, General Count (1879-   ): Son of Terauchi Masaki; War Minister; War Councillor.

TERAUCHI MASAKI, Field Marshal Count, Choshu (1852-1919): 18th Premier (Oct. 1916-Sept. 1918); War Minister during Russo-Nipponese War and continued through Saionji's 1st Cabinet; Governor-General of Korea; Premier.

TING JU-CH'ANG, Chinese Admiral (-1895): Commander of the Chinese North Sea Fleet; committed suicide when defeated by the Nipponese at Weihaiwei.

TO-AN: Saionji's pen-name.

TOKUDAIJI KINZUMI (1821-1883): Court noble; father of Sanenori, Saionji Kimmochi, Sumitomo Kichizayemon (Takamaro); Minister of Right.

TOKUDAIJI SANENORI, Prince (1839-1919): Saionji's elder brother; entered Department of Imperial Household in 1871; Minister of Imperial Household, Grand Chamberlain, Lord Keeper of Privy Seal.

TOKUDAIJI TAKAMARO (*see* SUMITOMO KICHIZAYEMON).

TOGO HEIHACHIRO, Fleet-Admiral Marquis, Satsuma (1847-1934): Captain of the *Naniwa* in Sino-Nipponese War and sank the *Kowshing;* Commander of Combined Fleet and victor of the Tsushima Battle during Russo-Nipponese War.

TOKUGAWA IYEYASU (1542-1616): Founder of Tokugawa Shogunate which dictated over the country from 1603 to 1867; took possession of Edo Castle.

GLOSSARY

TOKUTOMI ROKA (KENJIRO) (1868-1927): One of the foremost novelists in Meiji Period and author of *Hototogisu*.

TOYAMA MITSURU (1855-   ): Founder of *Kokuryukai* or Black Dragon Society; Patriarch of Nipponese patriots.

TOYOTOMI HIDEYOSHI (1568-1595): Peasant born dictator.

UCHIDA KOSAI, Count (1865-1936): Ambassador to the U. S.; Foreign Minister in Saionji's 2nd Cabinet and three other Cabinets and Acting Premier; President of South Manchurian Railway Co.

UME: Name of a maid at an inn at Ikaho.

UYEHARA YUSAKU, Field Marshal Viscount (1856-1935); Satsuma: War Minister in Saionji's 2nd Cabinet, succeeding General Ishimoto; Chief of General Staff.

WAKATSUKI REIJIRO, Baron (1866-   ): 26th and 28th Premier (Jan. 1926-April 1927, April-Dec. 1931); Finance Minister and Home Minister; President of the Kenseikai Party; Premier; Chief Delegate to London Naval Limitation Conference; President of the Minseito Party; member of House of Peers.

WATANABE JOTARO, General (1874-1936): Director of Military Education, one of the victims of the Feb. 1936 military mutiny in Tokyo.

WATANABE KUNITAKE, Viscount (1846-1919): Finance Minister in Ito's 2nd and 4th Cabinets.

YAMAGATA ARITOMO, Field Marshal, Genro, Prince (1838-1922), Choshu: 3rd and 9th Premier (Dec. 1887-May 1891, Nov. 1898-Oct. 1900); Saionji's Chief Aide in Echigo sector during Restoration wars; War Minister and Home Minister many times; Premier; Chief of General Staff during Russo-Nipponese War; President of Privy Council.

YAMAGATA ISABURO (1858-1927): Yamagata Aritomo's adopted son and heir; Communications Minister in Saionji's 1st Cabinet.

YAMAGUCHI MOTOOMI (1846-1904); General Viscount, Choshu: Commander of Nipponese troops at Peking, China, during the Boxer Uprisings in 1900.

YAMAMOTO GOMBEI, Admiral Count, Satsuma (1852-1933): 16th and 22nd Premier (Feb. 1913-April 1914, Sept. 1923-Jan. 1924); Navy Minister in many Cabinets; largely responsible for the fast development of Nipponese Navy.

YAMAMOTO TATSUO, Baron (1856-   ): President of Bank of Nippon; Finance Minister in Saionji's 2nd and other Cabinets.

YASUDA ZENJIRO (1838-1921): Founder of Yasuda Financial House; assassinated.

YOSHIHITO, CROWN PRINCE (*see* TAISHO EMPEROR).

YUAN SHIH-KAI (1859-1916): Chinese Statesman; Minister to Korea before Sino-Nipponese War; Premier under the last Manchu dynasty; 1st President of Chinese Republic.

YUI-NO-SHOSETSU (-1651): Famous military strategist and rebel.

NIPPONESE WORDS

AKAHO RONIN: Masterless *samurai* of the late Lord Akaho who took vengeance on their lord's enemy in 1684; considered the model for the ways of *samurai;* their action dramatized as *Chushingura.*

AMADO: Wooden slides of the Nipponese house; literally rain-doors.

AOI-MATSURI: Aoi (hollyhock) Festival of the Shimogamo Shrine, Kyoto, held on May 15, originated in the 6th century, revived in 1885.

ASHIGARU: A footman or common soldier, the lowest class of *samurai.*

BANTO: Chief Clerk of traditional commercial houses.

BANZAI: Nipponese *hurrah!* originated at the time of military reviews following the proclamation ceremonies of the Imperial Constitution in 1889.

BASHAYA: A horse-carriage driver.

BENI: Rouge made of vegetable juice.

BIWA: A string instrument, like the mandolin in shape, imported from China in the 7th century, considered to be originally either Hindu or Egyptian.

BUMMEI KAIKA: *Bummei,* civilization; *kaika,* enlightenment, culture.

CAPPORE: A fast jazz-like dance.

CHUSHINGURA: A classic play, dramatization of the Akaho Ronin's accomplishment.

DAIMYO or DAIMIO: Local lord or prince in feudal times.

DAN-NA: Mister! or Master! used by commercial people to their employers and customers.

DONO: Esquire (used as suffix; Saionji-*dono* or Saionji Kimmochi-*dono*), very formal, usually in written form.

ETA: An outcast class; formerly there were four social classes; *samurai,* farmer, artisan, merchant, and *eta,* who were segregated from the others.

FUJIN: Lady, Madame, Mrs. (used as suffix: Saionji-*fujin*), formal; also a married woman, a wife, the fair sex.

GEISHA: A female entertainer with dance, music and song.

GENJI MONOGATARI: *Tales of Genji* written by Murasaki-Shikibu or Lady Murasaki.

GENKAN: Vestibule or formal approach to a Nipponese house.

GENRO: Elder statesman; the term first applied to a group of noted statesmen who were personally consulted by the Emperor on important national affairs, particularly in the choice of a new Premier, with no special meaning; towards the end of the Meiji era it appeared as an institution supreme over all the political organizations based on the Imperial Constitution; Emperor Taisho (reigned from 1912 to 1925) for the first time officially called the still active Inouye, Matsukata, Oyama, Yamagata *Genro* which group Saionji (also Okuma Shigenobu) was commanded to join in 1916.

GENRO-IN: Equivalant to Senate or Upper House existing in 1880's.

GO-INKYO-SAN: 'Honorable,' retired head of a family.

GO-ISSHIN: Enlightened 'new deal' or renascence.

HAIKAI (*See* HOKKU).

HAKAMA: Divided skirt, worn by men in formal dress.

HAORI: A surcoat.

HARAKIRI or SEPPUKU: Stomach-cutting; Suicide by disembowelment.

HATAMOTO: Name of direct vassals of the Tokugawa Shogun.

HATSUSE: Name of a warship.

HICHIRIKI: A flute.

HINOMARU: National flag with the emblem of the sun in the center of a white rectangle.

HOKAN: A male entertainer or jester.

HOKKU or HAIKAI: Seventeen-syllable poem.

JINRIKISHA: A two-wheeled carriage, invented in Nippon.

JOROYA: A house of prostitution.

JOSHO: A female operator of a 'tea-house.

KABUKI: Classic drama.

KAGOKAKI: A palanquin bearer.

KAJIKA: A singing-frog.

KWANNON: The Goddess of Mercy.

KEMBAN: A geisha registry house.

KOKU: 47.7 gallons.

KOKURYUKAI: Black Dragon Society, patriotic organization first formed to arouse the people against Russia before the Russo-Nipponese War.

KOMACHI: A synonym for a beautiful woman, derived from the name of Onono Komachi who lived many centuries ago.

KOTATSU: A fire (charcoal) place covered with a quilt.

KUGE: A court noble.

KUN: Mr. (usually among and addressed to young friends: Saionji-*kun*.)

KURUMAYA: A jinrikisha man.

MAIKO: A dancing girl.

MARUMAGE: A traditional style of hairdressing for a married woman.

MEIJI: Name of the period, 1868-1912 ('Enlightened Administration'); from which the title was post-humously applied to the late Emperor who ruled the Meiji era—Emperor Meiji.

MEIJI RESTORATION: The 1868 revolution; the term 'revolution' never used in Nippon in connection with this great change.

MITSU-TOMOE: A crest with three conventionalized waves in the shape of circling comets; Saionji's family coat of arms.

MIYAKO: Poetic term for old Imperial Capital.

MONTSUKI: A kimono with family crests dyed on it in white.

MOSHI: Hello!

NAGAJUBAN: A long undergarment for women.

NANIWA: Name of a warship.

OBENTO: A lunch.

OBI: A sash.

OGI: A folding fan.

OKUGATA: Lady, Mrs., used in higher circles (Saionji-*no-okugata*); less frequently used now.

OKUGE-SAMA: An honorable court noble. (*See* KUGE.)

OKUSAMA: Lady, Mrs. (Saionji-*no-okusama*), polite form of *Okusan*; a married lady, a wife.

OKUSAN: Common form of *Okusama*.

ORIZUME: Food packed in a small thin wooden box.

OSHAKU: A waitress.

OSOBA: (*See* SOBA.)

O-TENSHI-SAMA: Enlightened Emperor.

PING-YUEN: Name of a Chinese warship, 7,000 ton iron-clad sister ship of the *Ting-Yuen*, the largest afloat in the Orient before Sino-Nipponese War, 1894-1895.

RONIN: A masterless *samurai*; an unemployed man; a vagabond.

SADAIJIN: The Minister of the Left (of the old order).

SAKAZUKI: A rice wine cup.

SAKE: Rice wine.

SAKURA: Cherry.

SAMA: Most common form of salutation for both man and woman (Saionji-*sama*).

SAMIDARE: Poetic term for the rain in early summer (in May).

SAMISEN: A musical instrument with three strings.

SAMPAN: A small flat-bottom boat.

SAMURAI: A warrior; a warrior-class; about five hundred thousand families in Nippon in feudal times.

SAN: Friendly salutation (Saionji-*san*).

SAYONARA: Good-bye!

SEKISHI: A true child or beloved subject.

SEPPUKU: (*See* HARAKIRI).

SHAKUHACHI: A flute with eight holes.

SHI: Chinese-style poetry.

SHIMADAI: An ornamental stand used at a wedding ceremony.

SHIMBUN: Newspaper

SHOGI: Nipponese chess.

SHOGITAI: A band of the Tokugawa Shogun's sympathizers defeated by the Government's forces in Tokyo.

SHOGUN: Generalissimo or dictator. (Tokugawa Shogun.)

SHOJI: A paper (sliding) screen.

SOBA: Buckwheat noodle.

SOKUHATSU: European style coiffure for a woman.

SORIDAIJIN: A Premier.

SOTOBA: A long, narrow wooden tablet on the new grave; a stupa.

SUKIYAKI: Slices of beef and vegetables cooked à la japonaise.

SUMO: Nipponese wrestling.

TABI: Socks made of cotton or silk cloth.

TAI: Porgy.

TAIKO-MUSUBI: A knot of a sash in the shape of a drum.

TAISHO: Name of an era (1912-1925) during the reign of Emperor Taisho.

TAN: Measurement for textiles, 27 ft.

TOMABUNE: A boat with a rush-mat awning.

TORI-I: A gateway erected at the approach to a Shinto shrine.

TSUBO: About four square yards.

UCHIWA: A round fan.

UKIYOE: A genre painting.

UTAI: The singing of the *No* drama.

WAKA: A poem of thirty-one syllables.

WAKIZASHI: A short sword.

YAKATABUNE: A house-boat.

YAMASAKURA: Wild cherry.

YUKATA: A summer kimono, originally a bath-kimono.

PLACES

AIZU: City in Fukushima Prefecture, Northeast Honshu Island, population 46,000.

AKASAKA DETACHED PALACE or AKASAKA RIKYU: In Akasaka Ward, Tokyo; was Emperor Meiji's temporary residence from 1872 to 1888, while the present Imperial Palace was being constructed.

AMUR RIVER (Chinese: Heilungkiang): Between Manchuria and the Far Eastern region, Soviet Russia, Asia, formed by Argun and Shilka Rivers, runs northeast to Saghalien Gulf, 2,600 miles including Argun and Shilka Rivers.

AOYAMA CEMETERY: One of the largest and best known in Tokyo.

ARASHIYAMA or RANZAN: A scenic spot, a little way north-west of Kyoto, noted for varied vegetation, especially for cherry and maples.

ASAKUSA PARK: In Asakusa Ward, Tokyo, where the Asakusa Temple and *Kwannon* are located; it is one of the busiest sections in the Capital.

ASAN: Town, West Coast Korea, now *Seikan*, site of 1894 battle between Nippon and China.

ASHIO COPPER MINE: In Tochigi Prefecture, central Honshu Island, the largest of its kind in the country.

ATAMI: Town on East coast of Izu Peninsula, Shizuoka Prefecture, population 6,000; hot spring and resort.

BEPPU: Town, Oita Prefecture, Northeast Kyushu Island, population 14,000; one of the best hot springs.

CHANGCHUN: Now *Hsinking*, Capital of Manchukuo, Kirin Province, Manchuria, population 134,000.

CHEMULPO or CHEMULPHO: Now *Jinsen*, West coast Korea, population 60,000, port of Seoul, former Korean Capital, memorable for 1904 naval battle between Russia and Nippon.

CHION-IN: Buddhist monastery located in North Sakyo Ward, Kyoto, the Mecca of the *Jodo* sect, founded by Honen-shonin in the twelfth century.

CHOSHU: Old province, Southwest end of Honshu Island, now Yamaguchi Prefecture; home of military and political leaders since the 1868 Restoration.

DAIBUTSU or GREAT BUDDHA: A bronze image of Buddha in sitting posture, at Kamakura, Kobe and Nara; the last one is the largest and best known and is located in the *Daibutsu-den* of the Todaiji Temple, Nara.

DAIREN, formerly *Dalny:* Capital of the Japanese leased territory of Kwantung, South Manchuria, population 232,000.

ECHIGO: Old Province, North central Honshu Island, now Niigata Prefecture.

EDO, often YEDO: Now Tokyo, headquarters of the Tokugawa Shoguns from 1603 to 1868, renamed Tokyo or Eastern Capital. (*See* TOKYO.)

FUKIAGE TERRACE: Imperial Garden adjacent to Tokyo Imperial Palace Grounds.

FUKUI PREFECTURE: Central Honshu Island.

FUKUOKA PREFECTURE: North Kyushu Island; FUKUOKA CITY, capital of the prefecture, population 291,000; devastated by Mongolian invasions in 1274 and 1281.

FUJISAN, FUJIYAMA or FUJI-NO-YAMA: Sacred and highest mountain (inactive volcano), 12,395 feet high; South central Honshu Island.

FUSHIMI: Formerly town, southern gateway to Kyoto together with Toba, now annexed to Kyoto City, site of the first battle of the 1868 Restoration War.

FORMOSA or TAIWAN: Island in South China Sea, 13,889 square miles, population 5,213,000, belongs to Nippon; Tokyo sent expeditionary forces in 1874; at the conclusion of the Sino-Nipponese War, 1894-1895, ceded by China to Nippon by Shimonoseki treaty together with Liaotung Peninsula.

GENYOSHA: Social club among the former *samurai* founded by Toyama Mitsuru and his friends in the 1880's in Fukuoka city, later became a patriotic organization.

GINZA STREET: 'Great White Way' of Tokyo, between Shimbashi and Kyobashi bridges; is the famous shopping district in Tokyo.

GOBI: Desert in central Asia, mostly in Mongolia, 500,000 square miles.

GOLDEN PAVILION or *Kinkakuji:* At the foot of Kinugasa mountain, Kamikyo Ward, Kyoto, built by Ashikaga Yoshimitsu (1368-1394).

GOTEMBA: Town on the northeast slope of Fujisan, popular starting point for the climber of the mountain, seventy miles south from Tokyo; Saionji's summer home located.

GUNKAKU-RO: At Oiso, Kanagawa Prefecture, a tea-house.

HACHIMAN SHRINE: At Kamakura, dedicated to Emperor Ojin (270-310), popularly believed the God of War, originally founded in 1063 and transferred to the present site in 1191 by Minamoto Yoritomo.

HAKONE: The mountainous district northeast of Fujisan, about sixty miles south of Tokyo.

HAYAMA: Resort, west coast of Miura Peninsula, a little over forty miles south of Tokyo; Imperial villa located.

HIBIYA PARK: In Kojimachi Ward, Tokyo, laid out partly Nipponese and partly Western fashion, formerly the site of daimyo's mansions and still later a drill ground, now containing many large public and private buildings.

HIGASHIYAMA: Mountains, the eastern wall of Kyoto city.

HIROSHIMA CITY: Capital of Hiroshima Prefecture, Southwest Honshu Island, on the Inland Sea, population 310,000; the Imperial Military Headquarters established during Sino-Nipponese War, 1894-1895.

HOKKAIDO: One of the largest Islands of Nippon, north of Honshu Island, formerly Yezo or Ezo Island.

HONSHU or HONDO: Main or largest island of Nippon, 87,028 square miles, population 49,000,000; important cities and historic places mostly located on this island.

HYOGO PREFECTURE: West Honshu Island, of which Kobe is local capital. (Kobe was formerly called Hyogo or Hiogo.)

IKAHO: Town in Gumma Prefecture, known for hot spring; about ninety miles northwest of Tokyo, on high altitude.

ISE: Ise Daijingu or Great Shrines of Ise, dedicated to the Sun Goddess or Amaterasu Omikami and the Goddess of Farms, Crops, Food, and Sericulture;

located at Uji Yamada, in Miye Prefecture, three hundred miles southwest from Tokyo.

ISHIYAMA TEMPLE: At Ishiyama, on the southern shore of Lake Biwa; founded in the eighth century; on the site is a building supposed to have been used by Lady Murasaki when she wrote the *Genji Monogatari* or *Tales of Genji*; nine miles east of Kyoto.

IZU PENINSULA: Extending south of the Hakone district, divides Sagami Bay on the east and Suruga Bay on the west.

JAPAN: (*See* NIPPON.)

KAGOSHIMA: Capital of old Satsuma Province and Kagoshima Prefecture; on Kagoshima Bay, South Kyushu Island, population 182,000; 249 miles from Moji and 900 miles from Tokyo; Satsuma province is noted for navy and political leaders of new Nippon.

KAIYUAN: Town, Fengtien Province, Manchuria, population 20,000; 1905 Russo-Nipponese battle.

KAMAKURA: Town and resort, Kanagawa Prefecture, South Honshu Island, population 10,000, 32 miles from Tokyo, fourteen miles from Yokohama; Minamoto Yoritomo established first Shogun government there in 1192, many historic places and structures such as the Hachiman Shrine and the Kamakura *Daibutsu* or Great Buddha.

KAMO SHRINES: Upper and Lower Kamo Shrines in northern suburb of Kyoto.

KAMOGAWA or KAMO RIVER: Romantic river running through Kyoto from north to south, through eastern part of the city.

KANDA BRIDGE: In Kanda Ward, Tokyo.

KARUISAWA: Mountain resort in Nagano Prefecture, ninety-one miles from Tokyo.

KEGON WATERFALL: Lies below Lake Chuzenji, Nikko, Tochigi Prefecture, three hundred thirty feet high, one of the finest in the country.

KIAOCHOW BAY: Southeast Shantung, China, on which former German leased town, Tsingtao, is located.

KIYOMIZU TEMPLE: In HIGASHIYAMA section, Kyoto, founded in 805, is famous for its scenic view of the city and its *Kwannon* image.

KIYOMI-GA-SEKI: Name of the old toll-barrier located at present Okitsu, Shizuoka Prefecture.

KOMPIRA SHRINE: At Tadotsu, Shikoku, dedicated to the god believed to protect seamen and voyagers; nationally popular.

KOTO: Romantic name applied to the section east of the Sumida River, Tokyo.

KOYOKAN: High class restaurant in Shiba Park, Tokyo, used to be patronized by only well-to-do people.

KOZU: Town on Sagami Bay, Kanagawa Prefecture, 48 miles from Tokyo.

KURIL ISLANDS: Thirty-six islands lying between Hokkaido and Kamchatka; Nipponese name, *Chishima*, 6,140 square miles, population 6,000, formerly Russian territory and exchanged in 1875 with Saghalien Island.

KUSATSU: Famous hot spring, west Gumma Prefecture, 125 miles northeast of Tokyo.

KWANTO: Region around Tokyo consisting of eight old provinces east of the old Hakone barrier.

KYOTO or KIOTO: Imperial Capital from 805 to 1868, in Kyoto Prefecture, West Honshu Island, population 1,081,000; the center of old native culture and civilization, 326 miles from Tokyo.

KYUJYO: Tokyo Imperial Palace, located in the center of the Capital, completed and occupied by Emperor Meiji in 1889; built on the site of Edo Castle of the former Tokugawa Shogun; (term applied only to this Palace).

KYUSHU or KIUSHU: Southwesternmost of the Nipponese Main Islands, 16,591 square miles, population 9,100,000.

LIAOTUNG PENINSULA: Extending into Yellow Sea, South Fentien Province, Manchuria, part of which, including Port Arthur and Dairen was ceded to Japan by China as one of the major prizes of the Sino-Nipponese War, 1894-1895, returned to China on the advice of Germany, France, Russia, only to be leased by Czar and ten years later, after a hard struggle, returned to Nippon at Portsmouth Conference, 1905.

LIAOYANG: In Fengtien Province, Manchuria, population 92,000; one of the major battles fought between the Nipponese and Russian armies, 1904.

MANCHURIA: The three Northeast Provinces of China, Fengtien, Kirin and Heilungkiang, 401,173 square miles, population 30,866,000; since 1932, independent *Manchukuo*, including Inner Mongolia besides the three provinces, 460,265 square miles, population 34,075,000, Capital Hsinking, former Changchun.

MEIJI SHRINE: In Shibuya Ward, Tokyo, dedicated to the Emperor Meiji and his Empress, completed in 1920.

MIHO-NO-MATSUBARA: Pine groves on a sandy Miho promontory on the western shore of Suruga Bay forming Kiyomi Inlet; features in many romantic tales and one of the scenic spots on the Tokaido shores between Tokyo and Kyoto.

MIURA PENINSULA: In Kanagawa Prefecture, dividing the waters of Edo (Tokyo) Bay on the east and Sagami Bay on the west, with Boso Peninsula forms the Uraga Strait, the entrance of Edo Bay; embraces many resorts and historic places, particularly on its Sagami Bay shores.

MOMOYAMA MAUSOLEA: The tombs of the Emperor Meiji and His Empress located at Momoyama, four miles from Kyoto, situated on the former site of Toyotomi Hideyoshi's famous castle.

MORIOKA: Capital of Iwate Prefecture, North Honshu Island, population 69,000; 332 miles north from Tokyo.

MUKDEN or MUOKDEN or FENGTIEN: Capital of Fengtien Province, and traditional Capital of Manchuria, population 422,000, the decisive battle between the Nipponese and Russian armies fought in 1905; *Hoten* in Nipponese.

MUSASHINO or MUSASHI VALLEY: Northwest of Tokyo, consisting of part of Tokyo and Saitama Prefectures.

NAGASAKI: Capital of Nagasaki Prefecture, northwest Kyushi Island, population 212,000, one of the oldest seaports and not entirely closed for trade even during the Tokugawa isolation period.

NAGATACHO: Street in Kojimachi Ward, Tokyo, where the official residence of the Premier and other government buildings are located.

NARA: Capital of Nara Prefecture, west Honshu Island, population 56,000, historic city of great importance next only to Kyoto; *Daibutsu* or Great Buddha is located there; Imperial Seat before it was permanently settled in Kyoto.

NIJUBASHI or DOUBLE-BRIDGE: Main entrance to the Tokyo Imperial Palace.

NIHOMBASHI: Bridge in Nihombashi Ward, Tokyo, was formerly considered the center of the city and the distance to all the points in the country was measured from here.

NIKKO: Town and tourist resort, Tochigi Prefecture, central Honshu Island, famous shrines dedicated to the founder of Tokugawa Shogunate, Iyeyasu, and his grandson.

NIPPON: Properly Japan, originally NIHON, 'Origin of Light' or 'Sun Origin,' hence 'Land of the Rising Sun,' later conventionalized Nippon; Island chain extending East Asia from Kamchatka to Formosa, main group of Nippon Proper consisting of Honshu, Hokkaido, Kyushu, Shikoku, with their adjoining smaller islands, 147,593 square miles, population 69,251,000; Nippon Teikoku or Nippon Empire including Formosa, Korea, Saghalien, Kwantung, etc., 262,082 square miles, population 97,695,000; Capital, Tokyo.

NIPPONESE: (*See* NIPPON.)

NISHI-HONGANJI: Buddhist temple, Kyoto, one of the meccas of the *Shinshu* sect, a specimen of the finest Buddhist architecture in existence.

ODAWARA: Town on Sagami Bay, Honshu Island, 50 miles southwest Tokyo, historic spot dating back to the sixteenth century.

OISO: Noted seaside resort on Sagami Bay, 42 miles southwest Tokyo; Prince Saionji's *Rin-so* was located.

OKITSU: Town on Suruga Bay, Shizuoka Prefecture, central Honshu Island, noted for its mild climate and natural beauty, 109 miles southwest of Tokyo; Prince Saionji's *Zagyoso* is located.

OMAYEZAKI: Cape of Omaye located West Suruga Bay, Shizuoka Prefecture, central Honshu Island.

OMI-HAKKEI: Eight scenic spots around Lake Biwa in Omi Province, South central Honshu Island.

OMORI: Tokyo suburb, 7.5 miles southwest Tokyo; Prince Saionji's home was formerly located here.

OSAKA: Second largest city in the country, in Osaka Prefecture, West Honshu Island, on Osaka Bay, population 2,990,000; once Imperial Capital, chief commercial and industrial center; 353 miles southwest Tokyo.

OSHIMA: Volcanic island off Izu Peninsula.

O-UCHIYAMA: Poetic allusion to the Tokyo Imperial Palace Grounds.

PEKING or PEIPING: Former Chinese Capital, Hopeh Province, North China, population 1,300,000; scene of Boxer Uprisings in 1900.

RIN-SO: Name of Prince Saionji's Oiso home.

RYOGOKU BRIDGE: On the Sumida River, Tokyo; fireworks display there in July.

SADO: Island off northwest coast of Honshu Island, now part of Niigata Prefecture.

SAGAMI BAY: East coast, Honshu Island, between Miura and Izu Peninsulas, Kanagawa Prefecture.

SAGA PREFECTURE: Northwest Kyushu Island; local capital, Saga City.

SAGHALIEN ISLAND: Nipponese name, *Karafuto*, South of fifty degrees, 13,934 square miles, population 300,000, ceded by Russia to Nippon by Portsmouth Peace treaty, 1905; formerly Nippon claimed the Island, but waived her claim in exchange of Kuril Islands, in 1875.

SAKASHITA GATE: Usual entrance to the Imperial Household Department and other government offices on the Imperial Palace Grounds.

SAKURADA GATE: In Kojimachi Ward, Tokyo, former main entrance of the Tokugawa Shogun's Edo Castle (now Imperial Palace).

SATSUMA: Old Province, South Kyushu Island, now Kagoshima Prefecture, noted since the 1868 Restoration as a home of statesmen and admirals.

SEIFUSO: Prince Saionji's Kyoto home in Tanaka, Sakyo Ward, northeast Kyoto.

SEIKENJI: or Kiyomi-dera at Okitsu, Shizuoka Prefecture, temple founded in 672 and noted for its surrounding excellent views.

SEIYOKEN: One of the earliest Western style restaurants of high class, Uyeno Park, Tokyo.

SEOUL: Now Keijyo, former Korean Capital, Governor-General from Tokyo resides there, population 340,000.

SHIKENDO: Four Sages' Arbor at Prince Ito's '*Sorokaku*' at Oiso.

SHIMONOSEKI or BAKAN: At southwest extremity of the Honshu Island, with Moji on north Kyushu Island forms the western gateway of the Inland Sea, population 133,000, 703 miles from Tokyo.

SHIMIZU: Port, Shizuoka Prefecture, South central Honshu Island, population 61,000, 113 miles from Tokyo.

SHINAGAWA: Former seaport for Tokyo and the first of 53 posts between Tokyo and Kyoto in feudal days; now a Tokyo Ward.

SHIRAKUMO-JINSHA: Prince Saionji's family shrine, still intact within Kyoto Imperial Palace Grounds.

SHIZUOKA: Capital of Shizuoka Prefecture, central Honshu Island, population 201,000, 119 miles south of Tokyo.

SHUISHINYING: Near Port Arthur, Liaotung Peninsula, where General Nogi and General Stoessel met after the fall of Port Arthur.

SOROKAKU: Prince Ito's Oiso home.

SURUGA BAY: Formed by Izu Peninsula on the east and Omaye-zaki on the west, Shizuoka Prefecture, central Honshu Island.

SURUGADAI: In Kanda Ward, Tokyo, noted for colleges and schools; Prince Saionji's Tokyo home located.

TAGO-NO-URA: Sandy shore of Suruga Bay south of Numazu, Shizuoka Prefecture, covered with pine groves toward Okitsu, referred to in old poems and literature, exact location is debated.

TAMBA: Old Province West Honshu Island (west of Kyoto), now divided into Kyoto and Hyogo Prefectures; Prince Saionji commanded the Imperial Army to pacify the province in 1868.

TIEHLING: Fengtien Province, Manchuria, population 55,000, 40 miles north of Mukden; 1905 Russo-Nipponese battle.

TIENTSIN: City, treaty port, Hopeh Province, international settlements, population 1,389,000.

TOCHIGI PREFECTURE: Central Honshu Island, north of Tokyo.

TODAIJI: In Nara City, one of the seven great temples of the city, founded by Emperor Shomu (724-748), possesses the Great Buddha, 'Nara-no-Daibutsu.'

TOKAIDO: Old region between Kyoto and Tokyo along the seacoast; Tokaido highway between the two cities with 53 posts was a chief means of communications and transportation in feudal days; now Tokaido railway line also connects the cities.

TOKYO: Nation's Capital since 1869, formerly Edo, the Tokugawa Shoguns' governing seat; the place was practically unknown until 1457 when Ota Dokan built the castle that was later Edo Castle and still later the Tokyo Imperial Palace, its importance increased after Tokugawa Iyeyasu took over the castle and eventually in 1603, became the Shogun, population (of Greater Tokyo) 5,875,000, 19 miles from Yokohama, once in Tokugawa times it was estimated at two million, it fell to 583,000 in 1877; earthquake and fire, Sept. 1, 1923, heavily damaged the city; in Tokyo Prefecture, central Honshu Island, on east coast (on Edo Bay).

TSINGTAO: Treaty port on Kiaochow Bay, Shantung Province, China, population 61,000; held by Germany, 1898-1914 and by Nippon 1914-1922, returned to China.

TSUSHIMA: Island in Korea Strait; Tsushima Straits, Nipponese name of Korea Strait; in naval battle 1905, the Nipponese Navy under Admiral Togo defeated the Baltic Fleet.

UYENO PARK: In Shitaya Ward, Tokyo, covers over 200 acres, formerly Tokugawa Shogun's family temple grounds, now one of the best parks in the Capital.

WAKAYAMA PREFECTURE: South Honshu Island.

WEIHAIWEI: Treaty port, North Shantung, China, population 180,000 in 1895, occupied by Nipponese, soon leased by British and held until 1930.

YALU RIVER: *Oryoko* by Nipponese, between Manchuria and Korea, 300 miles to Yellow Sea; naval battle between Chinese and Nipponese fleets near its mouth in 1894.

YASUKUNI-JINSHA: A Shinto shrine dedicated to those who died for the Imperial cause, during and after the Restoration in 1868. In the square in front of the Shrine there is a bronze statue of Omura Masujiro erected in 1888. Omura's is said to be the oldest among the seven hundred bronze statues in Nippon.

YOKOHAMA: Port, commercial city, capital of Kanagawa Prefecture, East central Honshu Island, on west shore of Edo Bay, population 704,000; port for Tokyo; earthquake and fire, Sept. 1, 1923, destroyed the city.

YOSHIWARA: Famous licensed prostitute quarter in Asakusa Ward, Tokyo.

YOYOGI: Section in Shibuya Ward, Tokyo, contains the Meiji Shrine, the Parade Grounds, etc.

ZAGYOSO: Prince Saionji's present home at Okitsu, Shizuoka Prefecture.